AN INTRODUCTION
TO
ADVANCED DYNAMICS

ADDISON-WESLEY SERIES IN MECHANICS

Eric Reissner, *Consulting Editor*

———————

Bisplinghoff, Ashley, and Halfman—Aeroelasticity

McCuskey—An Introduction to Advanced Dynamics

AN INTRODUCTION
TO
ADVANCED DYNAMICS

S. W. McCUSKEY

Department of Mathematics
Case Institute of Technology

ADDISON-WESLEY PUBLISHING COMPANY, INC.

READING, MASSACHUSETTS, U.S.A.

The Library of Congress has cataloged this book as follows:

McCuskey, Sidney Wilcox.
    An introduction to advanced dynamics. Reading, Mass.,
Addison-Wesley Pub. Co. [1959]
      264 p. illus. 26 cm. (Addison-Wesley series in mechanics)
      Includes bibliography.

    1. Dynamics.
    QA845.M3   531.3   59—7553 ‡
    Library of Congress

PREFACE

In view of its dominant place in the development of scientific thought, theoretical mechanics should be a part of the educational background of every serious student of physics and engineering. In physics, particularly, modern ideas of quantum mechanics can be more thoroughly assimilated if the student is conversant with the essential contributions of past masters such as Newton, Lagrange, D'Alembert, Hamilton, Jacobi, and many others.

The purpose of this introductory book is to familiarize advanced undergraduate students in science and mathematics with a few of the ideas of classical dynamics not ordinarily treated in their courses in elementary mechanics. Its aim is to bridge the gap between the undergraduate study of mechanics and the work normally covered in the first semester of graduate study in theoretical physics. The book does not treat exhaustively any one topic nor many topics in advanced dynamics. Nor has the aim been to present a wide variety of applications. The emphasis is on the underlying principles and a few simple and familiar applications for illustrative purposes only.

A one-semester course covering the material presented here has been given for several years to senior students in physics. Emphasis has been placed to a large extent upon student participation in solving and discussing the problems. Only by such individual activity will the student learn thoroughly the dynamical concepts involved. Students who have taken the course have been prepared in differential equations and in advanced calculus, including some vector analysis. A knowledge of matrix algebra has not been assumed; therefore the discussion of rigid-body motion and oscillatory systems is somewhat more cumbersome than would be the case in matrix notation. In general, the mathematical tools used have not been elaborated upon. If the student is forced to seek some supplementary mathematics, so much the better.

It is a pleasure to acknowledge the many helpful discussions with my colleagues and students at Case during the preparation of this material. In particular I wish to thank Dr. L. L. Foldy and Dr. F. J. Milford, who read parts of the manuscript in detail and made many valuable suggestions.

October 1958   S. W. M.

CONTENTS

CHAPTER 1

FUNDAMENTALS OF NEWTONIAN DYNAMICS

Mechanics is one of the oldest of the sciences. Problems of a mechanical nature have led to the invention of some of the most elegant parts of mathematics. One need only mention, for example, the works of Newton, Laplace, and Lagrange and their efforts to create the mathematical analysis appropriate for describing the movements of the planets. Long before them, practical mechanical problems attracted the attention of Archimedes and of Galileo.

That part of mechanics which treats of systems in equilibrium is called *statics*. The part which deals with motion, and the interplay of forces that produce motion, is called *dynamics*. Today it is necessary to distinguish between those ideas which have been influential in explaining the mechanical behavior of systems of macroscopic size and those which are appropriate to describe systems of atomic dimensions. The former comprise *classical mechanics;* the latter comprise *quantum mechanics*. Needless to say, many of the ideas and techniques of classical mechanics are also of value in quantum mechanics. In this book we shall discuss only certain aspects of the classical dynamics of particle and of rigid-body motion.

1–1 Kinematical preliminaries. Consider the motion of a single point which describes a curve in space, whose equation in vector form may be written $\mathbf{r} = \mathbf{f}(t)$, where t is the time reckoned from an arbitrary instant. Suppose the particle starts at P_0, Fig. 1–1, and in Δt sec moves along the curve $\mathbf{r} = \mathbf{f}(t)$ to P. Its radius vector changes by an amount $\Delta \mathbf{r} = \mathbf{r} - \mathbf{r}_0$. We therefore define its velocity as

$$\lim_{\Delta t \to 0} \frac{\Delta \mathbf{r}}{\Delta t} = \frac{d\mathbf{r}}{dt} = \mathbf{v},$$

where the necessary continuity conditions are assumed for $\mathbf{f}(t)$.

We may write $\Delta \mathbf{r}/\Delta t = (\Delta \mathbf{r}/\Delta s) (\Delta s/\Delta t)$, where Δs is the arc length from P_0 to P along the curve. In the limit, we have

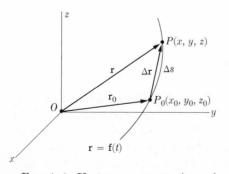

Fig. 1–1. Vector representation of space curve.

$$\lim_{\Delta s \to 0} \frac{\Delta \mathbf{r}}{\Delta s} \cdot \lim_{\Delta t \to 0} \frac{\Delta s}{\Delta t} = \mathbf{u}_\tau \frac{ds}{dt},$$

1

where $\mathbf{u}_\tau$ is a unit vector tangent to the curve and ds/dt is the speed of the particle, which we designate by v. Thus the *velocity is a vector of magnitude v tangent to the curve along which the point moves.*

$$\mathbf{v} = v\mathbf{u}_\tau. \tag{1-1}$$

As P moves along the curve, the velocity vector changes direction as well as magnitude. If, in time Δt, the vector $\mathbf{v}$ changes by an amount $\Delta \mathbf{v}$, the acceleration is $\lim_{\Delta t \to 0}(\Delta \mathbf{v}/\Delta t) = \mathbf{a}$. Insight into the nature of $\mathbf{a}$ may be gained by differentiating Eq. (1-1), bearing in mind that $\mathbf{u}_\tau$ changes in direction as the point moves along the curve. We have

$$\mathbf{a} = \frac{d\mathbf{v}}{dt} = \frac{dv}{dt}\,\mathbf{u}_\tau + v\,\frac{d\mathbf{u}_\tau}{dt}. \tag{1-2}$$

The first term on the right in Eq. (1-2) is a vector tangent to the curve. To interpret the second term, we use the fact that $\mathbf{u}_\tau$ is a vector of constant unit magnitude and hence $\mathbf{u}_\tau \cdot \mathbf{u}_\tau = 1$. Therefore

$$\mathbf{u}_\tau \cdot \frac{d\mathbf{u}_\tau}{dt} + \frac{d\mathbf{u}_\tau}{dt} \cdot \mathbf{u}_\tau = 0, \qquad \text{or} \qquad 2\mathbf{u}_\tau \cdot \frac{d\mathbf{u}_\tau}{dt} = 0.$$

This implies that $\mathbf{u}_\tau$ and $d\mathbf{u}_\tau/dt$ are mutually perpendicular vectors. We write, therefore,

$$\frac{d\mathbf{u}_\tau}{dt} = \left(\frac{d\mathbf{u}_\tau}{ds}\right)\left(\frac{ds}{dt}\right) = v\,\frac{d\mathbf{u}_\tau}{ds} = v\left|\frac{d\mathbf{u}_\tau}{ds}\right|\mathbf{u}_n, \tag{1-3}$$

where $\mathbf{u}_n$ is a unit vector normal to the curve and $|d\mathbf{u}_\tau/ds|$, the scalar magnitude of $d\mathbf{u}_\tau/ds$, is the curvature of $\mathbf{r} = \mathbf{f}(t)$. The reciprocal of the curvature is defined to be the radius of curvature, ρ. Hence we interpret the second term on the right in Eq. (1-2) to be a vector normal to the curve and of magnitude v^2/ρ. The acceleration expressed in tangential and normal components is, therefore,

$$\mathbf{a} = \frac{dv}{dt}\,\mathbf{u}_\tau + \frac{v^2}{\rho}\,\mathbf{u}_n. \tag{1-4}$$

In plane motion under the action of a force directed toward or away from a fixed center, it is convenient to resolve the acceleration and the velocity vectors into components along the radius vector $\mathbf{r}$ and perpendicular to it. In Fig. 1-2 let the motion be in a plane and let the point P have polar coordinates (r, θ) at time t. The vector joining O to P may be written $\mathbf{r} = r\mathbf{u}_r$, where $\mathbf{u}_r$ is a unit vector in the radial direction. From the definition of velocity,

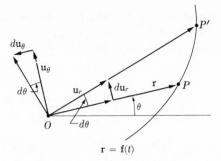

$$\mathbf{r} = \mathbf{f}(t)$$

FIG. 1–2. Vector resolution into radial and transverse components.

$$\mathbf{v} = \frac{d\mathbf{r}}{dt} = \frac{dr}{dt}\,\mathbf{u}_r + r\,\frac{d\mathbf{u}_r}{dt}. \qquad (1\text{–}5)$$

Since $\mathbf{u}_r$ is a unit vector and $d\mathbf{u}_r/dt$ is perpendicular to $\mathbf{u}_r$, we shall define a unit vector $\mathbf{u}_\theta$ to specify this direction. From Fig. 1–2 it is evident that as the particle moves from P to P', the unit vector $\mathbf{u}_r$ changes direction by an amount $d\theta$, the tip of $\mathbf{u}_r$ moving on a circle of unit radius. This implies that $(d\mathbf{u}_r/dt) = (d\theta/dt)\mathbf{u}_\theta$, so that

$$\mathbf{v} = \frac{dr}{dt}\,\mathbf{u}_r + r\,\frac{d\theta}{dt}\,\mathbf{u}_\theta,$$

or

$$\mathbf{v} = \dot{r}\mathbf{u}_r + r\dot{\theta}\mathbf{u}_\theta. \qquad (1\text{–}6)$$

To obtain the acceleration, we differentiate once more.

$$\mathbf{a} = \ddot{r}\mathbf{u}_r + \dot{r}\dot{\mathbf{u}}_r + \dot{r}\dot{\theta}\mathbf{u}_\theta + r\ddot{\theta}\mathbf{u}_\theta + r\dot{\theta}\dot{\mathbf{u}}_\theta. \qquad (1\text{–}7)$$

This involves an interpretation of $\dot{\mathbf{u}}_\theta$ which we may obtain by an inspection of Fig. 1–2. As the unit vector $\mathbf{u}_r$ changes direction by an amount $d\theta$, so does the unit vector $\mathbf{u}_\theta$. Hence, $\dot{\mathbf{u}}_\theta = -(d\theta/dt)\mathbf{u}_r$. We have, by grouping terms,

$$\mathbf{a} = [\ddot{r} - r\dot{\theta}^2]\mathbf{u}_r + [2\dot{r}\dot{\theta} + r\ddot{\theta}]\mathbf{u}_\theta. \qquad (1\text{–}8)$$

This is the resolution of $\mathbf{a}$ into radial and transverse components.

1–2 Mass and force. Basic to any study of dynamics are the definitions of mass and force. We usually associate the former with a loosely conceived notion of "inertia," or the resistance of a body to being set in motion. Our subjective idea of a force is a push or a pull which sets a body in motion. These are not satisfactory definitions in the scientific sense. We shall lay down certain more precise definitions and postulates and build upon them.

We first define as a *dimensionless entity* a particle which has the properties of (a) *position* in space and time, (b) a quality called *inertia*, measured by its *mass*, so far an undefined term, and (c) certain relations or interactions with other particles. What follows will be restricted to particles.

Consider two particles, 1 and 2, isolated in space from all others. This is an idealized situation, but at least it may be imagined. We assume that these particles interact upon each other somehow, and accelerated motion results. The acceleration of particle 1 relative to an arbitrary coordinate system we designate by $\mathbf{a}_{12}$, the subscript 2 denoting the accelerating agency. Similarly $\mathbf{a}_{21}$ denotes the acceleration of particle 2 due to the presence of 1. Then we lay down

POSTULATE 1. *The ratio $a_{12}/-a_{21}$ is a positive scalar which is invariant with respect to the relative position and the relative velocity (small compared with the velocity of light) of the particles, and with respect to time and space.* We designate this constant ratio by μ_{21}.

Consider now a third particle, 3, and let it be associated first with particle 1, and then independently with particle 2. We obtain two other scalar constants:

$$\frac{a_{13}}{-a_{31}} = \mu_{31} \quad \text{and} \quad \frac{a_{23}}{-a_{32}} = \mu_{32}. \quad (1\text{–}9)$$

These lead us to

POSTULATE 2. *The ratios, Eqs. (1–9), are not independent constants, but are related by the equation*

$$\mu_{32} = \frac{\mu_{31}}{\mu_{21}} \quad (1\text{–}10)$$

for any three particles whatever. This is not a randomly selected postulate. It is founded on experience. As nearly as experimental procedures can fulfill the definitions laid down for particles and for isolation, we observe this to be true.

By combining Eqs. (1–9) and (1–10) we have, in vector form,

$$\mu_{21}\mathbf{a}_{23} = -\mu_{31}\mathbf{a}_{32}. \quad (1\text{–}11)$$

This expresses the interaction of particles 2 and 3, but we observe that the constants involved, μ_{21} and μ_{31}, are expressed in terms of the behavior of particle 1, which otherwise does not enter. Particle 1 may be designated as a standard particle in terms of whose behavior the interaction of particles 2 and 3 is described. We *define*, therefore, the constant μ_{21} to be the *mass* of 2 relative to 1. Similarly μ_{31} is the mass of particle 3 relative to 1.

It should be emphasized that this definition of mass is quite arbitrary. When so defined, the mass of a particle satisfies our "push-pull" sense by measuring the resistance of the particle to being set in motion. The latter property of the particle we have described by the term "inertia." Henceforth we shall designate the masses of particles by m_1, m_2, $m_3 \ldots$, understanding that we refer to masses relative to some standard.

In terms of the mass and acceleration, we now define force. We observe that the product of mass and acceleration in the interaction of two particles is a quantity which is the same in magnitude for both but opposite in sign. This leads to

POSTULATE 3. *The quantity* ma *for a given interaction between two particles depends only on the relative position of the two, or on the relative velocity, or on the time, or upon all three.* This quantity is called the *force* exerted by one particle on another. From experience, we form

POSTULATE 4. *When several forces act upon a particle, each acts independently of the others.*

The definitions of mass and force given here, together with the postulates, are adequate to formulate the differential equations defining the motion of a particle.

1–3 Newton's laws of motion. The fundamental physical laws upon which the analysis of dynamical problems rest are those enunciated by Isaac Newton in the *Principia* (1686). These are three in number.

First Law. A particle of constant mass remains at rest, or moves with constant velocity in a straight line, unless acted upon by a force.

Second Law. A particle acted upon by a force moves so that the time rate of change of its linear momentum equals the force.

Third Law. If two particles act on each other, the force exerted by the first on the second is equal in magnitude and opposite in direction to the force exerted by the second on the first.

To represent these mathematically, it is convenient to use vector notation, as we have done in Section 1–1. We first define the *linear momentum* of a particle to be $\mathbf{p} = m\mathbf{v}$. Then Newton's Second Law becomes

$$\frac{d(m\mathbf{v})}{dt} = \mathbf{F}, \tag{1-12}$$

where, according to Postulates 3 and 4, $\mathbf{F}$ is, in general, a vector function of position, velocity, and the time, and is also the vector sum of all external forces acting on the particle.

In many physical problems, the mass remains constant and Eq. (1–12) becomes the familiar

$$m \frac{d\mathbf{v}}{dt} = m\mathbf{a} = \mathbf{F}. \tag{1–13}$$

But in rocket propulsion where the projectile is losing mass, or in relativistic mechanics where mass is a function of the velocity, variations in mass are important.

If $\mathbf{F} = 0$ in Eq. (1–13), we see that $\mathbf{v}$ is a constant and the Second Law of motion reduces to the First Law.

The Third Law of Newton is embodied in Eq. (1–11). For two particles of masses m_1 and m_2, we have

$$m_1\mathbf{a}_{12} = -m_2\mathbf{a}_{21}, \tag{1–14}$$

and, by definition, $m_1\mathbf{a}_{12} = \mathbf{F}_{12}$, the force on m_1 due to m_2, while $m_2\mathbf{a}_{21} = \mathbf{F}_{21}$, the force on m_2 due to m_1. Hence

$$\mathbf{F}_{12} = -\mathbf{F}_{21}, \tag{1–15}$$

as Newton's Third Law asserts.

This approach to a dynamical problem is by no means the only one. D'Alembert, Lagrange, and Hamilton have formulated other methods for setting up the equations of motion that are based on the kinetic and potential energies of the particles. These methods lead ultimately to the same differential equations obtainable from Newton's laws. In many cases, however, the Lagrange-Hamilton formulation is more easily applied. In succeeding chapters we shall discuss these methods at some length.

In cartesian coordinates, the differential equations expressing Newton's Second Law of motion become

$$\frac{d(m\dot{x})}{dt} = X, \qquad \frac{d(m\dot{y})}{dt} = Y, \qquad \frac{d(m\dot{z})}{dt} = Z, \tag{1–16}$$

where X, Y, and Z are the components of force in the three coordinate directions.

To illustrate the application of Newton's Second Law, consider the following examples.

EXAMPLE 1. A particle of unit mass moves along the x-axis of a cartesian coordinate system under the action of a force $F(x, \dot{x}) = -x - \dot{x} + 4$. Let its position at time t be $x(t)$ and let $x(0) = x_0$, $\dot{x}(0) = v_0$. Then Newton's Second Law results in the initial value problem

$$\ddot{x} = -x - \dot{x} + 4, \qquad x(0) = x_0, \qquad \dot{x}(0) = v_0.$$

The differential equation, solved by standard methods, yields

$$x(t) = e^{-t/2}[c_1 \cos \sqrt{3/4}\, t + c_2 \sin \sqrt{3/4}\, t] + 4,$$

and, applying the initial conditions, we find, for the constants of integration,

$$c_1 = x_0 - 4, \qquad c_2 = \sqrt{4/3}\, (v_0 + \tfrac{1}{2}x_0 - 2),$$

so that

$$x(t) = e^{-t/2}[(x_0 - 4) \cos \sqrt{3/4}\, t + \sqrt{4/3}\, (v_0 + \tfrac{1}{2}x_0 - 2) \sin \sqrt{3/4}\, t] + 4.$$

The motion in this case is oscillatory, as indicated by the trigonometric functions. However, as $t \to \infty$, $e^{-t/2} \to 0$, and hence the oscillation dies out, leaving the particle ultimately at rest at $x = 4$.

EXAMPLE 2. A particle of mass m moves in a vertical plane under the action of gravity and of a force whose components are $X = -kx$ and $Y = -ky$, where k is a constant. Let $x(t)$ and $y(t)$ denote the coordinates of the particle at time t. Let $x(0) = x_0$, $y(0) = 0$, $\dot{x}(0) = 0$, and $\dot{y}(0) = v_0$. Then, by Eq. (1–16), we have to solve the system of equations

$$m\ddot{x} = -kx, \qquad m\ddot{y} = -ky - mg,$$

together with the given initial conditions. We find

$$x(t) = c_1 \cos \alpha t + c_2 \sin \alpha t \qquad (\alpha = \sqrt{k/m}),$$
$$y(t) = c_3 \cos \alpha t + c_4 \sin \alpha t - \frac{mg}{k},$$

and, using the initial values, we have

$$c_1 = x_0, \qquad c_2 = 0, \qquad c_3 = \frac{mg}{k}, \qquad c_4 = \frac{v_0}{\alpha},$$

so that the path of the particle is given by

$$x(t) = x_0 \cos \alpha t \qquad (\alpha = \sqrt{k/m}),$$
$$y(t) = \frac{mg}{k} (\cos \alpha t - 1) + \frac{v_0}{\alpha} \sin \alpha t.$$

EXAMPLE 3. Let a particle of mass m be projected from the origin of a cartesian coordinate system with a velocity

$$\mathbf{v}_0 = v_0 \cos \alpha \mathbf{i} + v_0 \cos \beta \mathbf{j} + v_0 \cos \gamma \mathbf{k},$$

where $\mathbf{i}$, $\mathbf{j}$ and $\mathbf{k}$ are unit vectors along the x-, y-, and z-axes respectively, and α, β, γ are the direction angles which $\mathbf{v}_0$ makes with the coordinate

In discussing Newton's laws of motion (Section 1–3), we defined the linear momentum of a particle by $\mathbf{p} = m\mathbf{v}$. Its *angular momentum*, or *moment of momentum*, about an origin O is

$$\mathbf{L} = \mathbf{r} \times m\mathbf{v} = \mathbf{r} \times \mathbf{p}. \qquad (1\text{–}25)$$

This vector is perpendicular to the instantaneous plane of $\mathbf{r}$ and $\mathbf{p}$. As we shall see, $\mathbf{L}$ and $\mathbf{N}$ are related through the rotational dynamics of the mechanical system.

1–5 Newton's Second Law applied to rotational motion. The fundamental law for linear motion expressed by Eq. (1–12) has its counterpart in rotational motion. To obtain it we differentiate Eq. (1–25) with respect to the time:

$$\dot{\mathbf{L}} = \dot{\mathbf{r}} \times m\mathbf{v} + \mathbf{r} \times \frac{d}{dt}\,(m\mathbf{v}). \qquad (1\text{–}26)$$

Since $\dot{\mathbf{r}} = \mathbf{v}$, the first term on the right vanishes, and by Eq. (1–12) the second term becomes $\mathbf{r} \times \mathbf{F} = \mathbf{N}$. Hence we have for Newton's Second Law applied to rotational motion: *the time rate of change of the angular momentum equals the torque*, or

$$\frac{d\mathbf{L}}{dt} = \mathbf{r} \times \mathbf{F} = \mathbf{N}. \qquad (1\text{–}27)$$

When the mass m is moving on a circular arc about some axis in such a way that the angular speed is $d\theta/dt$, we have the relation $r(d\theta/dt) = v$ (see Fig. 1–5). Then $L = mr^2(d\theta/dt)$. We define the quantity mr^2 to be the *moment of inertia* of the mass about the axis of rotation. Hence, calling this I, we write Eq. (1–27) as

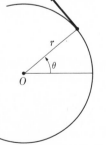

$$I\,\frac{d^2\theta}{dt^2} = \mathbf{N}, \qquad (1\text{–}28)$$

where $d^2\theta/dt^2$ denotes the angular acceleration of the moving mass. This equation plays the same part in pure rotational motion that Eq. (1–13) plays in linear motion. We shall consider the calculation of I in more detail in Chapter 4.

Fig. 1–5. Particle moving on circle.

1–6 Work and energy. The concepts of the work done by a force, and of the potential and kinetic energies, are important in many dynamical problems. Suppose that $\mathbf{F}$, the force acting on a particle, is a function of the particle's position in space. This means that X, Y, Z are functions of x, y, z. We call $\mathbf{F}$ a *vector point function* and its components X, Y, Z *scalar point functions*. For the present we shall ignore the possibility that these functions may involve the time explicitly.

Let a particle move along a curve $\mathbf{r} = \mathbf{f}(t)$ in the direction of increasing arc s, as shown in Fig. 1–6, under the influence of a force $\mathbf{F}$. Then the *work done by $\mathbf{F}$ as the particle moves from P to P' is defined by*

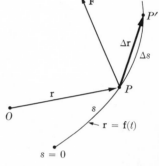

$$\Delta W = \mathbf{F} \cdot \Delta \mathbf{r}, \qquad (1\text{–}29)$$

where the dot denotes the scalar product of $\mathbf{F}$ and $\Delta \mathbf{r}$. Since

$$\Delta \mathbf{r} = (\Delta \mathbf{r}/\Delta s)\Delta s,$$

we have

$$\Delta W = \mathbf{F} \cdot (\Delta \mathbf{r}/\Delta s)\Delta s,$$

and in the limit as $\Delta \mathbf{r} \to 0$,

$$dW = \mathbf{F} \cdot \mathbf{u}_r \, ds, \qquad (1\text{–}30)$$

Fig. 1–6. Work done by a force in curvilinear motion.

where $\mathbf{u}_r = \lim_{\Delta s \to 0} (\Delta \mathbf{r}/\Delta s)$ is a unit vector tangent to the curve at P. If ϕ is the angle between $\mathbf{u}_r$ and $\mathbf{F}$, we may write Eq. (1–30) in the form

$$dW = F \cos \phi \, ds, \qquad (1\text{–}31)$$

and we note that the work done is the product of the component of F tangent to the path and the infinitesimal displacement along the path.

The total work done by $\mathbf{F}$ in a displacement of the particle along the arc C from $\mathbf{r} = \mathbf{a}$ to $\mathbf{r} = \mathbf{b}$ is given by the line integral

$$W = \int_C \mathbf{F} \cdot \mathbf{u}_r \, ds. \qquad (1\text{–}32)$$

If, in terms of cartesian coordinates, $\mathbf{F} = X\mathbf{i} + Y\mathbf{j} + Z\mathbf{k}$ and $\mathbf{u}_r = \cos \alpha \mathbf{i} + \cos \beta \mathbf{j} + \cos \gamma \mathbf{k}$, Eq. (1–32) becomes

$$W = \int_C (X \cos \alpha + Y \cos \beta + Z \cos \gamma) \, ds$$

$$= \int_C X \, dx + Y \, dy + Z \, dz, \qquad (1\text{–}33)$$

where C denotes the curve along which the integration is to be taken and α, β, γ are the direction angles made by $\mathbf{u}_r$ with the coordinate axes. It should be noted that, in general, the value of W depends upon the path of integration.

An important relationship links the work done by $\mathbf{F}$ along the curve and the change in kinetic energy of the particle. By the *kinetic energy* we mean the quantity $\frac{1}{2}mv^2$, where v is the instantaneous speed of the particle. From Eq. (1–32) and $\mathbf{v} = (ds/dt)\mathbf{u}_r$, we have

$$W = \int_C \mathbf{F}\cdot\mathbf{u}_r \, ds = \int_C \mathbf{F}\cdot\mathbf{v} \, dt = \int_C \frac{d(m\mathbf{v})}{dt}\cdot\mathbf{v} \, dt = m\int_C \mathbf{v}\cdot d\mathbf{v}, \qquad (1\text{–}34)$$

where the mass of the particle is assumed to be constant and C represents the curve over which the integration takes place. Now we recall that $d(\mathbf{v}\cdot\mathbf{v}) = d(v^2) = 2v \, dv$. Thus the work

$$W = m\int_C v \, dv = \frac{1}{2}mv_b^2 - \frac{1}{2}mv_a^2 \qquad (1\text{–}35)$$

if v_a, v_b are the speeds at the endpoints of C. This fundamental equation states *that the work done by* $\mathbf{F}$ *in a displacement along* C *equals the change in the kinetic energy of the particle from the beginning to the end of the path.*

As an example, consider the force $\mathbf{F} = 2xy\mathbf{i} + 3x^2\mathbf{j}$ moving a mass m in the plane curve $x^2 = 9y$ from the point $(0, 0)$ to $(3, 1)$. The application of Eq. (1–32) or Eq. (1–33) yields

$$W = \int_{(0,0)}^{(3,1)} 2xy \, dx + 3x^2 \, dy.$$

To evaluate this, replace y by $x^2/9$ and dy by $(2x \, dx)/9$. Then

$$W = \int_0^3 \left(\frac{2x^3}{9} + \frac{6x^3}{9}\right) dx = 18 \text{ units.}$$

If the force is in dynes and the displacement is in centimeters, the unit of W will be dyne·cm or ergs.

If the particle was initially at rest at $(0,0)$, its speed at $(3,1)$ is given by

$$v = \left(\frac{2\times 18}{m}\right)^{1/2} = \left(\frac{36}{m}\right)^{1/2} \text{ cm/sec.}$$

1–7 Conservative force fields. If, and only if, the work done by $\mathbf{F}$ between two points $\mathbf{r} = \mathbf{a}$ and $\mathbf{r} = \mathbf{b}$ is independent of the path of integration C (and hence the integral depends only upon the endpoints of C), we say that the force is *conservative* and that the totality of points where this takes place constitutes a *conservative force field*. In these circumstances the integrand in W, as given in Eq. (1–33), is the exact differential of some function $V(x,y,z)$. It is customary to take $dV = -dW$. Then we have

$$dW = -dV = X\,dx + Y\,dy + Z\,dz. \tag{1–36}$$

It follows from the definition of an exact differential that

$$X = -\frac{\partial V}{\partial x}, \qquad Y = -\frac{\partial V}{\partial y}, \qquad Z = -\frac{\partial V}{\partial z}. \tag{1–37}$$

The function $V(x,y,z)$ that occurs here is called the *potential energy* of the mass point. The change in V between points **a** and **b** is the amount of work done on the mass point by some external force in changing its position. In a conservative force field, therefore, by definition

$$W_\mathbf{b} - W_\mathbf{a} = \int_C \mathbf{F}\cdot\mathbf{u}_r\,ds = V_\mathbf{a} - V_\mathbf{b}, \tag{1–38}$$

where $V_\mathbf{a}$ and $V_\mathbf{b}$ denote the potential energies at $\mathbf{r} = \mathbf{a}$ and $\mathbf{r} = \mathbf{b}$ respectively.

If $V(x,y,z)$ is a function having continuous first and second partial derivatives in a given region, we have, from Eq. (1–37),

$$\frac{\partial Z}{\partial y} = -\frac{\partial^2 V}{\partial y \partial z} = \frac{\partial Y}{\partial z},$$

$$\frac{\partial X}{\partial z} = -\frac{\partial^2 V}{\partial z \partial x} = \frac{\partial Z}{\partial x}, \tag{1–39}$$

$$\frac{\partial X}{\partial y} = -\frac{\partial^2 V}{\partial y \partial x} = \frac{\partial Y}{\partial x}.$$

It would appear, then, that it will be possible to obtain a potential function $V(x,y,z)$ if

$$\frac{\partial Z}{\partial y} - \frac{\partial Y}{\partial z} = 0, \qquad \frac{\partial Z}{\partial x} - \frac{\partial X}{\partial z} = 0, \qquad \text{and} \qquad \frac{\partial Y}{\partial x} - \frac{\partial X}{\partial y} = 0. \tag{1–40}$$

These are both necessary and sufficient conditions for the existence of the function $V(x,y,z)$.* They may be expressed compactly by the equivalent vector statement

$$\operatorname{curl}\mathbf{F} = \nabla \times \mathbf{F} = 0. \tag{1–41}$$

---

* The reader is referred to any book on advanced calculus for a proof of this statement. See, for example, W. Kaplan, *Advanced Calculus*. Reading, Massachusetts: Addison-Wesley Publishing Company, Inc., 1952, p. 279.

1–8 Conservation laws. The laws of motion expressed in Eqs. (1–12) and (1–27) lead, in special circumstances, to two important properties of motion. These are the *laws of conservation of linear and of angular momentum*.

If the sum of the forces acting on a particle is zero, then by Eq. (1–12) *the linear momentum is constant in time*. Also, if the sum of the external torques acting on a particle vanishes, we observe from Eq. (1–27) that the *angular momentum is constant in time*.

Consider, for example, a planet moving about the sun. Newton has shown that such a body behaves dynamically as if all its mass were concentrated at its center. Hence, for practical purposes, it approximates a point mass. No external torque acts on this mass particle. We anticipate, therefore, that the angular momentum $\mathbf{L}$ is constant in time. This means that the motion takes place in a plane, the vector $\mathbf{L}$ being always perpendicular to the plane defined by $\mathbf{r}$ and $m\mathbf{v}$. Furthermore, since the magnitude of $\mathbf{L}$ is directly proportional to r and to v, its constancy demands an increase in v when a decrease in r occurs.

A third important conservation law is that of energy in a conservative field of force. Taking the scalar product of each side of Eq. (1–13) and $\mathbf{v}$, we find

$$ m\mathbf{v}\cdot\frac{d\mathbf{v}}{dt} = \mathbf{F}\cdot\mathbf{v}, $$

and integrating with respect to the time, we obtain

$$ m\int_{\mathbf{v}_0}^{\mathbf{v}_1} \mathbf{v}\cdot d\mathbf{v} = \int_{t_0}^{t_1} \mathbf{F}\cdot\mathbf{v}\,dt = \int_{s_0}^{s_1} \mathbf{F}\cdot\mathbf{u}_r\,ds, \qquad (1\text{--}42) $$

where $\mathbf{v}_0$ and $\mathbf{v}_1$ are the velocities of the particle at times t_0 and t_1, respectively, and s_0 and s_1 are the corresponding arc positions (Fig. 1–6). The last integral in Eq. (1–42) is the work done by $\mathbf{F}$ in the displacement from s_0 to s_1. By Eq. (1–38), if the force field is conservative, this is the change in potential energy during the motion. Hence we may write, upon integration of the left side of Eq. (1–42),

$$ \tfrac{1}{2}m\mathbf{v}_1^2 - \tfrac{1}{2}m\mathbf{v}_0^2 = V_0 - V_1, \qquad (1\text{--}43) $$

where V_0 and V_1 denote the potential energies of the particle at s_0 and s_1 respectively. Equation (1–43) may be written in the form

$$\tfrac{1}{2}mv_1^2 + V_1 = \tfrac{1}{2}mv_0^2 + V_0 = \text{constant.} \qquad (1\text{–}44)$$

Equation (1–44) expresses the law of *conservation of energy: the sum of the kinetic and potential energies of the particle remains constant during the motion.*

If the force field is nonconservative, Eq. (1–44) is no longer valid. Frictional forces, or other types which depend upon velocity or time, are examples of nonconservative forces. Suppose that the total force acting upon a particle is composed of a conservative part $\mathbf{F}_1(\mathbf{r})$ and a nonconservative part $\mathbf{F}_2(\mathbf{r},\mathbf{v},t)$. By Eq. (1–42), we have

$$\tfrac{1}{2}m(\mathbf{v}_1^2 - \mathbf{v}_0^2) = \int_{t_0}^{t_1} (\mathbf{F}_1 + \mathbf{F}_2)\cdot\mathbf{v}\,dt,$$

or, by Eq. (1–43),

$$\tfrac{1}{2}m(v_1^2 - v_0^2) = V_0 - V_1 + \int_{t_0}^{t_1} \mathbf{F}_2\cdot\mathbf{v}\,dt. \qquad (1\text{–}45)$$

Let $E_1 = \tfrac{1}{2}mv_1^2 + V_1$ and $E_0 = \tfrac{1}{2}mv_0^2 + V_0$ denote the total energies, as represented by the conservative part of the force field, at times t_1 and t_0. Then Eq. (1–45) states that the difference in total energy,

$$E_1 - E_0 = \int_{t_0}^{t_1} \mathbf{F}_2\cdot\mathbf{v}\,dt, \qquad (1\text{–}46)$$

equals the work done by the nonconservative force F_2 between the same two times. This may also be expressed by the statement that the time rate of change of E is the rate of working of the nonconservative force. That is,

$$\frac{dE}{dt} = \mathbf{F}_2\cdot\mathbf{v}. \qquad (1\text{–}47)$$

1–9 Energy diagrams. In many physical problems an analysis of the motion may be carried out qualitatively, and sometimes quantitatively, by using an energy diagram and the theorem on conservation of energy. As an illustration, we consider a simple harmonic oscillator.

A mass m is displaced from an origin O and thereafter moves on a horizontal line under the action of a force directed toward O (Fig. 1–7). Assume that the motion takes place without friction and that the force acting on m is $-kx$. Then, by Newton's Second Law,

$$m\ddot{x} = -kx. \qquad (1\text{–}48)$$

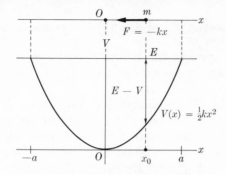

FIG. 1–7. Energy diagram for simple harmonic oscillator.

Multiplying by $\dot{x}$ and integrating both sides yields

$$m\dot{x}\ddot{x} = -kx\dot{x},$$

$$\frac{d}{dt}\left(\frac{1}{2}\, m\dot{x}^2\right) = -kx\,\frac{dx}{dt},$$

$$\tfrac{1}{2}m\dot{x}^2 = -\frac{kx^2}{2} + E, \qquad (1\text{–}49)$$

where we have written E for the constant of integration. This is simply the law of conservation of energy for the particle, E being the total energy. The potential energy, $V(x) = \frac{1}{2}kx^2$, has been plotted in the lower part of Fig. 1–7. This is the *energy diagram* for the motion. Equation (1–49), solved for the velocity, yields

$$\dot{x} = \pm\sqrt{(2/m)(E - \tfrac{1}{2}kx^2)} = \pm\sqrt{(2/m)(E - V)}. \qquad (1\text{–}50)$$

It is clear from this equation that $\dot{x} = 0$ when $E = V$; that $\dot{x}$ is real and hence motion can take place when $E > V$; that $\dot{x}$ is imaginary and hence there can be no motion when $E < V$. In Fig. 1–7, therefore, we have drawn a horizontal line to represent the total energy of the particle. Where this is drawn depends upon the initial conditions under which the motion is started. Motion is possible only within that range in x where the line $E = $ constant is above the curve $V(x)$. At any point such as x_0, the velocity of the particle is proportional to the square root of $E - V$. The particle comes to rest at $x = a$, and $x = -a$ and has its greatest velocity at $x = 0$. The particle cannot move to the right of $x = a$ nor to the left of $x = -a$. At the point $x = x_0$, the particle may be traveling either to the right or to the left, depending upon the sign chosen for the $\sqrt{(2/m)(E - V)}$.

The period P of the motion in this case is given by the time required for m to travel from $x = -a$ to $+a$ and back. We have

$$\frac{1}{2}P = \int_{-a}^{a}\frac{dx}{\dot{x}} = 2\int_{0}^{a}\frac{dx}{\sqrt{(2/m)(E - \frac{1}{2}kx^2)}}. \qquad (1\text{–}51)$$

The value of a must be given by the positive root of the equation $E - (\frac{1}{2}ka^2) = 0$; hence $a = \sqrt{2E/k}$.

Integrating Eq. (1–51), we have

$$\frac{1}{2}P = 2\sqrt{m/k}\,\sin^{-1}\left(\frac{x}{\sqrt{2E/k}}\right)\Bigg|_{0}^{\sqrt{2E/k}} = \pi\sqrt{m/k}, \qquad (1\text{–}52)$$

and the period is $2\pi\sqrt{m/k}$. This could have been obtained directly from the equation of motion. Writing Eq. (1–48) as $\ddot{x} + (k/m)x = 0$, and solving for x, we find that the quantity k/m is the square of the angular frequency ω. Hence, since $P = 2\pi/\omega$, we obtain $P = 2\pi\sqrt{m/k}$ as before.

To summarize, if we plot $V(x)$ against x and establish a total energy E for the particle, motion is possible for those ranges in x where $E - V(x)$ is positive. The idea may be visualized to a first approximation by considering a small ball rolling under the action of gravity on a track, as in Fig. 1–8. If we start it at a level y_1, its total energy is fixed at E_1. Neglecting frictional losses and the energy of rotation, we observe that the ball will move rapidly at the depths of the track and slowly at the maxima, and will continue indefinitely to the left. On the other hand, if we start it at a level y_2 so that its total energy is E_2, it will oscillate if caught in region a or move indefinitely far to the left if in region b. Motion is not possible in region c. Once we plot $V(x)$ for a given problem, we can obtain a qualitative idea of the motion under assumed boundary conditions.

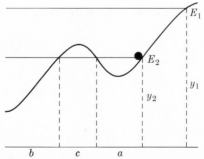

Fig. 1–8. Energy diagram for a ball on a vertical track.

1–10 Impulsive motion. In the preceding sections on work and energy we have been concerned with the effect of a force acting through a distance. In this section we shall discuss the time effect of a force. We define for this purpose the integral

$$\mathbf{I} = \int_{t_0}^{t_1} \mathbf{F}\, dt \qquad (1\text{–}53)$$

to be the *impulse* of the force during the time interval (t_0, t_1). Substituting for $\mathbf{F}$ its value according to Newton's Second Law of motion, we have

$$\mathbf{I} = \int_{t_0}^{t_1} \frac{d}{dt}\,(m\mathbf{v})\, dt = m\mathbf{v}(t_1) - m\mathbf{v}(t_0). \qquad (1\text{–}54)$$

The vector $\mathbf{I}$, therefore, is the change in the linear momentum of the particle in the interval (t_0, t_1).

Equation (1–54) is particularly useful in analyzing the result of applying a large force to the particle for a brief interval of time. The ensuing motion is called *impulsive* motion. An example will serve to illustrate the point.

Consider the motion that will occur if a force $F(t) = a\tau t - at^2$ is applied to a mass m for a time interval τ. The mass will be assumed to move in a straight line. The parameter a is arbitrary and positive. We shall denote the displacement at time t by x, and set $x = 0$ at $t = 0$. Figure 1–9 shows the force function. During the interval in which the force acts, we have

$$m\ddot{x} = a\tau t - at^2, \qquad (1\text{–}55)$$

and by integration

$$m\dot{x}(\tau) - m\dot{x}(0) = a\left[\frac{\tau t^2}{2} - \frac{t^3}{3}\right]_0^\tau = a\,\frac{\tau^3}{6}. \qquad (1\text{–}56)$$

The left side is the change in momentum $\Delta(m\dot{x})$ that occurs in the time interval $(0, \tau)$. We see that the change in velocity will be

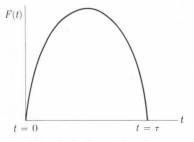

$$\Delta\dot{x} = \frac{a\tau^3}{6m}. \qquad (1\text{–}57)$$

A second integration, performed on Eq. (1–56), yields the change in x,

$$\Delta x = \frac{a\tau^4}{12m}. \qquad (1\text{–}58)$$

Fig. 1–9. Impulsive force.

Over the time interval concerned, the *average force* acting on m is

$$F_{av} = \frac{1}{\tau} \int_0^\tau (a\tau t - at^2)\, dt = \frac{a\tau^2}{6}, \qquad (1\text{--}59)$$

and if we express the changes in velocity and displacement in terms of F_{av}, we have

$$\Delta \dot{x} = \frac{\tau F_{av}}{m} \qquad \text{and} \qquad \Delta x = \frac{\tau^2 F_{av}}{2m}. \qquad (1\text{--}60)$$

Let us now suppose that F is allowed to increase; that is, we increase a, while at the same time τ is allowed to decrease. If this takes place in such a way that τF_{av} remains constant, or at least approaches a definite limit, it is apparent from Eq. (1–60) that

$$\Delta \dot{x} \rightarrow \frac{\text{constant}}{m} \qquad \text{and} \qquad \Delta x \rightarrow 0 \qquad \text{as} \qquad \tau \rightarrow 0. \qquad (1\text{--}61)$$

In the limit, therefore, we have an instantaneous change of velocity but no change in the position of the particle *during the time in which F acts*. Immediately after F acts, or ceases to act, the particle moves with its new velocity uniformly.

From Eq. (1–54) and from a similar integrated form of Newton's Second Law of rotational motion, Eq. (1–27), the changes in the linear and the angular momentum of a particle in a time interval (t_0, t_1) are

$$\Delta(m\mathbf{v}) = \int_{t_0}^{t_1} \mathbf{F}\, dt \qquad \text{and} \qquad \Delta\mathbf{L} = \int_{t_0}^{t_1} \mathbf{N}\, dt. \qquad (1\text{--}62)$$

These integrals represent the total linear and angular impulses with respect to the origin of reference. It should be emphasized that $\Delta(m\mathbf{v})$ and $\Delta\mathbf{L}$ are vectors.

The impulsive motion in one dimension illustrated in the example may now be generalized to three dimensions. If $\mathbf{r}$ is the position vector of the particle to which an impulsive force

$$\mathbf{F}_i = \lim_{t_1 \rightarrow t_0} \int_{t_0}^{t_1} \mathbf{F}\, dt$$

is applied, $\mathbf{r}$ does not change appreciably in the vanishing time interval (t_0, t_1). Hence we may write

$$\lim_{t_1 \rightarrow t_0} \int_{t_0}^{t_1} \mathbf{N}\, dt = \lim_{t_1 \rightarrow t_0} \int_{t_0}^{t_1} \mathbf{r} \times \mathbf{F}\, dt$$

$$= \mathbf{r} \times \lim_{t_1 \rightarrow t_0} \int_{t_0}^{t_1} \mathbf{F}\, dt = \mathbf{r} \times \mathbf{F}_i. \qquad (1\text{--}63)$$

This quantity is the *impulsive torque,* or moment, created by $\mathbf{F}_i$. For three-dimensional impulsive motion, therefore, we may write

$$\Delta(m\mathbf{v}) = \mathbf{F}_i \quad \text{and} \quad \Delta\mathbf{L} = \mathbf{N}_i, \tag{1–64}$$

where $\mathbf{N}_i$ is the *total* impulsive torque and $\mathbf{F}_i$ is the *total* impulsive force acting on the particle.

1–11 Impact and collision. An example of an impulsive motion is that produced by an impact or collision. Consider the impact of an elastic ball when it strikes a fixed wall as shown in Figs. 1–10 and 1–11. Before it strikes the wall, the ball has a velocity of magnitude v_1 to the right and consequently a momentum $m\mathbf{v}_1$. We assume that the wall is rigid and hence has zero velocity at all times.

At the interface (Fig. 1–11), when the ball strikes the wall, there will be an impulse $\mathbf{I}$ on the wall and, by Newton's Third Law, an impulse $-\mathbf{I}$ on the ball. During the time of contact, the ball will be compressed for a time interval $t = 0$ to $t = \tau_1$. On the rebound there will be an impulse of restitution due to expansion of the compressed portion of the ball. Let this take place from $t = \tau_1$ to $t = \tau$. Both the impulse of compression and of expansion act in the same direction. At time $t = \tau$, the contact between ball and wall is broken. Figure 1–12 shows schematically these two parts of the impulse as the areas under the force-time

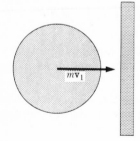
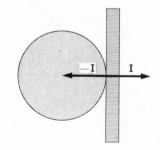

FIG. 1–10. Ball moving toward a wall.   FIG. 1–11. Ball striking a wall.

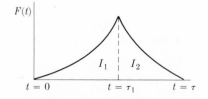

FIG. 1–12. Relation between impulse and force.

curve, I_1 being the magnitude of the compression impulse and I_2 that of the impulse of restitution. $F(t)$ is the magnitude of the force acting on the ball during the collision.

During the period of compression, the speed of the ball is reduced to zero. Hence, by the impulse-momentum theorem, Eq. (1–54), we have

$$\Delta(m\mathbf{v}_1) = -m\mathbf{v}_1 = \mathbf{I}_1. \tag{1–65}$$

Likewise, in the ensuing expansion during which $\mathbf{I}_2$ acts on the ball, we have

$$\Delta(m\mathbf{v}_2) = m\mathbf{v}_2 = \mathbf{I}_2, \tag{1–66}$$

where $\mathbf{v}_2$ is the final velocity of the ball as it leaves the wall on the rebound.

If no loss of energy occurred in this collision, the two impulses would be equal in magnitude as well as in direction, and as a consequence

$$m\mathbf{v}_1 = -m\mathbf{v}_2. \tag{1–67}$$

Thus the momenta before and after impact are equal in magnitude but opposite in direction.

On the other hand, we should consider that during the compression and expansion the internal elastic forces have done some work at the expense of the kinetic energy of the ball. To measure this, we introduce a coefficient of restitution e, defined by the equation

$$I_2 = eI_1, \tag{1–68}$$

where I_1 and I_2 are the magnitudes of the compression and expansion impulses, both of which act in the same direction. This definition is consistent with the experimentally established fact that the ratio of speed of the ball after impact to that before impact is e. Experiment indicates that e depends upon the materials of the objects in collision as well as on their sizes and shapes, and by its definition $0 \le e \le 1$. If $e = 0$, the collision is *inelastic;* if $e = 1$, the collision is *perfectly elastic.*

From Eqs. (1–67) and (1–68),

$$mv_2 = -emv_1, \tag{1–69}$$

and hence the loss of kinetic energy during the impact is

$$\Delta T = \tfrac{1}{2}m[v_1^2 - v_2^2] = \tfrac{1}{2}mv_1^2(1 - e^2). \tag{1–70}$$

When $e = 0$, we observe that all the kinetic energy is lost; in a perfectly elastic collision, when $e = 1$, no kinetic energy is lost.

When two spheres having different velocities collide, the foregoing results may be extended to a calculation of the velocities of the spheres after collision. This we leave as a problem for the reader. It should be emphasized that we have discussed here normal impact; that is, the impulses and velocities involved have been normal to the surfaces in contact. If oblique collisions are considered, the normal velocity components and normal components of the impulses still follow the laws discussed above.

1–12 Systems of particles. Let a group of n particles be described by their position vectors $\mathbf{r}_j(j = 1, 2, \ldots, n)$ relative to a fixed origin O, as shown in Fig. 1–13. The masses of the particles will be denoted by $m_j(j = 1, 2, \ldots, n)$. The center of mass of the system, denoted by $\mathbf{R}$, is defined to be

$$\mathbf{R} = \frac{1}{M} \sum_{j=1}^{n} m_j \mathbf{r}_j, \qquad (1\text{–}71)$$

where $M = \sum_{j=1}^{n} m_j$ is the total mass of the system.

The force acting on each particle consists of an external part, $\mathbf{F}_j$, and an internal part, $\sum_k \mathbf{f}_{jk}$ $(k \neq j)$, due to the action of the other particles on it. Hence, for the jth particle, Newton's Second Law becomes

$$m_j \frac{d^2 \mathbf{r}_j}{dt^2} = \mathbf{F}_j + \sum_k \mathbf{f}_{jk} \qquad (k \neq j), \qquad (1\text{–}72)$$

the summation extending over $n - 1$ particles of the system. Summing over all particles, we have

$$\sum_{j=1}^{n} m_j \frac{d^2 \mathbf{r}_j}{dt^2} = \sum_{j=1}^{n} \mathbf{F}_j + \sum_{j,k=1}^{n} \mathbf{f}_{jk} \qquad (j \neq k). \qquad (1\text{–}73)$$

Now we assume that the force on the jth particle due to the kth is equal in magnitude and opposite in direction to the force on the kth due to the

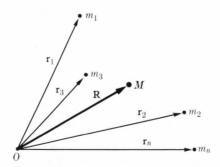

FIG. 1–13. Position vectors for a particle system.

jth and is directed along the line joining the two. That is, by Newton's Third Law,

$$\mathbf{f}_{jk} = -\mathbf{f}_{kj}. \tag{1-74}$$

With these restrictions,

$$\sum_{j,k=1}^{n} \mathbf{f}_{jk} = 0. \tag{1-75}$$

It is evident also that, by Eq. (1-71),

$$\sum_{j=1}^{n} m_j \ddot{\mathbf{r}}_j = M\ddot{\mathbf{R}}, \tag{1-76}$$

so that

$$M\ddot{\mathbf{R}} = \sum_{j=1}^{n} \mathbf{F}_j = \mathbf{F}, \tag{1-77}$$

where $\mathbf{F} = \sum_{j=1}^{n} \mathbf{F}_j$ is by definition the *resultant* of all the external forces.

Equation (1-77) states that the *motion of the center of mass is the same as if all the mass were concentrated at that point and were acted upon by the resultant of all the external forces.*

Two equally important theorems are concerned with the rotational properties of such a system of particles. Let $\mathbf{L}_0$ denote the angular momentum of the system about the origin O, and let $\mathbf{L}_c$ be the angular momentum about the center of mass. By definition,

$$\mathbf{L}_0 = \sum_{j=1}^{n} \mathbf{r}_j \times m_j \dot{\mathbf{r}}_j, \tag{1-78}$$

and

$$\mathbf{L}_c = \sum_{j=1}^{n} \mathbf{r}'_j \times m_j \dot{\mathbf{r}}'_j. \tag{1-79}$$

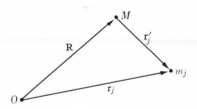

Fig. 1-14. Relation between center of mass and a particle.

If, in Eq. (1-78), we substitute for $\mathbf{r}_j$ its value $\mathbf{R} + \mathbf{r}'_j$ (see Fig. 1-14), we have

$$\mathbf{L}_0 = \sum_{j=1}^{n} m_j(\mathbf{R} \times \dot{\mathbf{R}} + \mathbf{r}'_j \times \dot{\mathbf{R}} + \mathbf{R} \times \dot{\mathbf{r}}'_j + \mathbf{r}'_j \times \dot{\mathbf{r}}'_j). \tag{1-80}$$

In Eq. (1-80), $\sum_{j=1}^{n} m_j \mathbf{R} \times \dot{\mathbf{R}} \,(= \mathbf{R} \times M\dot{\mathbf{R}})$ is the angular momentum about O of the entire mass considered as concentrated at the center of mass. By the definition of the center of mass

$$\sum_{j=1}^{n} m_j \mathbf{r}'_j = 0, \quad \text{and} \quad \sum_{j=1}^{n} m_j \dot{\mathbf{r}}'_j = 0.$$

Hence the second and third terms in Eq. (1–80) vanish. Thus we are left with

$$\mathbf{L}_0 = \mathbf{R} \times M\dot{\mathbf{R}} + \sum_{j=1}^{n} \mathbf{r}'_j \times m_j \dot{\mathbf{r}}'_j. \tag{1–81}$$

But the last term is the angular momentum of the system $\mathbf{L}_c$ about the center of .mass. Hence we find that *the angular momentum about a fixed origin O is equal to that of a particle whose mass is the entire mass of the system situated at and moving with the center of mass, together with the angular momentum of the particle system about the center of mass.*

We now differentiate Eq. (1–81) with respect to the time to obtain

$$\frac{d\mathbf{L}_0}{dt} = \dot{\mathbf{R}} \times M\dot{\mathbf{R}} + \mathbf{R} \times M\ddot{\mathbf{R}} + \frac{d\mathbf{L}_c}{dt}. \tag{1–82}$$

By the collinearity of the vectors involved, $\dot{\mathbf{R}} \times M\dot{\mathbf{R}} = 0$. Furthermore $\mathbf{R} = \mathbf{r}_j - \mathbf{r}'_j$ and $M\ddot{\mathbf{R}} = \sum_{j=1}^{n} \mathbf{F}_j$, and hence

$$\frac{d\mathbf{L}_0}{dt} - \sum_{j=1}^{n} \mathbf{r}_j \times \mathbf{F}_j = \frac{d\mathbf{L}_c}{dt} - \sum_{j=1}^{n} \mathbf{r}'_j \times \mathbf{F}_j, \tag{1–83}$$

or

$$\frac{d\mathbf{L}_0}{dt} - \mathbf{N}_0 = \frac{d\mathbf{L}_c}{dt} - \mathbf{N}_c, \tag{1–84}$$

where $\mathbf{N}_0$ and $\mathbf{N}_c$ are the torques about O and the center of mass respectively. By Newton's Second Law for rotational motion, the left side of Eq. (1–84) is zero. Hence we find that *the time rate of change of the angular momentum, for motion relative to the center of mass, equals the torque about the center of mass. This is true even if the center of mass has a translational motion relative to a fixed coordinate system.*

This is a very important theorem when applied to rigid-body motion. It means that when studying its rotational motion, we may ignore the translational motion of the center of mass of the body provided we refer all torques and angular momenta to the center of mass as origin. It is well to emphasize again, however, that the theorem is general and holds equally well for a swarm of particles in motion relative to one another.

It may be shown that the conservation laws for linear and for angular momentum (Section 1–8) hold also for a system of particles.

As an illustration of the theorems stated here, consider the two masses m_1 and m_2 linked by a rigid rod, as shown in Fig. 1–15. We shall assume that the rod has a mass which is negligible compared with m_1 and m_2. Let c denote the center of mass of the system. At $t = 0$, m_1 is at the origin and m_2 is rotating in the xy-plane, as shown by the arrow, with an

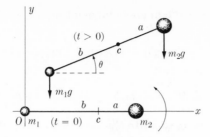

FIG. 1–15. Motion of two linked masses.

angular velocity $\dot\theta_0$. Let θ be the angle which the rod makes with the horizontal at some later time t when the masses have reached the upper position shown. Let $m = m_1 + m_2$ denote the entire mass of the system, and let (x_c, y_c) denote the coordinates of the center of mass at any time $t > 0$.

Then, by Eq. (1–77), we have as equations of motion for the center of mass

$$m\ddot{x}_c = 0, \qquad m\ddot{y}_c = - mg,$$

subject to the initial conditions

$$x_c(0) = b, \qquad \dot{x}_c(0) = 0,$$
$$y_c(0) = 0, \qquad \dot{y}_c(0) = b\dot\theta_0.$$

The solution of this initial value problem is

$$x_c(t) = b, \qquad y_c(t) = -\tfrac{1}{2}gt^2 + b\dot\theta_0 t,$$

and we have shown that the center of mass moves in a path which is identical with that of a single particle of mass m placed at the center of mass and acted upon there by the sum total of the forces on the system.

The total moment N_c of the forces $m_1 g$ and $m_2 g$ about the center of mass vanishes for $t > 0$. Hence by Newton's Second Law for rotational motion, Eq. (1–27), the angular momentum L_c is given by the system of equations

$$\frac{dL_c}{dt} = N_c = 0, \qquad L_c(0) = (m_1 b^2 + m_2 a^2)\dot\theta_0.$$

We observe that L_c is constant in time and equal to $L_c(0)$. Furthermore, the angular velocity $\dot\theta = \dot\theta_0$ for all $t > 0$.

In a similar way, the total moment about the origin O is found to be

$$N_0 = -m_1 g x_1 - m_2 g x_2 = - mg x_c = -mgb,$$

a constant. Therefore the angular momentum about O is given by

$$\frac{dL_0}{dt} = -mgb, \qquad L_0(0) = m_2(a+b)^2\dot\theta_0,$$

and

$$L_0(t) = -mgbt + m_2(a+b)^2\dot\theta_0.$$

Since $m_1 b = m_2 a$, we may write the last equation in the form

$$L_0 = -mgbt + m_2 a^2\dot\theta_0 + 2m_1 b^2\dot\theta_0 + m_2 b^2\dot\theta_0$$
$$= L_c - mgbt + mb^2\dot\theta_0.$$

But if all the mass $m = m_1 + m_2$ were concentrated at the center of mass, its angular momentum about O would be

$$mb\dot{y}_c = -mgbt + mb^2\dot\theta_0.$$

We see that this is precisely the last pair of terms in the expression for L_0 above. Hence in this simple example we have a verification of the theorem expressed by Eq. (1–81). The reader may verify also that Eq. (1–84) is valid here.

1–13 The energy of a particle system. The kinetic energy of the system of particles discussed in the preceding section is defined to be

$$T = \frac{1}{2}\sum_{j=1}^{n} m_j \dot{\mathbf{r}}_j^2. \tag{1-85}$$

But $\mathbf{r}_j = \mathbf{R} + \mathbf{r}'_j$ (Fig. 1–14), and hence

$$T = \frac{1}{2}\sum_{j=1}^{n} m_j[\dot{\mathbf{R}} + \dot{\mathbf{r}}'_j]^2$$

$$= \frac{1}{2}\sum_{j=1}^{n} m_j(\dot{\mathbf{R}}\cdot\dot{\mathbf{R}}) + \frac{1}{2}\sum_{j=1}^{n} m_j(\dot{\mathbf{r}}'_j\cdot\dot{\mathbf{r}}'_j) + \sum_{j=1}^{n} m_j(\dot{\mathbf{r}}'_j\cdot\dot{\mathbf{R}}). \tag{1-86}$$

By the definition of the center of mass, $\sum_{j=1}^{n} m_j \dot{\mathbf{r}}'_j$ vanishes and Eq. (1–86) reduces to

$$T = \frac{1}{2} M(\dot{\mathbf{R}}\cdot\dot{\mathbf{R}}) + \frac{1}{2}\sum_{j=1}^{n} m_j(\dot{\mathbf{r}}'_j\cdot\dot{\mathbf{r}}'_j). \tag{1-87}$$

The first term above is the kinetic energy of translation of the mass of the system considered as concentrated at the center of mass. The second term is the kinetic energy of the system of particles in their relative motion about the center of mass.

Again, let the jth particle be subjected to an external force $\mathbf{F}_j$ and an internal force $\mathbf{f}_{jk}$ due to the kth particle. Suppose the particle is given a displacement $d\mathbf{r}_j$. Then the work done on it by the external force is

$$dW_e = \mathbf{F}_j \cdot d\mathbf{r}_j. \tag{1-88}$$

But since, by Eq. (1-72), $\mathbf{F}_j = m_j\ddot{\mathbf{r}}_j - \sum_k \mathbf{f}_{jk}$ for the system of particles, we may write

$$dW_e = \sum_{j=1}^{n} m_j\ddot{\mathbf{r}}_j \cdot d\mathbf{r}_j - \sum_{j,k=1}^{n} \mathbf{f}_{jk} \cdot d\mathbf{r}_j \qquad (j \neq k). \tag{1-89}$$

However, since $d\mathbf{r}_j = \dot{\mathbf{r}}_j\, dt$, the first term on the right may be rewritten as

$$\frac{d}{dt}\left[\frac{1}{2}\sum_{j=1}^{n} m_j\dot{\mathbf{r}}_j^2\right] dt = dT, \tag{1-90}$$

where T is the kinetic energy.

The reduction of the second term in Eq. (1-89) is a little more complicated. Writing out several terms of this sum, we have

$$\mathbf{f}_{12}\cdot d\mathbf{r}_1 + \mathbf{f}_{21}\cdot d\mathbf{r}_2 + \mathbf{f}_{13}\cdot d\mathbf{r}_1 + \mathbf{f}_{31}\cdot d\mathbf{r}_3 + \mathbf{f}_{14}\cdot d\mathbf{r}_1 + \mathbf{f}_{41}\cdot d\mathbf{r}_4 + \ldots,$$

from which it is evident that the scalar products may be grouped in pairs. By Newton's Third Law, Eq. (1-74), this sum reduces to

$$\mathbf{f}_{12}\cdot(d\mathbf{r}_1 - d\mathbf{r}_2) + \mathbf{f}_{13}\cdot(d\mathbf{r}_1 - d\mathbf{r}_3) + \mathbf{f}_{14}\cdot(d\mathbf{r}_1 - d\mathbf{r}_4) + \ldots$$

or

$$\mathbf{f}_{12}\cdot d(\mathbf{r}_1 - \mathbf{r}_2) + \mathbf{f}_{13}\cdot d(\mathbf{r}_1 - \mathbf{r}_3) + \mathbf{f}_{14}\cdot d(\mathbf{r}_1 - \mathbf{r}_4) + \ldots.$$

But $\mathbf{r}_1 - \mathbf{r}_2$ is the vector from $\mathbf{r}_2$ to $\mathbf{r}_1$ and similarly, in general, $\mathbf{r}_j - \mathbf{r}_k$ is the vector joining the kth to the jth point. Call it $\mathbf{r}_{jk}$. Then the second sum in Eq. (1-89) becomes

$$-\sum_{j,k=1}^{n} \mathbf{f}_{jk}\cdot d\mathbf{r}_j = -\frac{1}{2}\sum_{j,k=1}^{n} \mathbf{f}_{jk}\cdot d\mathbf{r}_{jk} \qquad (j \neq k). \tag{1-91}$$

This quantity is the *internal potential energy* of the system. Call it dV_i. Let us assume that the external forces are conservative and define the external potential energy by

$$dV_e = -dW_e. \tag{1-92}$$

Then from Eqs. (1–89), (1–90), and (1–92) we have

$$dT + dV_i + dV_e = 0, \tag{1–93}$$

or

$$T + V_i + V_e = \text{constant}, \tag{1–94}$$

which expresses *the law of conservation of energy for the system*. For the case of a rigid body where the particles are fixed relative to one another, $dV_i = 0$ and the internal potential energy is constant.

As an example, consider again the two-mass system shown in Fig. 1–15. The kinetic energy of the system is

$$T = \tfrac{1}{2}[m_1(\dot{x}_1^2 + \dot{y}_1^2) + m_2(\dot{x}_2^2 + \dot{y}_2^2)],$$

where (x_1, y_1) and (x_2, y_2) are the positions of m_1 and m_2 at time $t > 0$. But here

$$x_1 = x_c - b \cos \theta, \qquad x_2 = x_c + a \cos \theta,$$

$$y_1 = y_c - b \sin \theta, \qquad y_2 = y_c + a \sin \theta.$$

Differentiating with respect to time, substituting in the expression for T, and simplifying, we find

$$T = \tfrac{1}{2}m(\dot{x}_c^2 + \dot{y}_c^2) + \tfrac{1}{2}(m_1 b^2 + m_2 a^2)\dot{\theta}^2.$$

The first term is the kinetic energy of translation of the center of mass; the second term is the rotational kinetic energy of the masses m_1 and m_2 about the center of mass. This result exemplifies Eq. (1–87).

1–14 Motion in a moving reference frame. In our discussion of motion in the preceding sections, we have assumed the existence of a coordinate system in which Newton's laws of motion are valid. Such a frame of reference is called a *primary inertial system*. By definition, according to Newton's First Law, in such a system a body subject to no forces moves in a straight line with constant velocity, and in accordance with its inertial characteristics only. Such a reference frame is difficult to realize in practice. One that seems to meet the requirements closely is a system of axes whose origin is the centroid of the fixed stars in the neighborhood of the sun. This we know is only an approximation, because these "fixed" stars are moving systematically with respect to the center of the galaxy. But the effect of this motion is so small and the motion is so uniform that its importance for dynamical studies on the surface of the earth is negligible.

A reference frame on the earth's surface, however, experiences a rotation about the earth's axis, and shares the earth's motion about the sun and the sun's motion relative to the fixed stars. In this section we shall see what modification of the laws of motion is necessary because of the motion of a reference frame on the earth relative to a primary inertial system.

In describing rotational motion, we shall define more fully the concept of *angular velocity*. We shall show that the angular velocity may be represented vectorially and, further, that angular velocities may be compounded by vector algebra.

In Fig. 1–16 let P be a point whose position vector relative to an origin O is $\mathbf{r}$. Let the unit vector $\mathbf{u}_n$ define the direction of an axis through O about which P moves, on a circle, to P'. The radius of the arc described by P is $r \sin \alpha$. Let the angle subtended by the arc PP' be $\Delta\theta$. Then, for small $\Delta\theta$, we have, approximately,

$$| \mathbf{r}' - \mathbf{r} | = | \Delta\mathbf{r} | \cong r \sin \alpha \, \Delta\theta,$$

but $r \sin \alpha = | \mathbf{u}_n \times \mathbf{r}. |$ Hence

$$\mathbf{r}' - \mathbf{r} = \Delta\mathbf{r} \cong \Delta\theta \mathbf{u}_n \times \mathbf{r}. \quad (1\text{--}95)$$

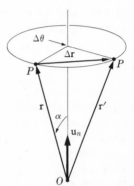

If Δt is the time interval during which P moves to P', we may write

$$\frac{\Delta\mathbf{r}}{\Delta t} = \frac{\Delta\theta}{\Delta t} \, \mathbf{u}_n \times \mathbf{r},$$

and in the limit as $\Delta t \to 0$

$$\frac{d\mathbf{r}}{dt} = \frac{d\theta}{dt} \, \mathbf{u}_n \times \mathbf{r}. \quad (1\text{--}96)$$

FIG. 1–16. Infinitesimal rotation.

We define the scalar $d\theta/dt$ to be the angular speed of rotation of P about the *axis* defined by $\mathbf{u}_n$. Furthermore, Eq. (1–96) suggests that the vector $(d\theta/dt) \, \mathbf{u}_n$ be called the *angular velocity of P*. It has a direction defined by $\mathbf{u}_n$ and is localized through the fixed point O.

If the axis of rotation is the x-axis of a cartesian system, the unit vector defining the direction of the angular velocity vector is $\mathbf{i}$. Then Eq. (1–96) may be written

$$\frac{d\mathbf{r}}{dt} = \omega_x \mathbf{i} \times \mathbf{r}, \quad (1\text{--}97)$$

where ω_x is the angular speed of rotation about Ox.

Suppose successive rotations of P relative to a fixed origin are performed about the coordinate axes as follows:

$$P \to P' \text{ about } Ox \text{ through angle } \Delta\theta_x,$$

$$P' \to P'' \text{ about } Oy \text{ through angle } \Delta\theta_y,$$

$$P'' \to P''' \text{ about } Oz \text{ through angle } \Delta\theta_z.$$

Then, by Eq. (1–95), we have successively, for initial radius vector $\mathbf{r}$,

$$\mathbf{r}' = \mathbf{r} + \Delta\theta_x \mathbf{i} \times \mathbf{r}, \qquad (1\text{–}98)$$

$$\mathbf{r}'' = \mathbf{r}' + \Delta\theta_y \mathbf{j} \times \mathbf{r}', \qquad (1\text{–}99)$$

$$\mathbf{r}''' = \mathbf{r}'' + \Delta\theta_z \mathbf{k} \times \mathbf{r}''. \qquad (1\text{–}100)$$

Substitution of Eqs. (1–98) and (1–99) into Eq. (1–100) and subsequent neglect of higher-order terms such as $\Delta\theta_x\,\Delta\theta_y$, $\Delta\theta_x\,\Delta\theta_y\,\Delta\theta_z$, yields

$$\mathbf{r}''' - \mathbf{r} = \Delta\mathbf{r} = (\Delta\theta_x \mathbf{i} + \Delta\theta_y \mathbf{j} + \Delta\theta_z \mathbf{k}) \times \mathbf{r}. \qquad (1\text{–}101)$$

Had we performed the rotations in any other order, we would have obtained the same value for $\Delta\mathbf{r}$. Dividing by Δt and proceeding to the limit as $\Delta t \to 0$, we have

$$\frac{d\mathbf{r}}{dt} = (\omega_x \mathbf{i} + \omega_y \mathbf{j} + \omega_z \mathbf{k}) \times \mathbf{r}, \qquad (1\text{–}102)$$

where $\omega_x = (d\theta_x/dt)$, $\omega_y = (d\theta_y/dt)$, $\omega_z = (d\theta_z/dt)$ are the angular speeds which the particle would have had if rotation had taken place about the Ox-, Oy-, or Oz-axes separately. Since Eq. (1–101) does not depend upon the order of addition, it is clear that the infinitesimal rotations and hence, by Eq. (1–102), the angular velocities may be added vectorially. The angular velocity $\boldsymbol{\omega} = \omega_x \mathbf{i} + \omega_y \mathbf{j} + \omega_z \mathbf{k}$ is localized along the axis of rotation through O and has for positive direction the sense of advance of a right-threaded screw.

For simplicity, we consider next two cartesian reference frames whose z-axes and origins coincide. Let the (x_0,y_0,z_0) axes be fixed in space and be such that the Newtonian equations of motion are valid. Let the (x,y,z) system, on the other hand, rotate with angular speed ω about the z_0 axis. The situation is shown in Fig. 1–17, where $\mathbf{i}$, $\mathbf{j}$, $\mathbf{k}$ are unit vectors along Ox, Oy, Oz in the moving system. Then $\mathbf{r} = x\mathbf{i} + y\mathbf{j} + z\mathbf{k}$, where, in general, as P moves, all the x, y, z, $\mathbf{i}$, $\mathbf{j}$ change with the time.

(a) Suppose, first, that P is *fixed* in the (x,y,z) system. An observer in the system (x_0,y_0,z_0) would say that P revolves about the z_0 axis with a linear velocity $r\omega \sin\alpha$. But vectorially this is $\boldsymbol{\omega} \times \mathbf{r}$, as shown in Eq. (1–102). An observer in the (x,y,z) system would say that P was stationary.

(b) Suppose, now, that P *moves* in the (x,y,z) system with a velocity $\mathbf{v} = x\mathbf{i} + y\mathbf{j} + z\mathbf{k}$. This would be the velocity measured by an observer rotating with this system. But to an outsider, that is, one in the (x_0,y_0,z_0) system, P would appear to have two motions, one described by $\mathbf{v}$ and one due to the rotating axes $\boldsymbol{\omega} \times \mathbf{r}$. To this observer, P would be moving with a velocity

$$\mathbf{v}_0 = \mathbf{v} + \boldsymbol{\omega} \times \mathbf{r}. \qquad (1\text{–}103)$$

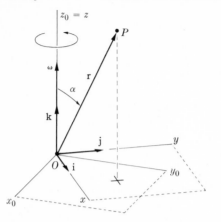

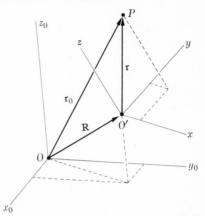

FIG. 1–17. Rotating reference frame.   FIG. 1–18. Translating and rotating reference frame.

To generalize the case above, we remove the restriction that the z-axes of the two systems coincide. At any instant let the angular velocity vector, referred to the moving axes, be $\boldsymbol{\omega} = \omega_x\mathbf{i} + \omega_y\mathbf{j} + \omega_z\mathbf{k}$. By definition, the velocity relative to the fixed system will be

$$\mathbf{v}_0 = \frac{d\mathbf{r}}{dt} = \dot{x}\mathbf{i} + \dot{y}\mathbf{j} + \dot{z}\mathbf{k} + x\frac{d\mathbf{i}}{dt} + y\frac{d\mathbf{j}}{dt} + z\frac{d\mathbf{k}}{dt}. \qquad (1\text{–}104)$$

But the first three terms of Eq. (1–104) comprise the velocity as observed in the (x,y,z) system. We have called it $\mathbf{v}$. Let us examine the last three terms.

The point $\mathbf{r} = \mathbf{i}$ in the (x,y,z) system is fixed relative to that system. Hence to an observer in (x_0,y_0,z_0) it behaves as described in (a) above. Thus $(d\mathbf{i}/dt) = \boldsymbol{\omega} \times \mathbf{i}$. In a similar way, $(d\mathbf{j}/dt) = \boldsymbol{\omega} \times \mathbf{j}$ and $(d\mathbf{k}/dt) = \boldsymbol{\omega} \times \mathbf{k}$. We conclude that

$$x\frac{d\mathbf{i}}{dt} + y\frac{d\mathbf{j}}{dt} + z\frac{d\mathbf{k}}{dt} = \boldsymbol{\omega} \times (x\mathbf{i} + y\mathbf{j} + z\mathbf{k}) = \boldsymbol{\omega} \times \mathbf{r}. \qquad (1\text{–}105)$$

When this is substituted in Eq. (1–104), we see the correspondence with the velocity $\mathbf{v}_0$ derived intuitively in Eq. (1–103).

If the (x,y,z) axes experience a translation relative to the (x_0,y_0,z_0) system (Fig. 1–18) the origins no longer coincide, and we have for P

$$\mathbf{r}_0 = \mathbf{R} + \mathbf{r}.$$

Hence for its velocity we obtain

$$\dot{\mathbf{r}}_0 = \dot{\mathbf{R}} + \dot{\mathbf{r}},$$

and, from Eq. (1–103),

$$\mathbf{v}_0 = \dot{\mathbf{R}} + \mathbf{v} + \boldsymbol{\omega} \times \mathbf{r}. \qquad (1\text{–}106)$$

Thus the linear velocity in the primary inertial system (x_0, y_0, z_0) is made up of three parts: (1) the velocity of transport of the moving origin O', (2) the velocity of the point as observed in the moving system, and (3) the velocity due to the rotation of the (x, y, z) axes.

The acceleration relative to the fixed axes is obtained by differentiating Eq. (1–106) with respect to the time. We obtain

$$\mathbf{a}_0 = \frac{d\mathbf{v}_0}{dt} = \ddot{\mathbf{R}} + \dot{\mathbf{v}} + \dot{\boldsymbol{\omega}} \times \mathbf{r} + \boldsymbol{\omega} \times \dot{\mathbf{r}}. \qquad (1\text{–}107)$$

But

$$\dot{\mathbf{v}} = \ddot{x}\mathbf{i} + \ddot{y}\mathbf{j} + \ddot{z}\mathbf{k} + \dot{x}\frac{d\mathbf{i}}{dt} + \dot{y}\frac{d\mathbf{j}}{dt} + \dot{z}\frac{d\mathbf{k}}{dt}.$$

Denoting $\ddot{x}\mathbf{i} + \ddot{y}\mathbf{j} + \ddot{z}\mathbf{k}$ by $\mathbf{a}$, we have

$$\dot{\mathbf{v}} = \mathbf{a} + \boldsymbol{\omega} \times \mathbf{v},$$

and, since $\dot{\mathbf{r}} = \mathbf{v} + \boldsymbol{\omega} \times \mathbf{r}$,

$$\mathbf{a}_0 = \ddot{\mathbf{R}} + \mathbf{a} + \boldsymbol{\omega} \times \mathbf{v} + \dot{\boldsymbol{\omega}} \times \mathbf{r} + \boldsymbol{\omega} \times \{\mathbf{v} + \boldsymbol{\omega} \times \mathbf{r}\},$$

or

$$\mathbf{a}_0 = \ddot{\mathbf{R}} + \mathbf{a} + 2\boldsymbol{\omega} \times \mathbf{v} + \dot{\boldsymbol{\omega}} \times \mathbf{r} + \boldsymbol{\omega} \times (\boldsymbol{\omega} \times \mathbf{r}), \qquad (1\text{–}108)$$

where:

$\mathbf{a}_0$ is the acceleration as observed in the (x_0, y_0, z_0) system.

$\ddot{\mathbf{R}}$ is the acceleration of the moving origin O'.

$\mathbf{a}$ is the apparent acceleration for an observer in the (x, y, z) system who shares in the motion of that system.

$2\boldsymbol{\omega} \times \mathbf{v}$ is the so-called Coriolis acceleration. Obviously for a particle at rest in the (x, y, z) system this term vanishes.

$\dot{\boldsymbol{\omega}} \times \mathbf{r}$ is the acceleration due to the rotational acceleration of the moving system. Since $\boldsymbol{\omega} = \omega_x\mathbf{i} + \omega_y\mathbf{j} + \omega_z\mathbf{k}$, its derivative

$$\dot{\boldsymbol{\omega}} = \dot{\omega}_x\mathbf{i} + \dot{\omega}_y\mathbf{j} + \dot{\omega}_z\mathbf{k} + \omega_x\frac{d\mathbf{i}}{dt} + \omega_y\frac{d\mathbf{j}}{dt} + \omega_z\frac{d\mathbf{k}}{dt}.$$

But, by analogy with Eqs. (1–104) and (1–105), the last three terms may be written $\boldsymbol{\omega} \times \boldsymbol{\omega} = 0$. Hence

$$\dot{\boldsymbol{\omega}} = \dot{\omega}_x\mathbf{i} + \dot{\omega}_y\mathbf{j} + \dot{\omega}_z\mathbf{k}, \qquad (1\text{–}109)$$

and $\dot{\boldsymbol{\omega}}$ may be taken either as the time rate of increase of $\boldsymbol{\omega}$ relative to the moving system or as the angular acceleration of the rotating system relative to the fixed system.

$\boldsymbol{\omega} \times (\boldsymbol{\omega} \times \mathbf{r})$ is the centripetal acceleration. Since $\boldsymbol{\omega} \times \mathbf{r}$ is perpendicular to the plane of $\boldsymbol{\omega}$ and $\mathbf{r}$, the product $\boldsymbol{\omega} \times (\boldsymbol{\omega} \times \mathbf{r})$ is a vector lying in the plane of $\boldsymbol{\omega}$ and $\mathbf{r}$. In expanded form,

$$\boldsymbol{\omega} \times (\boldsymbol{\omega} \times \mathbf{r}) = (\boldsymbol{\omega}\cdot\mathbf{r})\boldsymbol{\omega} - (\boldsymbol{\omega}\cdot\boldsymbol{\omega})\mathbf{r}. \qquad (1\text{–}110)$$

Factoring the scalar, $-\boldsymbol{\omega}\cdot\boldsymbol{\omega}$, or $-\omega^2$, out of Eq. (1–110), we have

$$-\omega^2 \left\{ \mathbf{r} - \left(\frac{\boldsymbol{\omega}\cdot\mathbf{r}}{\omega}\right)\frac{\boldsymbol{\omega}}{\omega} \right\}. \qquad (1\text{–}111)$$

Since $\boldsymbol{\omega}/\omega$ is a unit vector in the $\boldsymbol{\omega}$ direction, and the term in the braces is a vector in the $\boldsymbol{\omega}$ direction of magnitude $r \cos \theta$, where θ is the angle between $\mathbf{r}$ and $\boldsymbol{\omega}$, then $\mathbf{r} - (\mathbf{u}_\omega\cdot\mathbf{r})\mathbf{u}_\omega$ is a vector perpendicular to $\boldsymbol{\omega}$ and of magnitude $r \sin \theta$. Let $\mathbf{u}_n$ be the unit vector perpendicular to $\boldsymbol{\omega}$ and in the outward direction. Then

$$\boldsymbol{\omega} \times (\boldsymbol{\omega} \times \mathbf{r}) = -\omega^2 r \sin \theta \mathbf{u}_n. \qquad (1\text{–}112)$$

This is the *centripetal acceleration*. It is directed inward toward the instantaneous axis of rotation.

Since Newton's Second Law of motion is valid within the fixed reference frame, we have, for a particle of constant mass,

$$m\mathbf{a}_0 = m\ddot{\mathbf{R}} + m\mathbf{a} + 2m\boldsymbol{\omega} \times \mathbf{v} + m\dot{\boldsymbol{\omega}} \times \mathbf{r} + m\boldsymbol{\omega} \times (\boldsymbol{\omega} \times \mathbf{r}) = \mathbf{F},$$

where $\mathbf{F}$ is the resultant force on the particle. To an observer in the moving reference frame, the apparent equation of motion would be

$$m\mathbf{a} = \mathbf{F} - m\ddot{\mathbf{R}} - 2m\boldsymbol{\omega} \times \mathbf{v} - m\dot{\boldsymbol{\omega}} \times \mathbf{r} - m\boldsymbol{\omega} \times (\boldsymbol{\omega} \times \mathbf{r}). \qquad (1\text{–}113)$$

To him the mass would appear to move under the action of the entire force on the right of Eq. (1–113). Most of these terms are small. Some are automatically incorporated into a force measurement, as on the surface of the earth. We shall develop this more fully in the next section.

1–15 Motion on the rotating earth. Consider a particle moving on the surface of the earth. Let O be the center of the earth (Fig. 1–19), and let O' be the origin of a coordinate system fixed on the surface of the earth. The line NS designates the earth's axis. We neglect the translational acceleration of O due to the earth's motion about the sun and to the solar motion in space. In other words, we consider O and NS to define a reference frame with respect to which Newton's laws of motion are valid. Choose the z-axis to be the upward *direction of the plumb line.*

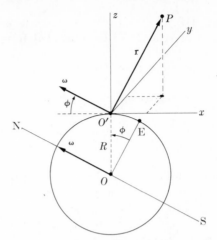

FIG. 1–19. Reference frame on the earth.

The x-axis points south; the y-axis points east. Let $\mathbf{i}, \mathbf{j}, \mathbf{k}$ be unit vectors in this system, which rotates about NS with angular velocity $\boldsymbol{\omega}$, assumed constant. We shall designate the latitude of O' by ϕ.

As in Section 1–14, let $\mathbf{r}$ and $\mathbf{v}$ be the position and velocity as observed in the (x,y,z) system. The position of O' relative to O is $\mathbf{R}$. Any point P is accelerated relative to O due to (1) the acceleration of O' about NS, (2) the rotation of the (x,y,z) axes about NS, and (3) the intrinsic acceleration of P in the (x,y,z) system. From Eq. (1–107),

$$\mathbf{a}_0 = \ddot{\mathbf{R}} + \mathbf{a} + 2\boldsymbol{\omega} \times \mathbf{v} + \boldsymbol{\omega} \times (\boldsymbol{\omega} \times \mathbf{r}) \tag{1–114}$$

$$= \boldsymbol{\omega} \times (\boldsymbol{\omega} \times \mathbf{R}) + \mathbf{a} + 2\boldsymbol{\omega} \times \mathbf{v} + \boldsymbol{\omega} \times (\boldsymbol{\omega} \times \mathbf{r}). \tag{1–115}$$

Suppose the external force acting at P is $\mathbf{F} = X\mathbf{i} + Y\mathbf{j} + Z\mathbf{k}$, and let the force exerted by the earth be $\mathbf{G}$. Then, by Eq. (1–113), we have

$$m\mathbf{a} = \mathbf{F} + \mathbf{G} - m[\boldsymbol{\omega} \times (\boldsymbol{\omega} \times \mathbf{R})] - 2m\boldsymbol{\omega} \times \mathbf{v} - m[\boldsymbol{\omega} \times (\boldsymbol{\omega} \times \mathbf{r})], \tag{1–116}$$

which yields the acceleration as observed on the earth's surface.

The acceleration due to gravity, as measured by a pendulum, refers to the attraction of the earth *and* to the centrifugal force due to the earth's rotation. That is, the plumb line has a direction defined by the vector $\mathbf{G} - m[\boldsymbol{\omega} \times (\boldsymbol{\omega} \times \mathbf{R})]$. In our coordinate system, therefore, the "force of gravity" is given by $-mg\mathbf{k}$.

Furthermore, since ω is 7.3×10^{-5} radians/sec, the term $\boldsymbol{\omega} \times (\boldsymbol{\omega} \times \mathbf{r})$ is of the order of magnitude of 10^{-10}, and we shall neglect it in comparison with the term $2\boldsymbol{\omega} \times \mathbf{v}$. Also,

$$\boldsymbol{\omega} \times \mathbf{v} = \begin{vmatrix} \mathbf{i} & \mathbf{j} & \mathbf{k} \\ \omega_x & \omega_y & \omega_z \\ \dot{x} & \dot{y} & \dot{z} \end{vmatrix} = \begin{vmatrix} \mathbf{i} & \mathbf{j} & \mathbf{k} \\ -\omega\cos\phi & 0 & \omega\sin\phi \\ \dot{x} & \dot{y} & \dot{z} \end{vmatrix}, \quad (1\text{–}117)$$

and $\mathbf{a} = \ddot{x}\mathbf{i} + \ddot{y}\mathbf{j} + \ddot{z}\mathbf{k}$.

Finally, as scalar equations of motion appropriate in a reference frame on the surface of the earth, we obtain

$$m\ddot{x} = X + 2m\omega\dot{y}\sin\phi,$$
$$m\ddot{y} = Y - 2m\omega(\dot{x}\sin\phi + \dot{z}\cos\phi), \quad (1\text{–}118)$$
$$m\ddot{z} = Z - mg + 2m\omega\dot{y}\cos\phi.$$

As an application of Eq. (1–118), consider a long Foucault pendulum whose point of support is on the z-axis at $(0,0,L)$ so that the bob, when at rest, is at the origin of the coordinate system (Fig. 1–20). The point of support is such that the pendulum can rotate freely about the z-axis. The length of the pendulum is L; the tension in the supporting wire is T. We assume that the mass of the wire is negligible in comparison with the mass m of the bob.

When the bob is at $P(x,y,z)$, the components of T in the coordinate directions are

$$X = -\frac{x}{L}\,T, \qquad Y = -\frac{y}{L}\,T, \qquad Z = \frac{L-z}{L}\,T. \quad (1\text{–}119)$$

These, together with the force of gravity, are the forces acting on the bob.

We shall study the motion under the following assumptions: (1) Oscillations of the bob are so small that terms of second order and higher in

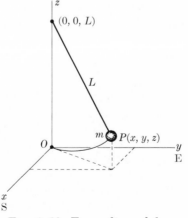

Fig. 1–20. Foucault pendulum.

coordinates and velocities may be neglected. (2) Oscillation in z will be neglected; i.e., the motion takes place approximately in the xy-plane; this means that $\dot{z}$ and $\ddot{z}$ are zero. (3) The angular velocity of the earth's rotation is so small (7.3×10^{-5} radians/sec) that squares and higher powers of ω are negligible compared with the angular velocity of swing of the pendulum in its plane. (4) Frictional torques produced by the support mechanism are negligible.

The equations of motion are

$$m\ddot{x} = -\frac{x}{L}\, T + 2m\omega\dot{y} \sin\,\phi, \qquad (1\text{--}120)$$

$$m\ddot{y} = -\frac{y}{L}\, T - 2m\omega(\dot{x} \sin\,\phi + \dot{z} \cos\,\phi), \qquad (1\text{--}121)$$

$$m\ddot{z} = \frac{L-z}{L}\, T - mg + 2m\omega\dot{y} \cos\,\phi. \qquad (1\text{--}122)$$

From Eq. (1–122), by virtue of assumption (2) and the fact that $z/L \ll 1$, we have

$$T = mg - 2m\omega\dot{y} \cos\,\phi. \qquad (1\text{--}123)$$

Substitution of this value for T in Eqs. (1–120) and (1–121) yields

$$m\ddot{x} = -\frac{x}{L}\, [mg - 2m\omega\dot{y} \cos\,\phi] + 2m\omega\dot{y} \sin\,\phi,$$

$$m\ddot{y} = -\frac{y}{L}\, [mg - 2m\omega\dot{y} \cos\,\phi] - 2m\omega[\dot{x} \sin\,\phi + \dot{z} \cos\,\phi],$$

and by using assumptions (1) and (2) these may be simplified to

$$m\ddot{x} = -\frac{x}{L}\, mg + 2m\omega\dot{y} \sin\,\phi, \qquad (1\text{--}124)$$

$$m\ddot{y} = -\frac{y}{L}\, mg - 2m\omega\dot{x} \sin\,\phi. \qquad (1\text{--}125)$$

Let $\alpha^2 = g/L$; then Eqs. (1–124) and (1–125) become

$$\ddot{x} + \alpha^2 x = 2\omega\dot{y} \sin\,\phi, \qquad (1\text{--}126)$$

$$\ddot{y} + \alpha^2 y = -2\omega\dot{x} \sin\,\phi. \qquad (1\text{--}127)$$

These are the equations for two-dimensional simple harmonic motion with the addition of a driving force in each coordinate proportional to the velocity in the mutually orthogonal direction. There is a *dynamic coupling* between the x- and y-components of the motion.

The behavior of the bob may be described concisely by using the notion of complex numbers. Multiplying Eq. (1–127) by i, where $i^2 = -1$, and adding the result to Eq. (1–126), we have

$$(\ddot{x} + i\ddot{y}) + \alpha^2(x + iy) = 2\omega(\dot{y} - i\dot{x})\sin\phi, \qquad (1\text{--}128)$$

or, factoring out the i on the right,

$$(\ddot{x} + i\ddot{y}) + \alpha^2(x + iy) = -2\omega i(\dot{x} + i\dot{y})\sin\phi. \qquad (1\text{--}129)$$

But this may be written

$$\ddot{u} + \alpha^2 u = -2\omega i\dot{u}\sin\phi, \qquad (1\text{--}130)$$

where $u = x + iy$, which we solve in a conventional way by writing $u = Ae^{\lambda t}$, where λ and A are to be determined. Substituting in Eq. (1–130), we find that

$$\lambda^2 + 2i\omega\lambda\sin\phi + \alpha^2 = 0 \qquad (1\text{--}131)$$

is a solution. This characteristic equation yields

$$\lambda = \tfrac{1}{2}[-2i\omega\sin\phi \pm \sqrt{-4\omega^2\sin^2\phi - 4\alpha^2}]$$

$$= -i\omega\sin\phi \pm i\sqrt{\omega^2\sin^2\phi + \alpha^2}.$$

But by assumption (3), $\omega^2\sin^2\phi \ll \alpha^2$ and may be neglected. Hence

$$\lambda = -i\omega\sin\phi \pm i\alpha. \qquad (1\text{--}132)$$

The general solution of the equation of motion then becomes

$$u = \{Ae^{i\alpha t} + Be^{-i\alpha t}\}e^{-i\omega t\sin\phi}, \qquad (1\text{--}133)$$

where A and B are constants that must be fixed by the initial conditions under which the pendulum is started.

In Eq. (1–133) let the quantity $Ae^{i\alpha t} + Be^{-i\alpha t} = u_0$. By Euler's relations $e^{i\alpha t} = \cos\alpha t + i\sin\alpha t$ and $e^{-i\alpha t} = \cos\alpha t - i\sin\alpha t$; therefore we may write $u_0 = C_1\cos\alpha t + iC_2\sin\alpha t$, where $C_1 = A + B$ and $C_2 = A - B$. The complex number $u_0 = x_0 + iy_0$ then has real and imaginary parts which change with time; that is,

$$x_0 = C_1\cos\alpha t, \qquad y_0 = C_2\sin\alpha t. \qquad (1\text{--}134)$$

But these are the parametric equations of an ellipse in the xy-plane. If we consider t fixed, the bob is describing an ellipse instantaneously.

The second factor in Eq. (1–133), $e^{-i\omega t\sin\phi}$, describes a rotation of the axes of the ellipse by an amount proportional to the time. To summarize the results of our analysis:

(1) The position of the bob at any instant is specified by the complex number $u = u_0 e^{-i\omega t \sin \phi}$.

(2) The modulus u_0 is periodic, with period $2\pi/\alpha$, so that the bob oscillates about the origin either in elliptic motion or in plane motion depending upon the initial conditions.

(3) The radius vector corresponding to the complex number u is rotating steadily in the xy-plane so as to make one rotation about the z-axis in $2\pi/\omega \sin \phi$ seconds. This is a rotation toward the x-axis and hence toward the west when the bob is south of the z-axis. The plane of the motion or, if the elliptical path is being followed, the axis of the ellipse, appears to rotate clockwise about the vertical as seen by an observer in the northern hemisphere.

PROBLEMS

1-1. A projectile is shot vertically upward from the earth's surface with an initial velocity v_0 ft/sec. The air resistance is proportional to the velocity. (a) If the projectile weighs W lb, write the differential equation of motion. (b) Find an expression for the height to which the projectile will rise and for the time at which it will strike the ground. (c) Compute this time and the height if $v_0 = 100$ ft/sec, $g = 32$ ft/sec^2, $k = 10^{-3}W$, where k is the coefficient of resistance. (Section 1–3)

1-2. A small particle of constant mass m is projected with velocity $\mathbf{v}_0$ from the earth's surface at an angle α with the horizontal, as shown in Fig. 1–21. It is acted upon by gravity and by a resisting force $-mkv$, where k is constant. At any point P of its path, the tangent makes an angle θ with the horizontal. Using Eq. (1–4), (a) write the equations of motion for the particle in terms of the speed v and the angle θ. (b) Solve for $v(\theta)$ and the velocity components $\dot{x}(\theta)$ and $\dot{y}(\theta)$. (c) Find θ as a function of t and hence the time at which the particle attains its maximum height. (Section 1–3)

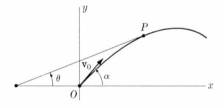

FIGURE 1–21

1-3. Suppose a rocket with its fuel has a mass m at time t. When fired vertically from the earth, the rocket itself had a mass m_r and its fuel a mass m_f. The mass of fuel consumed is proportional to the time. The rocket has an initial velocity v_0. Gravity is assumed to be the only force acting on the rocket other than the reaction due to the loss of fuel. Show that the differential equation of motion is

$$m\frac{dv}{dt} = -v'\frac{dm}{dt} - mg,$$

where v' is the absolute value of the velocity of the exhaust gas relative to the rocket. Solve the equation for v as a function of m, under the assumption that v' is constant. (Section 1–3)

1-4. A raindrop of initial mass m_0 gm falls from rest through a cloud whose thickness is a cm. As it falls, the drop gains mass at the rate of b gm/sec. The droplets of the cloud are at rest relative to the ground. The motion of the drop is resisted by a force proportional to the velocity. (a) Write the differential equation for the motion. (b) Find the velocity of the drop as it emerges from the cloud if, during the passage, its mass has been doubled. (c) What will be the limiting velocity of the drop after it leaves the cloud on the assumption that the air resistance outside the cloud is the same as within? (Section 1–3)

1–5. A particle whose mass is $m = m_0(1 + ct)$ moves in a horizontal line subject to a force of attraction proportional to the distance of the particle from an origin O. Write the differential equation for its motion and solve it, subject to the initial conditions, $x = x_0$, $\dot{x} = 0$ at $t = 0$. *Hint:* The resulting equation is reducible to a Bessel equation. (Section 1–3)

1–6. A bead of mass m slides without friction along a rod, one end of which is pivoted in such a way that the rod can be revolved about the z-axis at a constant angle α, as shown in Fig. 1–22. The rod is driven with constant angular velocity ω about Oz. Discuss the motion of the bead. In what circumstances will the bead be in equilibrium on the rod? (Sections 1–3 and 1–5)

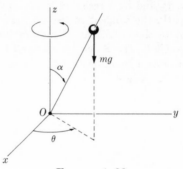

FIGURE 1–22

1–7. Show that for a constant mass Newton's Second Law of motion is valid in a coordinate system which is being uniformly translated in space. Does this result hold if the mass is a function of the time? (Section 1–3)

1–8. Determine whether each of the following forces is conservative and, if so, find a potential function. (Section 1–7)

(a) $\mathbf{F} = \dfrac{y}{\sqrt{x^2 + y^2}}\,\mathbf{i} - \dfrac{x}{\sqrt{x^2 + y^2}}\,\mathbf{j}.$

(b) $\mathbf{F} = xf(r)\mathbf{i} + yf(r)\mathbf{j}$, where $f(r)$ is an arbitrary function of the distance from the origin.

(c) $\mathbf{F} = \dfrac{y}{x^2 + y^2}\,\mathbf{i} - \dfrac{x}{x^2 + y^2}\,\mathbf{j}.$

(d) $\mathbf{F} = 2xy^3z^4\mathbf{i} + 3x^2y^2z^4\mathbf{j} + 4x^2y^3z^3\mathbf{k}.$

1–9. Rectilinear motion of a mass m takes place in a potential energy field given by $V(x) = -1/x + 1/x^2$. (a) Write the energy equation and draw an energy diagram for the system. Discuss the motion by means of the diagram. (b) Compute the period of oscillation for a given fixed total energy E. (c) For what value of E, and corresponding x, will the particle remain at rest? What is the force on the particle at this point? (Section 1–9)

1–10. A mass m describes straight-line motion in a potential field $V(s) = 2as^2 - as^4$, where a is a positive constant and s is the displacement of the particle at time t. Discuss the motion by means of an energy diagram and compute the period of small oscillations about points of lowest potential energy. (Section 1–9)

1–11. Suppose a mass m oscillates according to the equation $m\ddot{x} + a\dot{x} + bx = 0$. Describe the characteristics of its motion by means of an energy diagram. (Section 1–9)

1–12. A pendulum bob, mounted on a light stiff rod, is supported on a rotating table, as shown in Fig. 1–23. The plane of the pendulum motion is always

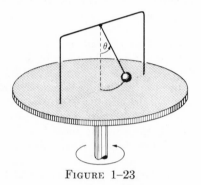

FIGURE 1–23

perpendicular to the plane of the supporting framework. Let the mass of the bob be m, length of pendulum l, moment of inertia of turntable about its axis I. Let θ be the angular displacement of the pendulum from the vertical at time t. The rod supporting the bob has negligible mass compared with m. The moment of inertia I is large compared with the moment of inertia of the bob about the vertical.

Initially $\theta = 0$, $v = v_0$ for the bob, where v is the velocity of the bob, and $\omega = \omega_0$, where ω is the angular velocity of the turntable at time t.

From the laws for conservation of energy and conservation of angular momentum, together with an energy diagram, discuss the motion of the system. (*Hint:* Expand $\sin \theta$ and $\cos \theta$ where necessary into Maclaurin series and retain ultimately terms to the fourth order in θ.) Distinguish between the situations when θ is small and when θ is large. Investigate the critical angular velocity $\omega_0 = \sqrt{g/l}$; i.e., state what happens when $\omega_0 < \sqrt{g/l}$ and when $\omega_0 > \sqrt{g/l}$. (Sections 1–8 and 1–9)

1–13. A mass m of 1000 gm hangs at the end of a vertical stiff rod whose mass is negligible compared with m. The rod is 100 cm long and is pivoted at a point 25 cm from its upper end. What is the magnitude of the smallest horizontal blow on the mass at the lower end of the rod which will make it describe a complete rotation about the pivot? (Sections 1–10 and 1–11)

1–14. A particle of mass $3m$ gm explodes into three equal pieces. Two of the pieces fly off at right angles to each other, one with a speed of $2a$ cm/sec, the other with a speed of $3a$ cm/sec. What is the magnitude and direction of the momentum of the third fragment? The explosion takes place in 10^{-5} sec. Find the average force acting on each piece during the explosion. (Sections 1–10 and 1–11)

1–15. A ping-pong ball is dropped from a height of 5 ft onto a hard, smooth, fixed tabletop. It bounces to a height of 4.05 ft. Compute the coefficient of restitution of the ball and the kinetic energy lost after 5 bounces of the ball. (Section 1–11)

1–16. A block whose coefficient of restitution is e slides without friction along a horizontal groove at a speed of v_1 cm/sec. It strikes a slower moving block of equal mass whose velocity is v_2 cm/sec in the same direction as the first.   Compute the direction and magnitude of the velocities of the two blocks after the collision. How much kinetic energy is lost in the collision? (Section 1–11)

1–17. The force on an electron of mass m, moving with a velocity $\mathbf{v}_0$ in an electric field $\mathbf{E}$ and magnetic field $\mathbf{B}$, is given by $\mathbf{F} = e[\mathbf{E} + \mathbf{v}_0 \times \mathbf{B}]$. The velocity $\mathbf{v}_0$ refers to a fixed coordinate system. Write the differential equation for the motion of the electron in (a) the fixed system, and (b) a system rotating with constant angular velocity $\boldsymbol{\omega}$ relative to the fixed system and having the same origin as the latter. Show that if $\boldsymbol{\omega} = -e\mathbf{B}/2m$, the Coriolis force vanishes and that $m\mathbf{a} \cong e\mathbf{E}$ if terms of second order in B are neglected. The angular frequency ω, thus found, is called the "Larmor frequency." (Section 1–14)

1–18. A mass m falls from height h to the surface of the earth. Neglecting frictional forces but taking into account the earth's rotation, find by how much and in what direction the particle will have been deflected from the vertical when it strikes the earth. Neglect terms in the square of the earth's angular speed of rotation. (Section 1–15)

1–19. A hurricane wind of velocity 100 mi/hr due north in latitude 45° N will be deflected by how much and in what direction due to the Coriolis force upon it? (Section 1–15)

1–20. A jet plane of weight W lb flying at 600 mi/hr in latitude 60° north is on a course N 45° E. (a) What is the magnitude and direction of the Coriolis force on the plane? (b) If the navigator, using a bubble sextant, is pointing to a star at right angles to the track of the plane, by how much will the bubble of his sextant deviate from a true indication of the vertical due to the Coriolis force? (Section 1–15)

1–21. A bullet of mass m is fired horizontally on the earth's surface with initial velocity components $\dot{x}_0$, $\dot{y}_0$. The velocity in the z-direction is zero. Assume the motion to start at $x = 0$ and $y = 0$. The velocity is very large, so that terms containing $\dot{x}_0$ and $\dot{y}_0$ are large compared with terms not containing them. Find the parametric equations, that is, x and y in terms of t, of the path of the bullet in the xy-plane. Show that the trajectory may be represented by the complex variable

$$u = (\dot{u}_0 t)e^{-i(\omega t \sin \phi - \psi)},$$

where $\dot{u}_0 e^{i\psi}$ is the complex representation of the initial velocity. Describe the motion of the bullet in terms of u. (Section 1–15)

CHAPTER 2

HAMILTON'S PRINCIPLE AND LAGRANGE'S EQUATIONS

In the preceding chapter we formulated the equations of motion by using the interplay of forces and masses, representing this interplay by Newton's laws. One may approach the same problem, however, by a consideration of the energy of the mechanical system. This requires a new postulational viewpoint of dynamics, which forms the content of this chapter.

Lagrange, in his famous treatise *Méchanique Analytique* (1788), derived equations equivalent to those based on Newton's laws but involving ideas of work and energy. Johann Bernoulli and D'Alembert had previously introduced the concepts of *virtual work* and *inertial forces*, by which dynamics and statics could be reduced to a common denominator, but Lagrange, and later Hamilton, cast these ideas into a form especially applicable in dynamical problems.

2–1 The principle of virtual work. In 1717 Johann Bernoulli enunciated his *principle of virtual work*, which is essentially a definition of equilibrium for the mechanical system. We shall confine our attention first to a single mass particle m, understanding that a summation over many particles or elements of a system may be made if required.

Let **r** be the position vector (Fig. 2–1) of the particle referred to an arbitrary origin. Several forces $\mathbf{F}_1 \ldots \mathbf{F}_n$ may act on the particle. These may be external applied forces, interactions between particles if the system is complex, or reactions due to the constraints of the system, i.e., the supports, strings, and so forth, which preclude complete freedom of motion of the particle.

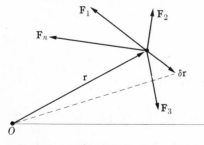

We define by δ**r** any small *imagined* displacement arbitrarily imposed upon the mass. This quantity δ**r** does not necessarily have to be the actual displacement of the particle under the acting force system. We do assume, however, that δ**r** is consistent with the constraints of the system. For example, if the particle rests upon an inclined plane, the

FIG. 2–1. Virtual displacement under a force system.

imagined, or *virtual*, displacement must be such that the particle remains on the plane. Otherwise $\delta\mathbf{r}$ is arbitrary.

The work done by the system of forces in such a displacement is

$$\mathbf{F}_1 \cdot \delta\mathbf{r} + \mathbf{F}_2 \cdot \delta\mathbf{r} + \cdots + \mathbf{F}_n \cdot \delta\mathbf{r} = \delta W, \qquad (2\text{--}1)$$

but since the scalar product is distributive and commutative, we may write

$$\delta\mathbf{r} \cdot \sum_{j=1}^{n} \mathbf{F}_j = \delta W. \qquad (2\text{--}2)$$

This is called the *virtual work* performed by the force system upon the particle. The *principle of virtual work* then states that: *if, and only if, for any arbitrary virtual displacement* $\delta\mathbf{r}$ *the virtual work* $\delta W = 0$ *under the action of the forces* $\mathbf{F}_j$, *the particle is in equilibrium.* An examination of Eq. (2–2) shows that $\delta W = 0$ for nonzero $\delta\mathbf{r}$ either if $\delta\mathbf{r}$ is perpendicular to $\sum_{j=1}^{n} \mathbf{F}_j$ or if

$$\sum_{j=1}^{n} \mathbf{F}_j = 0. \qquad (2\text{--}3)$$

Since Eq. (2–2) must hold for *any* $\delta\mathbf{r}$, the first possibility is ruled out. The second possibility, Eq. (2–3), expresses the condition that the vector resultant of the forces acting on the particle is zero, which is the well-known condition for equilibrium as formulated in elementary statics. In what follows we shall use the condition for equilibrium in the form

$$\delta W = \delta\mathbf{r} \cdot \mathbf{F} = 0, \qquad (2\text{--}4)$$

where $\mathbf{F}$ is the resultant of all forces acting on the particle.

If there are several particles in the system and we assume that the interaction forces between particles obey Newton's Third Law, the principle of virtual work remains valid. Suppose there are n particles in the system and that $\mathbf{F}_j$ represents the *resultant force* acting on the jth particle. Then the principle of virtual work states that the system will be in equilibrium when

$$\sum_{j=1}^{n} \mathbf{F}_j \cdot \delta\mathbf{r}_j = 0. \qquad (2\text{--}5)$$

Here $\delta\mathbf{r}_j$ is the virtual displacement of the jth particle and is arbitrary except for the constraint conditions.

A simple example will suffice to fix the ideas outlined above. Two masses rest on smooth inclined planes, as shown in Fig. 2–2, and are connected by an inextensible string running over a smooth disk D. By virtue of the constraints, a displacement $|\delta\mathbf{r}_1|$ of the mass m_1 must be

accompanied by an equal displace-
ment $|\delta\mathbf{r}_2|$ of the mass m_2. If $|\delta\mathbf{r}_1|$ is
taken arbitrarily up the first plane,
$|\delta\mathbf{r}_2| = |\delta\mathbf{r}_1|$ will be down the second
plane. Also by virtue of the smooth
planes and disk, the tension $|\mathbf{T}|$ is
the same on both sides of D. Hence,
$|\mathbf{T}_1| = |\mathbf{T}_2| = |\mathbf{T}|$. Applying the
principle of virtual work, we have
for the equilibrium condition

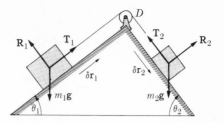

Fig. 2–2. Blocks on inclined planes.

$$\delta W = (m_1\mathbf{g} + \mathbf{R}_1 + \mathbf{T}_1)\cdot\delta\mathbf{r}_1 + (m_2\mathbf{g} + \mathbf{R}_2 + \mathbf{T}_2)\cdot\delta\mathbf{r}_2 = 0. \quad (2\text{–}6)$$

If we take the indicated scalar products and make use of the constraint
conditions, there results

$$(m_1 g \sin\theta_1 - m_2 g \sin\theta_2)|\delta\mathbf{r}_1| = 0. \quad\quad\quad (2\text{–}7)$$

We observe also that $\mathbf{R}_1\cdot\delta\mathbf{r}_1$ and $\mathbf{R}_2\cdot\delta\mathbf{r}_2$ vanish since the vectors are
mutually perpendicular. Hence the reaction forces do not influence the
virtual work. For equilibrium, therefore, $m_1 g \sin\theta_1 = m_2 g \sin\theta_2$, a
result we could have predicted from elementary considerations.

As a second example, consider a single mass particle in a conservative
force field of potential $V(x,y,z)$. The components of the force are

$$X = -\frac{\partial V}{\partial x}, \quad\quad Y = -\frac{\partial V}{\partial y}, \quad\quad Z = -\frac{\partial V}{\partial z},$$

and we write

$$\mathbf{F} = -\left[\frac{\partial V}{\partial x}\mathbf{i} + \frac{\partial V}{\partial y}\mathbf{j} + \frac{\partial V}{\partial z}\mathbf{k}\right].$$

The virtual displacement $\delta\mathbf{r} = \mathbf{i}\,\delta x + \mathbf{j}\,\delta y + \mathbf{k}\,\delta z$. Then

$$\delta W = \mathbf{F}\cdot\delta\mathbf{r} = -\frac{\partial V}{\partial x}\,\delta x - \frac{\partial V}{\partial y}\,\delta y - \frac{\partial V}{\partial z}\,\delta z = 0 \quad\quad (2\text{–}8)$$

for equilibrium. If δx, δy, δz are independent, we may choose them at
will, and if equilibrium is to occur, all the partial derivatives must be
zero. This is a necessary condition for an extremum of the function
$V(x,y,z)$. It may be a maximum value of V, or a minimum value, or
simply a point where V has a stationary value of another type.

Suppose, however, that the particle is constrained to move on a smooth
surface $f(x,y,z) = c$. Then the constraint imposes the condition that

$(\partial f/\partial x)\,\delta x + (\partial f/\partial y)\,\delta y + (\partial f/\partial z)\,\delta z = 0$, so that only two of δx, δy, δz are independent. If we eliminate δz from Eq. (2–8) by means of this constraint condition, we find as criteria for equilibrium

$$\frac{\partial V}{\partial x}\frac{\partial f}{\partial z} - \frac{\partial V}{\partial z}\frac{\partial f}{\partial x} = 0, \qquad \frac{\partial V}{\partial y}\frac{\partial f}{\partial z} - \frac{\partial V}{\partial z}\frac{\partial f}{\partial y} = 0. \qquad (2\text{–}9)$$

But these are just the conditions for an extremum of $V(x,y,z)$ subject to the constraint.

Let us examine this point further. Suppose we displace the particle from its position of equilibrium by a small amount and give it a small initial velocity. If, in its subsequent motion, the particle does not depart far from the equilibrium position and does not attain a high velocity, we classify the equilibrium as *stable*. The initial disturbance must be entirely arbitrary but small. For example, a small mass resting at the bottom of a spherical cup and subjected to the earth's gravitational field is in stable equilibrium. If it is displaced slightly and released from rest, it will oscillate about the bottom of the cup. On the other hand, if a mass rests on top of a sphere under similar circumstances, a small displacement will cause it to slide off, that is, depart from the equilibrium position. In this case the equilibrium is said to be *unstable*. A third type of equilibrium is represented by a sphere resting on a horizontal plane. Here a small displacement of the sphere in any direction on the plane, and subsequent release, leaves the sphere at rest. This is called *neutral* equilibrium.

To distinguish between stable and unstable equilibrium points in a conservative force field, we rely on a theorem due to the German mathematician Dirichlet; namely, *a position of equilibrium is stable if, and only if, the potential energy is a minimum in the equilibrium position.*

We shall not prove this theorem* but will illustrate its meaning by an example. Consider the one-dimensional motion of a particle of mass m in a conservative field for which the potential energy is represented by the diagram in Fig. 2–3. Let its displacement at time t be x. Consider the minimum in $V(x)$ at $x = x_A$. In the neighborhood of x_A we have $V(x) - V(x_A) > 0$. Suppose initially the particle is started from rest at the point $x = x_{A'}$, very near the minimum. Then its energy thereafter will be $E = V(x_{A'})$. As it gains velocity, we have

$$|v| = \sqrt{2/m[V(x_{A'}) - V(x)]} \leq \sqrt{2/m[V(x_{A'}) - V(x_A)]}. \qquad (2\text{–}10)$$

If A' is taken sufficiently close to A, the velocity can be made as small

---

* A proof will be found in G. Hamel, *Theoretische Mechanik.* Berlin: Springer-Verlag, 1949, pp. 268 ff.

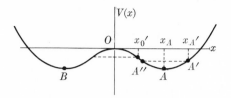

FIG. 2–3. Points of stable and unstable equilibrium.

as we please. The displacement cannot exceed $|x_{A'} - x_{A''}|$ under the imposed conditions. The equilibrium in position A is *stable*. A similar situation exists at B.

On the other hand, consider the neighborhood of the point O at which $\delta V = 0$ and $V(x)$ has a maximum. Suppose initially that the particle is started from rest at $x = x_{0'}$, where $0'$ is near O. This is not an equilibrium point, and the particle will begin to move. Its total energy $E = V(x_{0'})$ thereafter, and since its kinetic energy increases, its potential energy $V(x)$ will decrease. The particle can move only toward the right in the figure and *away from* the equilibrium point O. The point O is a position of unstable equilibrium.

We conclude that for one-dimensional motion of this type the possible equilibrium positions are given by values of x for which $dV/dx = 0$, but that the equilibrium will be stable only if $d^2V/dx^2 > 0$. For three-dimensional motion, the former condition is replaced by the three conditions $(\partial V/\partial x) = 0$, $(\partial V/\partial y) = 0$, $(\partial V/\partial z) = 0$, as indicated by Eq. (2–8). The conditions on the higher derivatives, sufficient for determining the stability of the equilibrium, are more complex and are omitted here.* By examining the function in the neighborhood of the critical point at which the three first partial derivatives vanish, one can sometimes tell the nature of the extremum.

2–2 D'Alembert's principle. In his *Traité de Dynamique* in 1743, D'Alembert proposed a principle which would reduce a problem in dynamics to an equivalent one in statics. By introducing so-called "inertial forces" he was able to apply Bernoulli's principle of virtual work to a system in which motion results from the action of the applied forces.

The *inertial force* acting on the jth particle of a system is $-m_j \ddot{\mathbf{r}}_j$, where $\ddot{\mathbf{r}}_j$ is the actual acceleration under the forces acting on it. Let the resultant force on the particle be $\mathbf{F}_j$. D'Alembert's principle then states that *the applied forces together with the forces of inertia form a system in equilibrium*. Expressed vectorially for a set of virtual displacements $\delta \mathbf{r}_j$,

---

* See, for example, D. V. Widder, *Advanced Calculus*. New York: Prentice-Hall, 1947, pp. 110–112.

the principle becomes

$$\sum_{j=1}^{n} (\mathbf{F}_j - m_j\ddot{\mathbf{r}}_j) \cdot \delta\mathbf{r}_j = 0. \tag{2-11}$$

Take as an example a free particle moving in space. Then $\mathbf{F} = X\mathbf{i} + Y\mathbf{j} + Z\mathbf{k}$, $\ddot{\mathbf{r}} = \ddot{x}\mathbf{i} + \ddot{y}\mathbf{j} + \ddot{z}\mathbf{k}$, and $\delta\mathbf{r} = \mathbf{i}\delta x + \mathbf{j}\delta y + \mathbf{k}\delta z$, so that we have from Eq. (2–11)

$$(X - m\ddot{x})\,\delta x + (Y - m\ddot{y})\,\delta y + (Z - m\ddot{z})\,\delta z = 0. \tag{2-12}$$

Since δx, δy, δz may be chosen arbitrarily and independently, this equation will be true if

$$X = m\ddot{x}, \qquad Y = m\ddot{y}, \qquad Z = m\ddot{z}, \tag{2-13}$$

which are the familiar Newtonian equations of motion for the particle.

We count the string tensions, surface- supports, and other reactive forces as part of the applied forces in D'Alembert's principle. For example, if a block is being pushed along a smooth horizontal plane under the action of an oblique force $\mathbf{F}$, as in Fig. 2–4, there will be a reactive force $\mathbf{R}$ as well as $\mathbf{F}$ acting on the block. The block will be accelerated toward the right, and we observe that the applied force $\mathbf{F} + \mathbf{R}$ is not collinear with the inertial force $-m\ddot{\mathbf{r}}$. In general, the $\mathbf{F}_j$ and $m_j\ddot{\mathbf{r}}_j$ will not be collinear. The vector difference $\mathbf{F}_j - m_j\ddot{\mathbf{r}}_j$, which enters D'Alembert's principle, represents a "lost force." In the example above, this would be $\mathbf{F} + \mathbf{R} - m\ddot{\mathbf{r}}$. The negatives of the inertial forces are sometimes called the "effective forces."

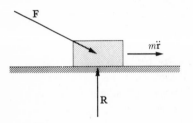

FIG. 2–4. Block moving under an oblique force.

To illustrate D'Alembert's principle, we shall use the masses on inclined planes shown in Fig. 2–2. The inertial forces are $-m_1\mathbf{a}_1$ and $-m_2\mathbf{a}_2$. We assume $\mathbf{a}_1$, the acceleration produced in m_1, to be positive upward on plane 1. Likewise $\mathbf{a}_2$, the acceleration of m_2, is assumed positive downward on plane 2. Then by virtue of the constraints $|\mathbf{a}_1| = |\mathbf{a}_2| = a$, where we denote by a the acceleration of the system.

D'Alembert's principle yields

$$(m_1\mathbf{g} + \mathbf{T}_1 + \mathbf{R}_1 - m_1\mathbf{a}_1) \cdot \delta\mathbf{r}_1 + (m_2\mathbf{g} + \mathbf{T}_2 + \mathbf{R}_2 - m_2\mathbf{a}_2) \cdot \delta\mathbf{r}_2 = 0. \tag{2-14}$$

Carrying out the scalar multiplications and substituting the constraint conditions, we have

$$[m_1 g \sin \theta_1 - m_2 g \sin \theta_2 - (m_1 + m_2)a]|\delta \mathbf{r}_1| = 0. \qquad (2\text{--}15)$$

Since $|\delta \mathbf{r}_1|$ is arbitrary, Eq. (2–15) will be satisfied if

$$a = \frac{m_1 g \sin \theta_1 - m_2 g \sin \theta_2}{m_1 + m_2}. \qquad (2\text{--}16)$$

The numerator is the net force acting on the total mass which appears in the denominator. In our succeeding discussion we will use D'Alembert's principle in the formulation of Hamilton's principle, which in turn will lead us to Lagrange's equations of motion.

2–3 Variational principles. We now make a slight digression to introduce briefly a few of the fundamental ideas of the calculus of variations. Consider, first, an example. We ask, "What will be the curve in a vertical xy-plane assumed by a perfectly flexible cable of length L hanging between points (a,b) and $(-a,b)$?" The situation is shown in Fig. 2–5. Although we shall not solve the problem completely, we will indicate what is involved.

Since the cable is in stable equilibrium, its potential energy is a minimum. If μ is its mass per unit length, assumed constant, the potential energy for an element will be $\mu g y\, ds$, and for equilibrium the integral

$$V = \mu g \int y \, ds \qquad (2\text{--}17)$$

will be a minimum. Integration here is along the curve from $(-a, b)$ to (a, b). Since ds is $\sqrt{1 + (y')^2}\, dx$, we may write Eq. (2–17) as

$$V = \mu g \int_{-a}^{a} y\sqrt{1 + (y')^2}\, dx, \qquad (2\text{--}18)$$

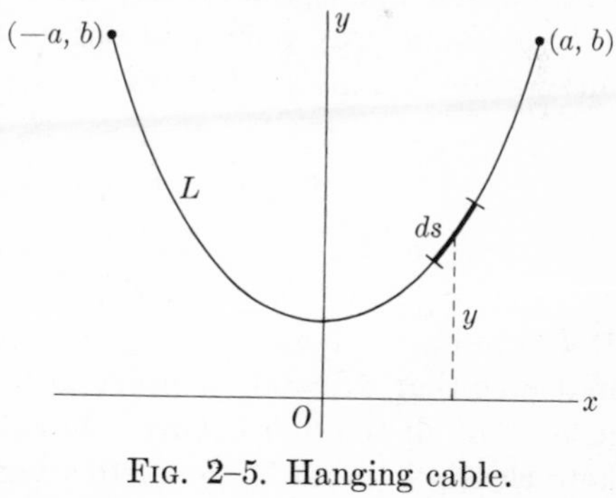

FIG. 2–5. Hanging cable.

y' standing, as usual, for the derivative of y with respect to x. Our problem, then, is to find y as a function of x such that V takes on its least value. This is a problem in the calculus of variations. We shall summarize the basic ideas needed to solve it and refer the reader to other sources* for the mathematical details. No attempt at rigor will be made here.

---

* See, for example, P. Franklin, *Methods of Advanced Calculus.* New York: McGraw-Hill Book Company, Inc., 1944, Chapter XII.

Consider that the integral

$$I = \int_a^c f(x,y,y') \, dx \qquad (2\text{--}19)$$

is to be maximized or minimized.
This is to be done by choosing a particular curve $y(x)$ among all curves
joining (a,b) and (c,d). Two such
curves are shown in Fig. 2–6. We
define the *variation in y*, labeled δy,
to be $y_2(x) - y_1(x)$, that is, to be

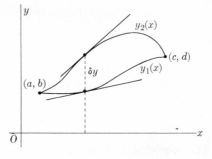

FIG. 2–6. Varied curves.

the change in y from curve to curve at the same value of x. The slope
of the curves, in general, also is different for the same x. The variation
in slope is $\delta y' = y_2'(x) - y_1'(x)$.

It is evident from the figure that as x changes from a to c, δy will
change and hence is a function of x which we will assume to be continuous at all points between $x = a$ and $x = c$. If we differentiate it with
respect to x, we have

$$\frac{d}{dx}(\delta y) = y_2'(x) - y_1'(x) = \delta y'. \qquad (2\text{--}20)$$

We shall have constant occasion to use this fundamental relation permit-
ting interchange of the operations of differentiation and variation.

In a similar way it may be shown that the operations of variation and
integration commute; that is,

$$\delta \int_a^b y \, dx = \int_a^b \delta y \, dx. \qquad (2\text{--}21)$$

Basically, if we vary y and hence y' in I, we produce a variation δI.
If I is to have a maximum or a minimum value, the calculus of variations
indicates that $\delta I = 0$ for every arbitrary change, δy, that we may make
in y. The distinction between δy and the usual differential dy should be
kept clearly in mind: δy refers to a variation *from curve to curve at a given x;*
dy refers to a differential change *along a given curve for a change in x.*
We find from the calculus of variations that I will have a stationary
value, usually a maximum or minimum, if $y(x)$ satisfies the Euler-Lagrange
differential equation,

$$\frac{d}{dx}\left(\frac{\partial f}{\partial y'}\right) - \frac{\partial f}{\partial y} = 0. \qquad (2\text{--}22)$$

This second order equation enables us to solve the minimum problem posed at the beginning of this section. For the hanging cable, we have

$$f(x,y,y') = y\sqrt{1 + (y')^2}.$$ (2–23)

Hence

$$\frac{\partial f}{\partial y'} = \frac{yy'}{\sqrt{1 + (y')^2}}, \qquad \frac{\partial f}{\partial y} = \sqrt{1 + (y')^2},$$ (2–24)

and the Euler-Lagrange equation becomes

$$\frac{d}{dx}\left(\frac{yy'}{\sqrt{1 + (y')^2}}\right) - \sqrt{1 + (y'^2)} = 0.$$ (2–25)

The solution of Eq. (2–25) subject to the given boundary conditions yields the equation of a catenary.

2–4 Hamilton's principle. We may interpret the virtual displacements used in discussing D'Alembert's principle as the small variations introduced in the preceding section. A particle in its motion will take a certain path described by $\mathbf{r} = \mathbf{f}(t)$ under the action of external forces. Varied paths *described in the same time* between two points in space may be imagined by changing the actual path by small variations $\delta\mathbf{r}$ for corresponding times. If we look upon the $\delta\mathbf{r}$ in this way, we are led to a fundamental variational postulate that serves as a basis for dynamics and which starts from energy concepts.

For simplicity, consider again n particles of masses m_j, located at points $\mathbf{r}_j$, and acted upon by resultant external forces $\mathbf{F}_j$. By D'Alembert's principle, we write

$$\sum_{j=1}^{n} (m_j\ddot{\mathbf{r}}_j - \mathbf{F}_j)\cdot\delta\mathbf{r}_j = 0.$$ (2–26)

This is the dynamical condition to be satisfied by the impressed forces and the inertial forces for arbitrary $\delta\mathbf{r}_j$ consistent with the constraints.

We observe first that $\sum_{j=1}^{n} \mathbf{F}_j\cdot\delta\mathbf{r}_j$ is the virtual work done by the forces. Call it δW. Furthermore,

$$\frac{d}{dt}\,(\dot{\mathbf{r}}_j\cdot\delta\mathbf{r}_j) = \dot{\mathbf{r}}_j\cdot\frac{d}{dt}(\delta\mathbf{r}_j) + \ddot{\mathbf{r}}_j\cdot\delta\mathbf{r}_j.$$ (2–27)

But by interchange of the derivative and variational operators,

$$\frac{d}{dt}(\delta\mathbf{r}_j) = \delta\dot{\mathbf{r}}_j.$$

This permits us also to conclude that $\dot{\mathbf{r}}_j\cdot\delta\dot{\mathbf{r}}_j = \delta(\frac{1}{2}\dot{\mathbf{r}}_j^2) = \delta(\frac{1}{2}v_j^2)$, where v_j is the speed of the jth particle. This last expression, however, when the mass m_j is included as a factor, is the *variation in the kinetic energy of the particle*. Thus we may write

$$\sum_{j=1}^{n} m_j \ddot{\mathbf{r}}_j \cdot \delta\mathbf{r}_j = \frac{d}{dt} \sum_{j=1}^{n} m_j \dot{\mathbf{r}}_j \cdot \delta\mathbf{r}_j - \delta T, \qquad (2\text{--}28)$$

where $T = $ the total kinetic energy $= \sum_{j=1}^{n} \frac{1}{2} m_j v_j^2$.

Putting all these results together, we have

$$\frac{d}{dt} \sum_{j=1}^{n} m_j \dot{\mathbf{r}}_j \cdot \delta\mathbf{r}_j = \delta T + \delta W. \qquad (2\text{--}29)$$

Consider two times, t_0 and t_1, at which we assume $\delta\mathbf{r}_j = 0$, that is, two times at which the dynamical path and all imagined variations of this path coincide. Integrating Eq. (2–29) between t_0 and t_1, we have

$$\sum_{j=1}^{n} m_j \dot{\mathbf{r}}_j \cdot \delta\mathbf{r}_j \bigg]_{t_0}^{t_1} = \int_{t_0}^{t_1} (\delta T + \delta W)\, dt. \qquad (2\text{--}30)$$

But the first term is zero by virtue of our restrictions on $\delta\mathbf{r}_j$. Hence

$$\int_{t_0}^{t_1} (\delta T + \delta W)\, dt = 0. \qquad (2\text{--}31)$$

We have assumed that variations in T and W arise from variations in the coordinates and velocities between the dynamical path and the varied path when these variations are taken at the same time. Thus throughout we have assumed $\delta t = 0$. If we assume further that W is a work function arising from a potential energy so that $W = -V(\mathbf{r}_j)$, Eq. (2–31) becomes

$$\delta \int_{t_0}^{t_1} (T + W)\, dt = \delta \int_{t_0}^{t_1} (T - V)\, dt = 0. \qquad (2\text{--}32)$$

The function $T - V = L$ is called the *kinetic potential*, or the *Lagrangian function*, or simply the *Lagrangian*, of the system.

Equation (2–32) is a mathematical statement of Hamilton's principle for a conservative dynamical system. We may state it thus: *of all paths in time which the coordinates $\mathbf{r}_j$ may be imagined to take between two instants t_0 and t_1, the dynamical path actually taken by the system will be that for which $\int_{t_0}^{t_1} (T - V)\, dt$ will have a stationary value.*

Let us make perfectly clear what "dynamical path" means in this sense. We imagine all $\mathbf{r}_j$ varying with the time. Corresponding to a given instant, we imagine a "representative point" whose coordinates are the n values $\mathbf{r}_j$ located in this n-dimensional space. By the "dynamical path" we mean the path of the representative point in the n-dimensional space.

As we shall see later, Hamilton's principle also holds for certain non-conservative systems in which a work function depending on the velocities as well as the coordinates is involved.

We shall illustrate by an example how Hamilton's principle leads to the differential equation of motion for a system with one degree of freedom, that is, a system completely specified by one coordinate. Consider a simple pendulum of length l with a bob of mass m. Its angular displacement from the vertical at any time t we shall take as θ, and we shall neglect the mass of the supporting wire. The kinetic energy of the system and its potential energy are

$$T = \tfrac{1}{2}ml^2\dot{\theta}^2, \qquad V = mgl(1 - \cos\theta), \qquad (2\text{–}33)$$

so that

$$L = T - V = \tfrac{1}{2}ml^2\dot{\theta}^2 - mgl(1 - \cos\theta). \qquad (2\text{–}34)$$

Hamilton's principle then states that the dynamical path will be obtained if

$$\int_{t_0}^{t_1} \delta[\tfrac{1}{2}ml^2\dot{\theta}^2 - mgl(1 - \cos\theta)]\,dt = 0. \qquad (2\text{–}35)$$

Carrying out the variation, we have

$$\int_{t_0}^{t_1} [ml^2\dot{\theta}\,\delta\dot{\theta} - mgl\sin\theta\,\delta\theta]\,dt = 0. \qquad (2\text{–}36)$$

The integral $\int_{t_0}^{t_1} ml^2\dot{\theta}\,\delta\dot{\theta}\,dt$ may be written as $\int_{t_0}^{t_1} ml^2\dot{\theta}[d(\delta\theta)/dt]dt$ by virtue of the operator interchange exhibited in Eq. (2–20). Integration by parts yields

$$\int_{t_0}^{t_1} ml^2\dot{\theta}\,\frac{d}{dt}\,(\delta\theta)\,dt = ml^2\dot{\theta}\,\delta\theta\Big]_{t_0}^{t_1} - ml^2\int_{t_0}^{t_1} \ddot{\theta}\,\delta\theta\,dt. \qquad (2\text{–}37)$$

But $\delta\theta$ is a variation which by definition is zero at t_0 and t_1. Hence the first term on the right side of Eq. (2–37) vanishes. Combining Eq. (2–37) with Eq. (2–36), we have

$$\int_{t_0}^{t_1} - [ml^2\ddot{\theta} + mgl\sin\theta]\,\delta\theta\,dt = 0. \qquad (2\text{–}38)$$

This must be true for an arbitrary assignment of $\delta\theta$. Therefore, we are led to

$$\ddot{\theta} + \frac{g}{l} \sin \theta = 0 \tag{2–39}$$

as the equation to be satisfied by θ for the dynamical path. Equation (2–39) is the familiar differential equation for the pendulum.

The Euler-Lagrange equation (2–22) applied here would have yielded the same result. We would have from Eq. (2–34)

$$\frac{\partial L}{\partial \dot{\theta}} = ml^2 \dot{\theta}, \qquad \frac{\partial L}{\partial \theta} = -mgl \sin \theta,$$

and hence by Eq. (2–22),

$$\frac{d}{dt}(ml^2 \dot{\theta}) + mgl \sin \theta = 0,$$

which reduces to Eq. (2–39).

In general, as we shall show, it is not necessary to use Hamilton's principle directly in the solution of dynamical problems. From it we derive equations equivalent to Eq. (2–22) for finding the stationary value of $\int_{t_0}^{t_1} L\, dt$. These are called Lagrange's equations. Their application is greatly facilitated by the use of generalized coordinates.

2–5 Generalized coordinates. In the example of the simple pendulum discussed above, we might have specified the position of the bob by giving its x- and y-coordinates. These are not independent coordinates, however, and we used, instead, the angle θ, which is a single parameter that suffices to specify the position of the bob at any time t. We say that the system has *one degree of freedom*. θ plays the part of a so-called *generalized coordinate*. In any physical system there will be just as many generalized coordinates as there are degrees of freedom. Or we may put it in another way: the generalized coordinates for a given system are the least number of variables required to specify the positions of the elements of the system at any given time.

As a second example, refer to the double pendulum illustrated in Fig. 2–7. Motion is confined to the xy-plane. Although we *may* give the x- and y-coordinates of m_1 and m_2 as functions of the time to describe the motion of the system, it will be more economical, however, to give the angles θ_1 and θ_2. These serve as the generalized coordinates. The cartesian coordinates of m_1 and m_2 can be expressed readily in terms of θ_1 and θ_2.

In general, let $\mathbf{r}_j$ be the position vector of a mass point m_j in cartesian space. Then we may write

$$\mathbf{r}_j = \mathbf{r}_j(q_1, q_2, \ldots, q_m), \tag{2–40}$$

where the q_k are the generalized coordinates for the system, one for
each degree of freedom. We shall
ignore for the moment a possible dependence of $\mathbf{r}_j$ explicitly on the time.
Equation (2–40) is equivalent to
the statement $x_j = x_j(q_1 \ldots q_m)$,
$y_j = y_j(q_1 \ldots q_m)$, $z_j = z_j(q_1 \ldots q_m)$,
where x_j, y_j, z_j are the cartesian coordinates of the mass point.

For the double pendulum, we
have

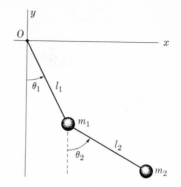

Fig. 2–7. Double pendulum.

$$x_1 = l_1 \sin \theta_1, \qquad x_2 = l_1 \sin \theta_1 + l_2 \sin \theta_2,$$
$$y_1 = -l_1 \cos \theta_1, \qquad y_2 = -l_1 \cos \theta_1 - l_2 \cos \theta_2. \tag{2–41}$$

It is important to note that the q_k may be any independent parameters
that specify uniquely the dynamical situation at a given time. They may
be angles, areas, lengths, or any other set of numbers. Since they are
independent, there can be no functional relation between them and
hence no integrable linear relation between the values of the δq_k. By this
we mean no relation $f(q_1, q_2, \ldots, q_m) = 0$, and hence no relation such as
$\sum_{k=1}^{m} (\partial f/\partial q_k) \delta q_k = 0$. There may, however, be nonintegrable relations
connecting the δq_k, such as $\sum_{k=1}^{m} a_k \delta q_k = 0$, where the coefficients a_k
are not the partial derivatives of some function with respect to the q_k.
We shall use generalized coordinates in much of our analysis henceforth.

2–6 Lagrange's equations. Consider a dynamical system composed of
n mass points located by the vectors $\mathbf{r}_j(j = 1, 2, \ldots, n)$ with respect
to some origin. The *resultant external force* acting on the jth mass will
be denoted by $\mathbf{F}_j$. We shall designate by $q_k(k = 1, 2, \ldots, m)$ the
generalized coordinates necessary to describe the system, and we seek
equations that will provide the q_k as functions of t.

From Eq. (2–40) we have

$$\delta \mathbf{r}_j = \sum_{k=1}^{m} \frac{\partial \mathbf{r}_j}{\partial q_k} \delta q_k \qquad \text{and} \qquad \dot{\mathbf{r}}_j = \sum_{k=1}^{m} \frac{\partial \mathbf{r}_j}{\partial q_k} \dot{q}_k, \tag{2–42}$$

where $\dot{\mathbf{r}}_j$ is the velocity of the jth mass.

We shall confine our attention here to *holonomic* dynamical systems,
that is, systems in which the δq_k are independent. *Nonholonomic* systems,
those in which there are nonintegrable relations between the δq_k, we shall
discuss later.

The kinetic energy of the n particles is

$$T = \frac{1}{2} \sum_{j=1}^{n} m_j \dot{\mathbf{r}}_j^2 = \frac{1}{2} \sum_{j=1}^{n} m_j \left\{ \sum_{p=1}^{m} \sum_{s=1}^{m} \left(\frac{\partial \mathbf{r}_j}{\partial q_p} \cdot \frac{\partial \mathbf{r}_j}{\partial q_s} \right) \right\} \dot{q}_p \dot{q}_s. \qquad (2\text{-}43)$$

The quantity in the brace comes from squaring the $\dot{\mathbf{r}}_j$ of Eq. (2–42) and summing. We may rewrite Eq. (2–43) as

$$T = \frac{1}{2} \sum_{p=1}^{m} \sum_{s=1}^{m} \left(\sum_{j=1}^{n} m_j \frac{\partial \mathbf{r}_j}{\partial q_p} \cdot \frac{\partial \mathbf{r}_j}{\partial q_s} \right) \dot{q}_p \dot{q}_s, \qquad (2\text{-}44)$$

where the parentheses enclose a quantity that we shall designate as a_{ps}. It depends entirely upon the generalized coordinates and not upon the velocities. This expression for T, namely,

$$T = \frac{1}{2} \sum_{p=1}^{m} \sum_{s=1}^{m} a_{ps} \, \dot{q}_p \dot{q}_s, \qquad (2\text{-}45)$$

is called a *homogeneous quadratic form* in the velocities $\dot{q}_k$.

Let us now examine the work done by the forces $\mathbf{F}_j$. We write for the virtual work, as usual,

$$\delta W = \sum_{j=1}^{n} \mathbf{F}_j \cdot \delta \mathbf{r}_j, \qquad (2\text{-}46)$$

and by Eq. (2–42)

$$\delta W = \sum_{j=1}^{n} \mathbf{F}_j \cdot \left\{ \sum_{k=1}^{m} \frac{\partial \mathbf{r}_j}{\partial q_k} \delta q_k \right\} = \sum_{k=1}^{m} \left\{ \sum_{j=1}^{n} \mathbf{F}_j \cdot \frac{\partial \mathbf{r}_j}{\partial q_k} \right\} \delta q_k. \qquad (2\text{-}47)$$

The quantity

$$\sum_{j=1}^{n} \mathbf{F}_j \cdot \frac{\partial \mathbf{r}_j}{\partial q_k}$$

is defined as the *generalized force*, Q_k, associated with the coordinate q_k. Hence the work done on the system becomes

$$\delta W = \sum_{k=1}^{m} Q_k \, \delta q_k. \qquad (2\text{-}48)$$

Now by Hamilton's principle we know that the dynamical path will be that for which

$$\int_{t_0}^{t_1} (\delta T + \delta W) \, dt = 0. \qquad (2\text{-}49)$$

But T is a function of q_k and $\dot{q}_k$, say $T(q_k, \dot{q}_k)$, and hence

$$\delta T = \sum_{k=1}^{m} \left(\frac{\partial T}{\partial q_k} \delta q_k + \frac{\partial T}{\partial \dot{q}_k} \delta \dot{q}_k \right).$$

Therefore, we may write

$$\int_{t_0}^{t_1} \sum_{k=1}^{m} \left\{ \frac{\partial T}{\partial \dot{q}_k} \delta \dot{q}_k + \frac{\partial T}{\partial q_k} \delta q_k + Q_k \, \delta q_k \right\} dt = 0. \qquad (2\text{–}50)$$

Consider $\int_{t_0}^{t_1} (\partial T / \partial \dot{q}_k) \, \delta \dot{q}_k \, dt$ for a given q_k. This we integrate by parts [as we did for the simple pendulum, Eq. (2–37)] to obtain

$$\int_{t_0}^{t_1} \frac{\partial T}{\partial \dot{q}_k} \frac{d}{dt} (\delta q_k) \, dt = \frac{\partial T}{\partial \dot{q}_k} \delta q_k \bigg]_{t_0}^{t_1} - \int_{t_0}^{t_1} \frac{d}{dt} \left(\frac{\partial T}{\partial \dot{q}_k} \right) \delta q_k \, dt. \qquad (2\text{–}51)$$

By virtue of the restrictions that at t_0 and t_1 all $\delta q_k = 0$, the first term on the right side of Eq. (2–51) vanishes. Thus Eq. (2–50) becomes

$$\int_{t_0}^{t_1} \sum_{k=1}^{m} \left\{ -\frac{d}{dt} \left(\frac{\partial T}{\partial \dot{q}_k} \right) + \frac{\partial T}{\partial q_k} + Q_k \right\} \delta q_k \, dt = 0. \qquad (2\text{–}52)$$

For this to be true for any arbitrarily assigned values of the δq_k, we find

$$\frac{d}{dt} \left(\frac{\partial T}{\partial \dot{q}_k} \right) - \frac{\partial T}{\partial q_k} = Q_k \qquad (k = 1, 2, \ldots, m). \qquad (2\text{–}53)$$

These m equations, one for each degree of freedom, are the celebrated Lagrange's equations of motion. They are second order differential equations which may be solved for the coordinates q_k as functions of the time. The quantity $\partial T / \partial \dot{q}_k$ in Eq. (2–53) is the momentum associated with the coordinate q_k.

If the force field is conservative, $\delta W = -\delta V$, where V is a function of the q_k only. Hence

$$-\delta V = \sum_{k=1}^{m} \left(-\frac{\partial V}{\partial q_k} \right) \delta q_k, \qquad (2\text{–}54)$$

and we observe by comparing this with Eq. (2–48) that

$$Q_k = -\frac{\partial V}{\partial q_k} \qquad (k = 1, 2, \ldots, m). \qquad (2\text{–}55)$$

Thus Lagrange's equations become

$$\frac{d}{dt}\left(\frac{\partial T}{\partial \dot{q}_k}\right) - \frac{\partial (T - V)}{\partial q_k} = 0 \qquad (k = 1, 2, \ldots, m). \qquad (2\text{-}56)$$

But $T - V = L$, the Lagrangian function, and since T is the only part of this which contains $\dot{q}_k$, we have $(\partial T/\partial \dot{q}_k) = (\partial L/\partial \dot{q}_k)$. This yields the form

$$\frac{d}{dt}\left(\frac{\partial L}{\partial \dot{q}_k}\right) - \frac{\partial L}{\partial q_k} = 0 \qquad (k = 1, 2, \ldots, m) \qquad (2\text{-}57)$$

for Lagrange's equations in the case of a conservative field.

We shall now apply Lagrange's equations to the solution of the double pendulum problem shown in Fig. 2–7. The potential energy of the system, reckoned from the point of support, is

$$V = -(m_1 + m_2)gl_1 \cos \theta_1 - m_2 gl_2 \cos \theta_2, \qquad (2\text{-}58)$$

while the kinetic energy is

$$T = \tfrac{1}{2}(m_1 + m_2)l_1^2\dot{\theta}_1^2 + \tfrac{1}{2}m_2 l_2^2\dot{\theta}_2^2 + m_2 l_1 l_2 \dot{\theta}_1 \dot{\theta}_2 \cos (\theta_1 - \theta_2) \qquad (2\text{-}59)$$

and the Lagrangian function is

$$L = \tfrac{1}{2}(m_1 + m_2)l_1^2\dot{\theta}_1^2 + \tfrac{1}{2}m_2 l_2^2\dot{\theta}_2^2 + m_2 l_1 l_2 \dot{\theta}_1 \dot{\theta}_2 \cos (\theta_1 - \theta_2)$$
$$+ (m_1 + m_2)gl_1 \cos \theta_1 + m_2 gl_2 \cos \theta_2. \qquad (2\text{-}60)$$

From L, we compute

$$\frac{\partial L}{\partial \dot{\theta}_1} = (m_1 + m_2)l_1^2\dot{\theta}_1 + m_2 l_1 l_2 \dot{\theta}_2 \cos (\theta_1 - \theta_2), \qquad (2\text{-}61)$$

$$\frac{\partial L}{\partial \dot{\theta}_2} = m_2 l_2^2\dot{\theta}_2 + m_2 l_1 l_2 \dot{\theta}_1 \cos (\theta_1 - \theta_2), \qquad (2\text{-}62)$$

$$\frac{\partial L}{\partial \theta_1} = -m_2 l_1 l_2 \dot{\theta}_1 \dot{\theta}_2 \sin (\theta_1 - \theta_2) - (m_1 + m_2)gl_1 \sin \theta_1, \qquad (2\text{-}63)$$

$$\frac{\partial L}{\partial \theta_2} = m_2 l_1 l_2 \dot{\theta}_1 \dot{\theta}_2 \sin (\theta_1 - \theta_2) - m_2 gl_2 \sin \theta_2. \qquad (2\text{-}64)$$

Then the Lagrangian equations of motion are

$$(m_1 + m_2)l_1\ddot{\theta}_1 + m_2 l_2 \ddot{\theta}_2 \cos (\theta_1 - \theta_2)$$
$$+ m_2 l_2 \dot{\theta}_2^2 \sin (\theta_1 - \theta_2) + (m_1 + m_2)g \sin \theta_1 = 0, \qquad (2\text{-}65)$$

$$l_2\ddot{\theta}_2 + l_1\ddot{\theta}_1 \cos (\theta_1 - \theta_2) - l_1\dot{\theta}_1^2 \sin (\theta_1 - \theta_2) + g \sin \theta_2 = 0. \qquad (2\text{-}66)$$

These simultaneous differential equations are to be solved for the co-ordinates θ_1 and θ_2 as functions of the time. The reader should examine for himself the physical significance of the terms in Eqs. (2–65) and (2–66) and, furthermore, he should try to obtain these equations by applying Newton's laws of motion directly. The advantages of the approach through Lagrange's equations become quite impressive.

We observe in the kinetic energy terms, Eq. (2–59), that not only the squares of the generalized velocities occur but also a cross-product term in $\dot{\theta}_1\dot{\theta}_2$. This is an instance of *dynamic coupling* between the two degrees of freedom of the system. Furthermore, we see that T is homogeneous of degree 2 in the velocities, as it should be according to Eq. (2–45), and that the coefficients of the quadratic velocity terms are functions of the coordinates.

The pulley and mass system shown in Fig. 2–8 serves as a second illustration of Lagrange's equations. We shall assume that the pulleys have negligible mass, turn without friction, and hence do not enter dynamically into the problem. Let r be the radius of each pulley, l_1 the length of the upper cord, l_2 the length of the lower cord. For generalized coordinates we choose q_1 and q_2. Then at any instant the masses m_1, m_2, m_3 are at distances $l_1 - \pi r - q_1$, $q_1 + l_2 - \pi r - q_2$, and $q_1 + q_2$, respectively, below the axis of the upper fixed pulley which we take as the origin of our coordinate system. The velocities are:

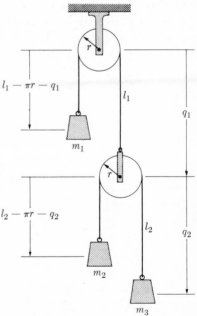

for m_1, $-\dot{q}_1$;

for m_2, $\dot{q}_1 - \dot{q}_2$;

for m_3, $\dot{q}_1 + \dot{q}_2$.

Therefore the kinetic energy is

$$T = \tfrac{1}{2}\{(m_1 + m_2 + m_3)\dot{q}_1^2 \\ + (m_2 + m_3)\dot{q}_2^2 \\ + 2(m_3 - m_2)\dot{q}_1\dot{q}_2\}. \quad (2\text{–}67)$$

For the potential energy, we find

$$V = -g\{m_1(l_1 - \pi r - q_1) \\ + m_2(q_1 + l_2 - \pi r - q_2) \\ + m_3(q_1 + q_2)\}, \qquad (2\text{–}68)$$

and hence a Lagrangian function $L = T - V$.

Fig. 2–8. Mass and pulley system.

Taking partial derivatives, we have

$$\frac{\partial L}{\partial \dot{q}_1} = (m_1 + m_2 + m_3)\dot{q}_1 + (m_3 - m_2)\dot{q}_2,$$

$$\frac{\partial L}{\partial \dot{q}_2} = (m_2 + m_3)\dot{q}_2 + (m_3 - m_2)\dot{q}_1,$$

$$\frac{\partial L}{\partial q_1} = (-m_1 + m_2 + m_3)g,$$

$$\frac{\partial L}{\partial q_2} = (m_3 - m_2)g.$$

From these, and using Eq. (2–57), we obtain the Lagrangian equations of motion:

$$(m_1 + m_2 + m_3)\ddot{q}_1 + (m_3 - m_2)\ddot{q}_2 + (m_1 - m_2 - m_3)g = 0, \quad (2\text{–}69)$$

$$(m_3 - m_2)\ddot{q}_1 + (m_2 + m_3)\ddot{q}_2 + (m_2 - m_3)g = 0, \quad (2\text{–}70)$$

which may be solved simultaneously for the accelerations $\ddot{q}_1$ and $\ddot{q}_2$. Again, the reader should interpret physically the terms in these equations and relate them to the physical system.

As a third example of the application of Lagrange's equations, we shall formulate the equations of motion for the governor shown in Fig. 2–9. The rods are pivoted at the origin and at each mass in such a way that, as the masses m move outward, the mass M can move smoothly in the vertical direction along the rod Oy. Let the cartesian reference frame,

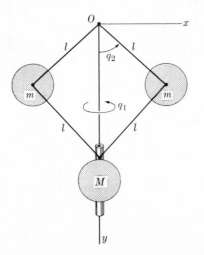

Fig. 2–9. Governor.

as shown, rotate about Oy so that at any instant its position is given by the angle q_1 with respect to some arbitrary initial plane. Then the angular velocity of rotation is $\dot{q}_1$ about Oy.

Let q_2 denote the angle at the origin which one of the bars makes with Oy (Fig. 2–9). The numbers q_1 and q_2, as functions of the time, are adequate to fix the positions of all three masses, and hence they serve as the generalized coordinates for the problem.

If I denotes the moment of inertia of M about the Oy axis and we consider the masses m as essentially particles, we have for the rotational kinetic energy about Oy

$$T_1 = \tfrac{1}{2}\{I + 2ml^2 \sin^2 q_2\}\dot{q}_1^2.$$

For the kinetic energy of motion in the xy-plane, we have

$$T_2 = \tfrac{1}{2}\{2ml^2\dot{q}_2^2 + 4Ml^2 \sin^2 q_2\,\dot{q}_2^2\},$$

and hence the total kinetic energy is

$$T = \tfrac{1}{2}\{(I + 2ml^2 \sin^2 q_2)\dot{q}_1^2 + (2ml^2 + 4Ml^2 \sin^2 q_2)\dot{q}_2^2\}. \qquad (2\text{–}71)$$

The potential energy may be written immediately as

$$V = -2mgl \cos q_2 - 2Mgl \cos q_2 = -2gl(m + M) \cos q_2. \qquad (2\text{–}72)$$

From $L = T - V$, we find the partial derivatives

$$\frac{\partial L}{\partial \dot{q}_1} = (I + 2ml^2 \sin^2 q_2)\dot{q}_1,$$

$$\frac{\partial L}{\partial \dot{q}_2} = (2ml^2 + 4Ml^2 \sin^2 q_2)\dot{q}_2,$$

$$\frac{\partial L}{\partial q_1} = 0,$$

$$\frac{\partial L}{\partial q_2} = 2l^2 \sin q_2 \cos q_2(m\dot{q}_1^2 + 2M\dot{q}_2^2) - 2gl \sin q_2(m + M).$$

Lagrange's equations for the system are

$$\frac{d}{dt}\left[(I + 2ml^2 \sin^2 q_2)\dot{q}_1\right] = 0, \qquad (2\text{–}73)$$

$$(2ml^2 + 4Ml^2 \sin^2 q_2)\ddot{q}_2 + 4Ml^2 \sin q_2 \cos q_2\,\dot{q}_2^2$$
$$-2ml^2 \sin q_2 \cos q_2\,\dot{q}_1^2 + 2gl \sin q_2(m + M) = 0. \qquad (2\text{–}74)$$

These may be solved for $\ddot{q}_2$ and $\ddot{q}_1$ to complete the problem. One fact is apparent immediately, namely,

$$(I + 2ml^2 \sin^2 q_2)\dot{q}_1 = \text{constant.}$$

This quantity is the angular momentum of the system about Oy. The acceleration $\ddot{y}_M$ with which M moves along Oy can be found from $\ddot{q}_2$ by using the relation $y_M = 2l \cos q_2$.

Two important properties of the Lagrangian equations of motion should be mentioned. Suppose the coordinates q_k are changed to another coordinate system by some point transformation. To be specific, this might be a change from cartesian to spherical coordinates, or from cartesian to cylindrical coordinates. When the Lagrangian equations are also transformed to the new coordinate system, they still express the condition for the vanishing of $\int_{t_0}^{t_1} (\delta T + \delta W) \, dt$ in the new coordinates. In the second place, when using Lagrange's equations, one does not need to calculate the inertial forces acting on each part of the mechanical system, as when applying D'Alembert's principle. The scalar function $L(q_k, \dot{q}_k)$ is sufficient to yield the differential equations for the dynamical system.

2–7 Nonholonomic and nonconservative systems.

In deriving Lagrange's equations from Hamilton's principle, we assumed in obtaining Eqs. (2–53) from Eq. (2–52) that the δq_k were independently assignable. We made no stipulation, however, that the generalized forces Q_k should be conservative. Eqs. (2–53) are, therefore, applicable to nonconservative systems. The independence of the δq_k, which is the condition for a holonomic system, can be removed to a certain extent so that some types of nonholonomic systems can be included in this type of analysis.

We assume that in establishing the q_k's for a given system all integrable constraint conditions have been applied, i.e., any functional relationship between the q_k's has been taken into account. If a particle moves on the surface $x^2 + y^2 = 4z$, for example, we can eliminate one of (x,y,z) as generalized coordinates of the particle. All three of the virtual displacements δx, δy, δz are not independent, since $2x \, \delta x + 2y \, \delta y - 4 \, \delta z = 0$ by the constraint condition. Two degrees of freedom are all the particle possesses.

If the constraint condition is nonintegrable but yet is in the form $\sum_{k=1}^{m} a_k \, \delta q_k = 0$, we may reduce the number of degrees of freedom and solve the problem by use of Lagrange's multipliers. An example of such a nonintegrable constraint is furnished by the pure rolling motion of a ball on a horizontal plane along a curve C as pictured in Fig. 2–10. The position and orientation of the ball at any time are specified by the x- and y-coordinates of its center (hence the point of contact with the plane)

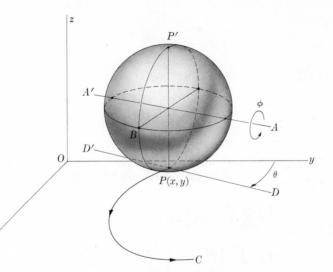

Fig. 2–10. Sphere rolling on a plane.

together with the angles θ and ϕ. The angle θ gives the orientation of the plane PBP' relative to the yz-plane, while ϕ gives the rotational orientation of the plane ABA' about AA'. The velocity of the center of the sphere then is given instantaneously by

$$\dot{x} = r\dot{\phi}\cos\theta, \qquad \dot{y} = -r\dot{\phi}\sin\theta, \qquad (2\text{--}75)$$

where r is the radius of the sphere. The constraint conditions are

$$\delta x - r\cos\theta\,\delta\phi = 0, \qquad \delta y + r\sin\theta\,\delta\phi = 0. \qquad (2\text{--}76)$$

These cannot be obtained from a functional relation between the coordinates x, y, θ, and ϕ. We speak of Eqs. (2–76) as nonintegrable constraint conditions.

At first we shall assume only one condition of constraint of the form

$$\sum_{k=1}^{m} a_k\,\delta q_k = 0. \qquad (2\text{--}77)$$

Equation (2–77) will still be true if we multiply by an unknown parameter λ, whose value will be determined in the course of the solution. This parameter is called *Lagrange's undetermined multiplier*. λ may be a function of the time, but for our discussion we shall assume it is not.

Multiplying Eq. (2–77) by λ and by dt and integrating between times t_0 and t_1, as we did in discussing Hamilton's principle, yields

$$\int_{t_0}^{t_1} \sum_{k=1}^{m} \lambda a_k \, \delta q_k \, dt = 0. \tag{2-78}$$

If the system is conservative, we may combine Eqs. (2–78) and (2–52) to yield

$$\int_{t_0}^{t_1} \sum_{k=1}^{m} \left\{ \frac{\partial L}{\partial q_k} - \frac{d}{dt}\left(\frac{\partial L}{\partial \dot{q}_k}\right) + \lambda a_k \right\} \delta q_k \, dt = 0. \tag{2-79}$$

We cannot assign values independently and arbitrarily to *all* the δq_k in this expression. However, we may rewrite Eq. (2–79) as

$$\int_{t_0}^{t_1} \sum_{k=1}^{m-1} \left\{ \frac{\partial L}{\partial q_k} - \frac{d}{dt}\left(\frac{\partial L}{\partial \dot{q}_k}\right) + \lambda a_k \right\} \delta q_k \, dt$$

$$+ \int_{t_0}^{t_1} \left\{ \frac{\partial L}{\partial q_m} - \frac{d}{dt}\left(\frac{\partial L}{\partial \dot{q}_m}\right) + \lambda a_m \right\} \delta q_m \, dt = 0. \tag{2-80}$$

Now suppose we choose λ so that the second integral vanishes; that is,

$$\frac{\partial L}{\partial q_m} - \frac{d}{dt}\left(\frac{\partial L}{\partial \dot{q}_m}\right) + \lambda a_m = 0. \tag{2-81}$$

This is necessary since δq_m is *not* independent but is restricted according to Eq. (2–77). Having done this, we are free to choose $\delta q_1, \delta q_2, \ldots, \delta q_{m-1}$ in the first integral arbitrarily, and if this integral is to vanish, we must have

$$\frac{\partial L}{\partial q_k} - \frac{d}{dt}\left(\frac{\partial L}{\partial \dot{q}_k}\right) + \lambda a_k = 0 \qquad (k = 1, 2, \ldots, m-1). \tag{2-82}$$

Equations (2–81) and (2–82) give us m equations to solve for the values $q_1, q_2, \ldots, q_m$, but we also must obtain λ. For this we adjoin to Eqs. (2–81) and (2–82) the constraint condition, Eq. (2–77), rewritten in the form

$$\sum_{k=1}^{m} a_k \, \dot{q}_k = 0. \tag{2-83}$$

This can be done since the constraint condition is essentially a linear differential form, $\sum_{k=1}^{m} a_k \, dq_k$, and hence remains so if each term is divided by dt.

Since a holonomic constraint $\phi(q_1, q_2, \ldots, q_m) = 0$ is equivalent to a differential equation

$$\sum_{k=1}^{m} \frac{\partial \phi}{\partial q_k} \, dq_k = 0, \tag{2-84}$$

we may treat holonomic systems by the undetermined multiplier method. Here the $(\partial\phi/\partial q_k)$ play the part of the a_k in Eq. (2–77). If there are several conditions of constraint, such as

$$\sum_{k=1}^{m} a_{1k}\,\delta q_k = 0, \quad \sum_{k=1}^{m} a_{2k}\,\delta q_k = 0, \ldots \sum_{k=1}^{m} a_{pk}\,\delta q_k = 0, \quad (2\text{–}85)$$

this procedure can be modified appropriately by introducing as many undetermined multipliers as we have conditions. In this case the equations to be solved are

$$\frac{d}{dt}\left(\frac{\partial L}{\partial \dot{q}_k}\right) - \frac{\partial L}{\partial q_k} - \sum_{j=1}^{p} \lambda_j\, a_{jk} = 0 \qquad (k = 1, 2, \ldots, m), \quad (2\text{–}86)$$

together with Eq. (2–85) modified to

$$\sum_{k=1}^{m} a_{jk}\,\dot{q}_k = 0 \qquad (j = 1, 2, \ldots, p). \tag{2–87}$$

To illustrate the method of undetermined multipliers, we shall consider a mass m sliding under gravity without friction on the inner surface of a paraboloid $r^2 = cz$. In cylindrical coordinates, we have

$$T = \tfrac{1}{2}m[\dot{r}^2 + r^2\dot{\theta}^2 + \dot{z}^2],$$

$$V = mgz,$$

$$L = T - V,$$

and the constraint condition, derived from the equation of the paraboloid, is $2r\,\delta r - c\,\delta z = 0$. There will be only one λ needed here: $a_r = 2r$, $a_\theta = 0$, $a_z = -c$. The equations of motion will be

$$m\ddot{r} - mr\dot{\theta}^2 - 2r\lambda = 0,$$

$$mr^2\ddot{\theta} + 2m\dot{r}\dot{\theta}r = 0,$$

$$m\ddot{z} + mg + c\lambda = 0.$$

Furthermore, $2r\dot{r} - c\dot{z} = 0$. These are the equations that correspond to Eqs. (2–82) and (2–83). From them we obtain r, θ, z, and λ.

We may naturally inquire into the physical significance of the λ_j in the equations of motion. If there were no constraints on the system but generalized forces were applied so as to keep the motion of the system the same as that described by Eqs. (2–86), these generalized forces would have to be identical with the quantities $\sum_{j=1}^{p} a_{jk}\lambda_j$. Thus when we find the λ_j, the constraint forces are supplied automatically as part of the answer to our problem.

If the force field is nonconservative, Lagrange's equations are still valid in the form given in Eqs. (2–53). We can define in some cases a generalized potential $V(q_k, \dot{q}_k)$, dependent upon both velocities and coordinates, in such a way that

$$Q_k = -\frac{\partial V}{\partial q_k} + \frac{d}{dt}\left(\frac{\partial V}{\partial \dot{q}_k}\right). \tag{2-88}$$

Then Lagrange's equations in the homogeneous form, Eq. (2–57), still represent the system. The function $V(q, \dot{q})$ is called a *velocity-dependent potential*.

Suppose, in the example just given, the mass m sliding on the surface $r^2 = cz$ is resisted by a force proportional to the velocity, $\mathbf{F} = a\mathbf{v}$. This force would have components $a\dot{r}$, $ar\dot{\theta}$, and $a\dot{z}$ in the cylindrical coordinate system. If we remove the constraint directly by using the equation of the surface, we have

$$T = \frac{1}{2}\, m\left[\left(1 + \frac{4r^2}{c^2}\right)\dot{r}^2 + r^2\dot{\theta}^2\right],$$

$$V = \frac{mgr^2}{c},$$

for the conservative part of the field. In addition to the conservative forces, we have the frictional forces entering the Q_r and Q_θ, so that Lagrange's equations (2–53) become

$$\frac{d}{dt}\left[m\dot{r}\left(1 + \frac{4r^2}{c^2}\right)\right] - \frac{4mr\dot{r}^2}{c^2} - mr\dot{\theta}^2 + \frac{2mgr}{c} = a\dot{r}, \tag{2-89}$$

$$\frac{d}{dt}\,[mr^2\dot{\theta}] = ar^2\dot{\theta}, \tag{2-90}$$

in terms of the generalized coordinates r, θ. The nonconservative parts of the force are exhibited on the right sides of Eqs. (2–89) and (2–90).

2–8 Impulsive motion. In Section 1–10 we examined the effect of impulsive forces on the particles of a mechanical system. The result on a particle was a change in its velocity without a corresponding change in its position during the time the impulsive force was acting. Let us now see how impulsive forces may be brought within the framework of Lagrange's equations.

For each degree of freedom of the system, we have

$$\frac{d}{dt}\left(\frac{\partial T}{\partial \dot{q}_k}\right) - \frac{\partial T}{\partial q_k} = Q_k \qquad (k = 1, 2, \ldots, m). \tag{2-91}$$

We multiply through by dt, integrate from t_0 to t_1 as we did in discussing Hamilton's principle, and take the limit as $t_1 \to t_0$. The result is

$$\left(\frac{\partial T}{\partial \dot{q}_k}\right)_{t_0}^{t_1} - \lim_{t_1 \to t_0} \int_{t_0}^{t_1} \frac{\partial T}{\partial q_k}\, dt = \lim_{t_1 \to t_0} \int_{t_0}^{t_1} Q_k\, dt. \qquad (2\text{–}92)$$

But $(\partial T/\partial q_k)$ remains finite during this time interval. Hence the second integral on the left side of Eq. (2–92) vanishes as $t_1 \to t_0$. Furthermore, we define

$$\lim_{t_1 \to t_0} \int_{t_0}^{t_1} Q_k\, dt$$

to be the generalized impulse associated with the coordinate q_k. We will designate it by Q_k'. Thus the Lagrangian equations appropriate to impulsive motion are

$$\left(\frac{\partial T}{\partial \dot{q}_k}\right)_f - \left(\frac{\partial T}{\partial \dot{q}_k}\right)_i = Q_k' \qquad (k = 1, 2, \ldots, m). \qquad (2\text{–}93)$$

Observe that the left side of Eqs. (2–93) is the *change in the momentum* $(\partial T/\partial \dot{q}_k)$ *from the initial to the final time of action of the impulse.* These equations are not differential equations, but simply algebraic relations which are satisfied by the momenta under the action of the impulses.

The quantities Q_k' are found in a manner analogous to the generalized forces Q_k. The virtual work done on a single particle during the action of an impulse $\mathbf{F}_i$ will be

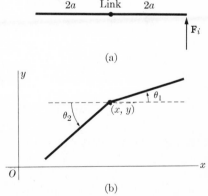

$$\delta W = \sum_{k=1}^{m} \left(\mathbf{F}_i \cdot \frac{\partial \mathbf{r}}{\partial q_k}\right) \delta q_k, \qquad (2\text{–}94)$$

(a)

and we identify the quantity $\mathbf{F}_i \cdot (\partial \mathbf{r}/\partial q_k)$ as the generalized impulse Q_k'. Extension of the definition to a system of n particles leads to a relation for Q_k' analogous to that for Q_k in Eq. (2–47).

As an illustration of these equations, we consider the effect of a blow on one end of a linked pair of rods, as shown in Fig. 2–11. Two bars, each

(b)

Fig. 2–11. Linked rods.

of length $2a$, lie on a smooth horizontal plane in a straight line, as shown in Fig. 2–11(a). A sharp blow $\mathbf{F}_i$ is struck at the right end of the system. We are to find the velocities imparted to the bars by this impulse. The position of the system at any time after the impulse may be specified by the angles θ_1 and θ_2 and the coordinates x, y of the link, as indicated in Fig. 2–11(b). These we shall take as the generalized coordinates.

The kinetic energy of a rod due to its rotation about an axis through the center of mass will be shown in Chapter 4 to be $\frac{1}{2}I_0\omega^2$, where I_0 is its moment of inertia about the axis and ω is the angular velocity. Furthermore, it can be shown that there is a point in the rod at distance k from the axis where a point mass m can be placed and produce the same moment of inertia as that produced by the distributed mass of the rod. Hence we have $I_0 = mk^2$, where m is the mass of the rod. The distance k is called the radius of gyration. The moment of inertia about the end of the rod is then

$$I = I_0 + ma^2 = m(a^2 + k^2), \tag{2-95}$$

where $2a$ is the length of the rod.

Using Eq. (2–95), together with the equations for the translational motion of the center of mass of each rod, we find that the kinetic energy at any time t will be

$$T = \tfrac{1}{2}m\big\{2\dot{x}^2 + 2\dot{y}^2 + (a^2 + k^2)(\dot{\theta}_1^2 + \dot{\theta}_2^2) + 2a\dot{x}(\dot{\theta}_2 \sin\theta_2 - \dot{\theta}_1 \sin\theta_1)$$
$$+ 2a\dot{y}(\dot{\theta}_1 \cos\theta_1 - \dot{\theta}_2 \cos\theta_2)\big\}. \tag{2-96}$$

The momenta are

$$\frac{\partial T}{\partial \dot{x}} = \frac{m}{2}\big\{4\dot{x} + 2a(\dot{\theta}_2 \sin\theta_2 - \dot{\theta}_1 \sin\theta_1)\big\}, \tag{2-97}$$

$$\frac{\partial T}{\partial \dot{y}} = \frac{m}{2}\big\{4\dot{y} + 2a(\dot{\theta}_1 \cos\theta_1 - \dot{\theta}_2 \cos\theta_2)\big\}, \tag{2-98}$$

$$\frac{\partial T}{\partial \dot{\theta}_1} = \frac{m}{2}\big\{2(a^2 + k^2)\dot{\theta}_1 - 2a\dot{x} \sin\theta_1 + 2a\dot{y} \cos\theta_1\big\}, \tag{2-99}$$

$$\frac{\partial T}{\partial \dot{\theta}_2} = \frac{m}{2}\big\{2(a^2 + k^2)\dot{\theta}_2 + 2a\dot{x} \sin\theta_2 - 2a\dot{y} \cos\theta_2\big\}. \tag{2-100}$$

We are interested in the change in these quantities during impact, and we bear in mind that initially $\theta_1 = \theta_2 = 0$, $\dot{\theta}_1 = \dot{\theta}_2 = 0$, $\dot{x} = \dot{y} = 0$. The velocities change during the impact, but the coordinates do not. Hence we have, from Eq. (2–93),

$$\Delta\left(\frac{\partial T}{\partial \dot{x}}\right) = 2m\dot{x} = Q'_x, \tag{2-101}$$

$$\Delta\left(\frac{\partial T}{\partial \dot{y}}\right) = 2m\dot{y} + ma(\dot{\theta}_1 - \dot{\theta}_2) = Q'_y, \tag{2-102}$$

$$\Delta\left(\frac{\partial T}{\partial\dot\theta_1}\right) = ma\dot y + \frac{4}{3}\,ma^2\dot\theta_1 = Q'_{\theta 1}, \qquad (2\text{--}103)$$

$$\Delta\left(\frac{\partial T}{\partial\dot\theta_2}\right) = -ma\dot y + \frac{4}{3}\,ma^2\dot\theta_2 = Q'_{\theta 2}, \qquad (2\text{--}104)$$

where we have used $k^2 = \frac{1}{3}a^2$ for the rods. Here Δ stands for the change in momentum during the action of the impulse.

To evaluate the generalized impulses Q'_k, we use the fact that the virtual work δW must be the same whether expressed in terms of the actual forces or in terms of the generalized forces. Thus we may write

$$\delta W = Q'_x\,\delta x + Q'_y\,\delta y + Q'_{\theta_1}\,\delta\theta_1 + Q'_{\theta_2}\,\delta\theta_2 = F_i\,\delta y_e, \qquad (2\text{--}105)$$

where δy_e is the virtual displacement of the right end of the right bar. But

$$\delta y_e = \delta y + 2a\,\delta\theta_1. \qquad (2\text{--}106)$$

Comparing coefficients in Eq. (2–105), after replacing δy_e by Eq. (2–106), we obtain

$$Q'_x = 0, \qquad Q'_y = F_i, \qquad Q'_{\theta_1} = 2aF_i, \qquad Q'_{\theta_2} = 0. \qquad (2\text{--}107)$$

With these values substituted into Eqs. (2–101), (2–102), (2–103), and (2–104), we can solve simultaneously to obtain

$$\dot x = 0, \qquad \dot y = -\frac{F_i}{m}, \qquad \dot\theta_1 = \frac{9F_i}{4ma}, \qquad \dot\theta_2 = -\frac{3F_i}{4ma}. \qquad (2\text{--}108)$$

These are the velocities resulting from the impact. To study the subsequent motion of the system, we would use Eqs. (2–108) as initial conditions.

2–9 Relativistic dynamics. The fundamental dynamical laws of Newton (Chapter 1) imply that the reference system used for their specification is fixed with respect to the average position of the stars in the solar neighborhood. This so-called primary inertial system is realizable only to a certain degree of approximation on a moving rigid body such as the earth (Sections 1–14 and 1–15). On the other hand, we can readily show that a reference system moving with constant velocity relative to a primary system is itself an inertial system according to Newtonian dynamics (see Problem 1–7), provided that the mass is a constant.

These conclusions, verifiable experimentally by astronomical observations and by laboratory experiments on the earth, are questionable when the magnitude of the velocity involved approaches the speed of light. In particular, an observer in a primary inertial system observes a spherical wave front emanating from a source of light at the origin with velocity c, but the same velocity would not be assigned to the wave front by an observer *moving* with respect to the primary inertial system. Suppose, for example, that with respect to a fixed origin O a point on the wave front is given by $\mathbf{r} = ct\mathbf{u}_n$, where $\mathbf{u}_n$ is a unit normal to the wave. Then the velocity of the wave front as observed in the fixed system would be $\dot{\mathbf{r}} = c\mathbf{u}_n$. But to an observer in a system moving with velocity $\mathbf{v}$ relative to O, the wave front would appear to advance with velocity $c\mathbf{u}_n - \mathbf{v}$, and the waves would not appear spherical to him since the velocity of advance depends on the direction.

Experiments of an optical nature, such as the Michelson-Morley experiment, indicated that the velocity of light is independent of such relative motions of source and observer. This possibility led Einstein, following the work of Lorentz,* to replace the postulates of Newtonian dynamics with new concepts of time and simultaneity and with these postulates: (1) The laws by which the states of physical systems undergo change are the same whether these changes of state are referred to one or the other of two systems of coordinates moving uniformly in translation with respect to one another. This is the *postulate of equivalence*. (2) The velocity of light is constant and the same in all systems of coordinates and is independent of the relative motion of source and observer.

The consequences of these postulates were far reaching; from them developed Einstein's special theory of relativity. We shall not dwell in detail upon the transformation theory underlying the differences between the Newtonian formulation of dynamical laws and those of relativistic dynamics, but shall indicate only the changes in the equations of motion resulting from the viewpoint of the special theory of relativity.

The special theory indicates that if the mass of a particle, instead of being a scalar constant, is taken as

$$m = \frac{m_0}{\sqrt{1 - (v/c)^2}},\qquad(2\text{–}109)$$

then the Newtonian *form* of the equations of motion is preserved. Here m_0 is called the *rest mass* of the particle, m is the *relativistic mass*, and the constant c is the velocity of light. It is apparent from Eq. (2–109) that m is meaningless if $v > c$. This fact is confirmed by experiment; no observed particle velocity has ever been found to be greater than the speed of light. We have, then, the equation of motion,

---

* See, for example, an interesting series of translations of the original papers entitled *The Principle of Relativity*. New York: Dover Publications, Inc.

$$\frac{d}{dt}\left(\frac{m_0\mathbf{v}}{\sqrt{1 - (v/c)^2}}\right) = \mathbf{F}. \qquad (2\text{--}110)$$

As in the Newtonian dynamics, we define the kinetic energy T to be that function of the velocity which satisfies the equation

$$\frac{dT}{dt} = \mathbf{F}\cdot\mathbf{v}. \qquad (2\text{--}111)$$

But by Eq. (2–110),

$$\frac{dT}{dt} = \mathbf{v}\cdot\frac{d}{dt}\left(\frac{m_0\mathbf{v}}{\sqrt{1 - (v/c)^2}}\right). \qquad (2\text{--}112)$$

Let $\mathbf{u}_v$ be a unit vector defining the direction of the velocity, and let $\beta = v/c$. Then Eq. (2–112) becomes

$$\frac{dT}{dt} = m_0 c^2 \beta \mathbf{u}_v \cdot \frac{d}{dt}\left(\frac{\beta \mathbf{u}_v}{\sqrt{1 - \beta^2}}\right)$$

$$= m_0 c^2 \beta \dot{\beta}(1 - \beta^2)^{-3/2}$$

$$= \frac{d}{dt}\left[\frac{m_0 c^2}{\sqrt{1 - \beta^2}}\right].$$

Integrating, we have

$$T = \frac{m_0 c^2}{\sqrt{1 - \beta^2}} + \text{constant}. \qquad (2\text{--}113)$$

If T is to vanish for $v = 0$, as in the nonrelativistic case, the constant must be $-m_0 c^2$. Hence

$$T = m_0 c^2 \left[\frac{1}{\sqrt{1 - (v/c)^2}} - 1\right]. \qquad (2\text{--}114)$$

We note that by using Eq. (2–109) this may be written as $T = (m - m_0)c^2$. If there are two particles with velocities v_1 and v_2, and hence masses m_1 and m_2, the difference in their kinetic energies is $T_2 - T_1 = (m_2 - m_1)c^2$. Hence there is an equivalence between mass and energy in the relativistic formulation of dynamics.

When β is small, the expression for T (2–114) can be expanded by the binomial theorem to yield

$$T = m_0 c^2 \left\{1 + \frac{1}{2}\frac{v^2}{c^2} + \cdots - 1\right\}.$$

As $v/c \to 0$, $T \to \frac{1}{2}m_0 v^2$, the nonrelativistic kinetic energy.

In the discussion of Lagrange's equations for constant mass and for a potential which was not velocity-dependent (Section 2–6), we found that $L = T - V$ was related to the momenta $m\dot{q}_k$ by the definition

$$\frac{\partial L}{\partial \dot{q}_k} = m\dot{q}_k \qquad (k = 1, 2, \ldots, m).$$

In the relativistic case for a single particle in a potential field that does not depend on the velocity, we demand a similar relationship between L and the relativistic momentum:

$$\mathbf{p} = \frac{m_0 \mathbf{v}}{\sqrt{1 - (v/c)^2}}. \qquad (2\text{–}115)$$

Thus the part of L which is velocity-dependent is given by the equation

$$\frac{\partial T^*}{\partial v} = \frac{m_0 v}{\sqrt{1 - (v/c)^2}},$$

which may be integrated directly to yield

$$T^* = -m_0 c^2 \sqrt{1 - (v/c)^2} + \text{constant}.$$

By analogy with the nonrelativistic case, it is customary to choose the constant so that T^* is zero when $v = 0$. With this choice, we have $T^* = m_0 c^2 [1 - \sqrt{1 - (v/c)^2}]$, and hence the Lagrangian function,

$$L = m_0 c^2 [1 - \sqrt{1 - (v/c)^2}] - V, \qquad (2\text{–}116)$$

where V is not velocity-dependent. Notice here that $L \neq T - V$, where T is the kinetic energy defined by Eq. (2–114). As in the non-relativistic case, L may be expressed in terms of generalized coordinates, and Lagrange's equations follow. The essential difference between them and those arising in the nonrelativistic dynamics is in the use of the relativistic mass $m = m_0 (1 - \beta^2)^{-1/2}$, where $\beta = v/c$.

As a simple example, consider the motion of a particle of rest mass m_0 on a horizontal line under the action of a linear restoring force $-kx$, where x is the displacement from the origin. In the nonrelativistic case, this would be simple harmonic motion with period $P = 2\pi\sqrt{m_0/k}$. We shall find the period of the relativistic oscillator for comparison.

By Eq. (2–116) we have

$$L = m_0 c^2 [1 - \sqrt{1 - (v/c)^2}] - \tfrac{1}{2} k x^2,$$

$$\frac{\partial L}{\partial v} = \frac{m_0 v}{\sqrt{1 - (v/c)^2}},$$

$$\frac{\partial L}{\partial x} = -kx,$$

and hence the Lagrangian equation of motion is

$$\frac{d}{dt}\left(\frac{m_0 v}{\sqrt{1-(v/c)^2}}\right) + kx = 0. \tag{2–117}$$

This could, of course, be written directly by use of Eq. (2–110).
  By writing Eq. (2–117) in the form

$$\frac{d}{dx}\left[\frac{m_0 v}{\sqrt{1-(v/c)^2}}\right]\frac{dx}{dt} + kx = 0,$$

and setting $dx/dt = v$, we can integrate directly to obtain

$$\frac{m_0 c^2}{\sqrt{1-(v/c)^2}} = -\frac{1}{2}kx^2 + E, \tag{2–118}$$

where E is a constant to be determined. Suppose the maximum excursion
of the oscillator is $x = a$. At this point $v = 0$. Hence, from Eq. (2–118),

$$E = m_0 c^2 + \tfrac{1}{2}ka^2. \tag{2–119}$$

From Eqs. (2–118) and (2–119), we find

$$v = c\sqrt{\frac{[1+\alpha(a^2-x^2)]^2 - 1}{[1+\alpha(a^2-x^2)]^2}}, \tag{2–120}$$

where $\alpha = k/2m_0 c^2$. Since c^2 is very large, α is very small, in general.
  The period of the relativistic oscillator is

$$P = 4\int_0^a \frac{dx}{v}, \tag{2–121}$$

or, using Eq. (2–120),

$$P = \frac{4}{c}\int_0^a \frac{dx[1+\alpha(a^2-x^2)]}{\sqrt{[1+\alpha(a^2-x^2)]^2 - 1}}. \tag{2–122}$$

This may be written

$$P = \frac{4}{c\sqrt{2\alpha}}\int_0^a \frac{dx[1+\alpha(a^2-x^2)]}{\sqrt{a^2-x^2}\sqrt{1+\tfrac{1}{2}\alpha(a^2-x^2)}}.$$

By using the binomial expansion, since α is small, and retaining terms
to the first power in α, we have

$$P = \frac{4}{c\sqrt{2\alpha}} \int_0^a \frac{dx}{\sqrt{a^2 - x^2}} \left[1 + \frac{3\alpha}{4} (a^2 - x^2) + \cdots \right]. \quad (2\text{--}123)$$

But $\sqrt{2\alpha} = (1/c)\sqrt{k/m_0}$, and direct integration of Eq. (2–123) yields, to terms of first order in α,

$$P \cong 2\pi\sqrt{m_0/k}\,[1 + \tfrac{3}{8}\alpha a^2]. \quad (2\text{--}124)$$

This is, to a high degree of approximation, the period of the oscillator. We observe that if α were set equal to zero we would have the period P for the nonrelativistic oscillator.

The reader will note that we have considered here only particle motion. In the study of electrodynamics particularly, the Lagrangian formulation of the equations of motion of an electron or other charged particle is useful. This is brought out in Problem 2–21. In general, the parts of nonrelativistic dynamics such as rigid body rotations and the like have no analog in the framework of relativistic dynamics.

PROBLEMS

2–1. An I-beam is hoisted by a sling composed of a cable of length equal to twice the distance between the sling supports, as in Fig. 2–12. The cable can slip freely over the hoisting hook, and we assume that the center of gravity of the I-beam is midway between sling supports. The beam weighs W lb. Discuss the equilibrium of the system by the use of Bernoulli's principle of virtual work. Verify your conclusion by computing the potential energy of the bar and finding its maximum or minimum value. (Section 2–1)

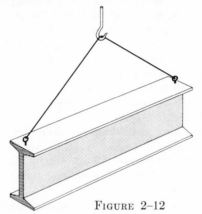

FIGURE 2–12

2–2. A rod of length a is placed on the inside of a spherical bowl of radius a. The ends of the rod slide smoothly on the interior of the bowl. Discuss the equilibrium of the rod by Bernoulli's principle. (Section 2–1)

2–3. A block of weight W_1 lb rests on a smooth table as shown in Fig. 2–13 and is connected by an inextensible string to a freely hanging weight W_2. The pulley has a moment of inertia I about its axis. Its radius is a. By use of D'Alembert's principle, find the acceleration of the system. (Section 2–1)

2–4. A block of mass M rests on a horizontal tabletop and is connected by inextensible cords to masses m_1 and m_2, as shown in Fig. 2–14. The system can move without friction, the cords sliding smoothly over pegs. Take $m_1 > m_2$. Discuss the motion of the system by D'Alembert's principle and verify by writing Newton's equation of motion directly. (Section 2–2)

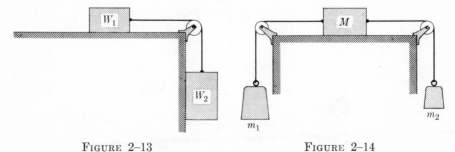

FIGURE 2–13   FIGURE 2–14

2–5. Verify the equation of motion for a simple pendulum of length l and mass of bob m by using D'Alembert's principle. (Section 2–2)

2–6. A particle of mass m describes simple harmonic motion according to the law $x = A \sin \omega t$ under the action of a restoring force $-m\omega^2 x$. Compute T and V and show directly that $\int_{t=0}^{t=\pi/8\omega} \delta(T - V)\, dt$ has a value zero for the prescribed dynamical path. (Section 2–4)

2–7. Suppose we choose a varied path for the simple harmonic oscillator of Problem 2–6, say $x = A\{\sin \omega t + c \sin 8\omega t\}$, which has the same endpoints in time as the path $x = A \sin \omega t$ of Problem 2–6. (a) Compute $\int_{t=0}^{t=\pi/8\omega} (T - V)\, dt$ for this varied path and (b) show that the integral is greater for either positive or negative c than the integral computed in Problem 2–6. (Section 2–4)

2–8. The force acting on a mass m has components $X = -kx$, $Y = -ly$, where k and l are positive constants. (a) By applying Hamilton's principle directly, find the equations of motion for the particle. (b) Describe the resulting path of the particle. (Section 2–4)

2–9. Write the Lagrangian equations of motion for the pendulum and turntable in Problem 1–12. (Section 2–6)

2–10. A spherical pendulum consisting of a large mass m suspended at the end of a light rod of length l is free to swing in any direction subject to the constraints. Write the Lagrangian equations of motion of the bob in appropriate generalized coordinates. Neglect the mass of the rod in comparison with the mass of the bob. (Section 2–6)

2–11. A pendulum of length l and bob m is suspended from a stiff spring, as shown in Fig. 2–15. The spring constant is k. We neglect the mass of the support wire and of the spring in comparison with m. The point of support of the pendulum is restricted to vertical motion. (a) Write Lagrange's equations of motion for the system. (b) Interpret physically the terms in these equations. (Section 2–6)

2–12. A bead of mass $3m$ is free to slide horizontally without friction on a wire, as shown in Fig. 2–16. Attached to the bead is a double pendulum. If the system is released from rest in a position near its equilibrium position, the masses oscillate, in the plane of the figure, about the vertical. (a) Write

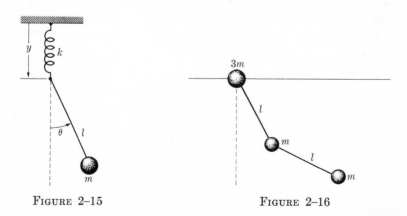

FIGURE 2–15   FIGURE 2–16

Lagrange's equations of motion for the system. (b) Find the accelerations when the displacements and velocities are small. (Section 2–6)

2–13. Two spheres each of mass m and bearing an electrostatic charge $+Q$ are suspended as pendulums, as shown in Fig. 2–17. The electrostatic force of repulsion between the spheres varies directly as the product of their charges and inversely as the square of the distance between their centers. Assuming that the displacements from equilibrium are small, so that the motion of the bobs vertically may be neglected, write the Lagrangian equations of motion for the pendulums. (Section 2–6)

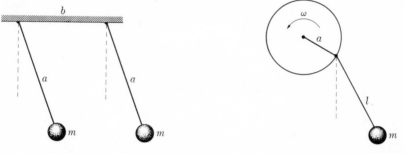

FIGURE 2–17   FIGURE 2–18

2–14. The point of support of a simple pendulum moves on a vertical circle of radius a, as shown in Fig. 2–18, with constant angular velocity ω. Write the equation of motion for the pendulum by Lagrange's method. (Section 2–6)

2–15. A mass m rests under the force of gravity at the vertex of the paraboloid $x^2 + y^2 = 4(4 - z)$. If displaced slightly, it will slide without friction on the surface. (a) Write the Lagrangian equations of motion, using the method of undetermined multipliers to represent the constraints. (b) What are the constraint forces? (c) At what height will the mass leave the paraboloid? (Section 2–7)

2–16. A wire hoop of radius b and mass m_1 per unit arc rolls without slipping over the curved cylindrical surface of radius a, as shown in Fig. 2–19. (a) Write the Lagrangian equations of motion, using the method of undetermined multipliers to represent the constraints. (b) At what angle θ will the hoop leave the cylinder? (Section 2–7)

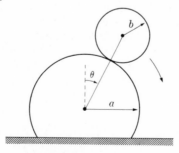

FIGURE 2–19

2–17. A bead of mass m slides under gravity along a wire bent into the form of the parabola $y = 1 + x^2$. The coefficient of friction between bead and wire is μ; hence the frictional force acting on the bead is μN, where N is the total force normal to the curve, and this force tends to oppose the motion. At the same time the plane of the wire rotates about Oy at constant angular speed ω. Discuss the motion of the bead by Lagrange's equations. (Section 2–7)

2–18. A horizontal rod of mass m and length $2l$ falls under gravity and strikes a knife-edge located one half of the way from center to end of the rod (see Fig. 2–20). Its velocity just before impact is $\mathbf{v}$. The coefficient of restitution between rod and knife-edge is e. Using Lagrange's equations, calculate (a) the velocity of the center of mass and (b) the angular velocity immediately after the rod strikes the obstruction. (Section 2–8)

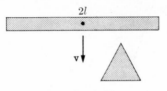

FIGURE 2–20

2–19. By writing $\mathbf{v} = v\mathbf{u}_v$, where $\mathbf{u}_v$ is a unit vector in the direction of $\mathbf{v}$, show from Eq. (2–110) that the acceleration component in the $\mathbf{u}_v$ direction has an associated mass $m_0[1 - (v/c)^2]^{-3/2}$, while the acceleration component perpendicular to $\mathbf{u}_v$ has an associated mass $m_0[1 - (v/c)^2]^{-1/2}$. These have been called the *longitudinal* and *transverse* masses respectively. (Section 2–9)

2–20. A particle of mass $m = m_0[1 - (v/c)^2]^{-1/2}$ moves on the x-axis under the action of a constant force F. (a) Find its velocity and its displacement at time $t > 0$ if the particle starts from rest at the origin. (b) How does the displacement compare with the value it would have if the nonrelativistic mass were used? (Section 2–9)

2–21. If m_0 is the rest mass of a particle, the mass given by the theory of relativity for a speed v is $m = m_0[1 - v^2/c^2]^{-1/2}$, where c is the velocity of light. Let $\mathbf{A}$ be a vector function of position such that $\mathbf{B} = \text{curl } \mathbf{A} = $ the magnetic induction. $\mathbf{A}$ is called the *vector potential* and is a function of position and time. The appropriate Lagrangian function here is $L = m_0c^2[1 - (1 - v^2/c^2)^{1/2}] + e(\mathbf{v}\cdot\mathbf{A}) - eV$, where e is the charge on the particle and V is the electrostatic potential. (a) Write the equations of motion for the particle in xyz-coordinates. (b) Compare these with the equations of motion obtained vectorially under the force law $\mathbf{F} = e[-\nabla V - \partial\mathbf{A}/\partial t + \mathbf{v} \times \mathbf{B}]$. (Section 2–9)

CHAPTER 3

CENTRAL FORCE MOTION

Central force motion is motion which takes place under the action of a force always directed toward or away from a point. Perhaps the first example of this type of motion to be recognized was that of the planets about the sun. A more modern example is the motion of the electrons in the accelerating device known as the betatron. Nuclear forces binding electrons to an atom undoubtedly have a central character. The importance of this kind of motion warrants a detailed study, which we shall undertake in this chapter. We shall use the method of Lagrange's equations to establish the equations of motion. The use of vector methods simplifies the discussion in certain aspects. To illustrate the economy of description by vector analysis, we shall also employ it in a supplemental way.

3-1 General properties of central force motion. Many characteristic features of the movement of a mass particle under the action of a central force do not depend specifically upon the force law. The only restriction is that the force be a central one.

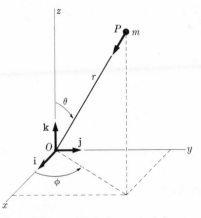

Fig. 3-1. Mass particle in central force motion.

Consider a mass particle at distance r from the force center O (Fig. 3-1). Let the force acting on this mass be $F(r)$ in magnitude and directed along the line OP. Suppose O to be fixed and the coordinate system to be a primary inertial system. Let the spherical coordinates r, θ, ϕ be chosen as generalized coordinates. Then the position vector of m is

$\mathbf{r} = r \sin \theta \cos \phi \mathbf{i} + r \sin \theta \sin \phi \mathbf{j} + r \cos \theta \, \mathbf{k}$; the velocity is

$$\mathbf{v} = \frac{d\mathbf{r}}{dt} = (\dot{r} \sin \theta \cos \phi + r \cos \theta \cos \phi \, \dot{\theta} - r \sin \theta \sin \phi \, \dot{\phi})\mathbf{i}$$

$$+ (\dot{r} \sin \theta \sin \phi + r \cos \theta \sin \phi \, \dot{\theta} + r \sin \theta \cos \phi \, \dot{\phi})\mathbf{j}$$

$$+ (\dot{r} \cos \theta - r \sin \theta \dot{\theta})\mathbf{k}.$$

The kinetic energy, $\frac{1}{2}mv^2$, becomes

$$T = \tfrac{1}{2}m[\dot{r}^2 + r^2 \sin^2 \theta \, \dot{\phi}^2 + r^2\dot{\theta}^2].$$

If $V(r)$ is the potential energy of the mass derivable from the force $F(r)$ when the latter is specified, then we form the Lagrangian function, $L = T - V$, which here becomes

$$L = \tfrac{1}{2}m[\dot{r}^2 + r^2 \sin^2 \theta \, \dot{\phi}^2 + r^2\dot{\theta}^2] - V(r). \tag{3-1}$$

To form Lagrange's equations (Section 2–6), we take the partial derivatives from Eq. (3–1) and use them in Eq. (2–57). We have

$$\frac{\partial L}{\partial \dot{r}} = m\dot{r}, \qquad \frac{\partial L}{\partial \dot{\phi}} = mr^2 \sin^2 \theta \, \dot{\phi}, \qquad \frac{\partial L}{\partial \dot{\theta}} = mr^2\dot{\theta}, \tag{3-2}$$

$$\frac{\partial L}{\partial r} = mr \sin^2 \theta \, \dot{\phi}^2 + mr\dot{\theta}^2 - \frac{dV}{dr},$$

$$\frac{\partial L}{\partial \phi} = 0, \tag{3-3}$$

$$\frac{\partial L}{\partial \theta} = mr^2 \sin \theta \cos \theta \, \dot{\phi}^2.$$

Hence Lagrange's equations (2–57) are

$$\frac{d}{dt}(m\dot{r}) - mr \sin^2 \theta \, \dot{\phi}^2 - mr\dot{\theta}^2 - F(r) = 0, \tag{3-4}$$

$$\frac{d}{dt}(mr^2 \sin^2 \theta \, \dot{\phi}) = 0, \tag{3-5}$$

$$\frac{d}{dt}(mr^2\dot{\theta}) - mr^2\dot{\phi}^2 \sin \theta \cos \theta = 0, \tag{3-6}$$

where for dV/dr we have written $-F(r)$ (see Section 1–7).

Equation (3–5) exhibits the first property of central force motion which we wish to note. From it we see that

$$mr^2 \sin^2 \theta \, \dot{\phi} = \text{constant} = k. \tag{3-7}$$

Here k denotes the angular momentum associated with the coordinate ϕ. Substituting $\dot{\phi}$ from Eq. (3–7) into Eqs. (3–4) and (3–6), we find

$$\frac{d}{dt}(m\dot{r}) - \frac{k^2}{mr^3 \sin^2 \theta} - mr\dot{\theta}^2 - F(r) = 0, \qquad (3\text{–}8)$$

$$\frac{d}{dt}(mr^2\dot{\theta}) - \frac{k^2 \cos \theta}{mr^2 \sin^3 \theta} = 0. \qquad (3\text{–}9)$$

These equations are entirely independent of ϕ. Hence there remain only two generalized coordinates, r and θ. The problem has been reduced from one of three degrees of freedom to one of only two degrees of freedom. The mass m moves in a plane, and its position at any time is given by the polar coordinates (r, θ).

This result is evident from physical considerations. Suppose the particle is projected initially in a plane perpendicular to the xy-plane. Thereafter the force F points toward O and hence lies in the plane determined by OP and Oz. There is no force component, and hence no motion, perpendicular to this plane.

Suppose the particle is projected so that it lies thereafter in the plane $\phi = $ constant (a plane POz). Then $\dot{\phi} = 0$ and hence $k = 0$. From Eq. (3–9),

$$\frac{d}{dt}(mr^2\dot{\theta}) = 0, \qquad (3\text{–}10)$$

and

$$mr^2\dot{\theta} = l = \text{constant}. \qquad (3\text{–}11)$$

The quantity $mr^2\dot{\theta}$ is the angular momentum associated with the coordinate θ. We call it the *orbital angular momentum*.

Had the particle been projected in such a way that the initial plane of motion did not contain the z-axis, we would have $k \neq 0$ in Eq. (3–7). The ensuing equations of motion, Eqs. (3–8) and (3–9), become more difficult to solve. We shall assume for simplicity that the orbit or path of the particle lies in a plane $\phi = $ constant.

We conclude from our analysis that: (1) the particle in central force motion moves in a plane; (2) the orbital angular momentum remains constant in time. These properties may be shown very simply by the use of vector analysis. Let $\mathbf{r} = \mathbf{f}(t)$ be the path of the particle as indicated in Fig. 3–2. The force is $F(r)\mathbf{u}_r$, where $\mathbf{u}_r$ is a unit vector along the radius vector. By definition (Section 1–4), the angular momentum is $\mathbf{L} = \mathbf{r} \times m\mathbf{v}$, and hence

$$\frac{d\mathbf{L}}{dt} = \mathbf{r} \times \mathbf{F} = \mathbf{r} \times F(r)\mathbf{u}_r = 0.$$

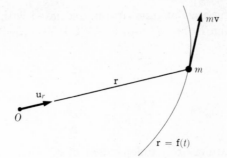

F$_{\text{IG}}$. 3–2. Linear momentum of a mass in central force motion.

Therefore **L** is a constant vector. This implies constancy of direction (which means that the particle moves in a plane whose normal is parallel to **L**) as well as magnitude.

As a consequence of the motion being restricted to the plane $\phi =$ constant, the equations of motion, (3–8) and (3–9), become

$$\frac{d}{dt}\,(m\dot{r}) - mr\dot{\theta}^2 = F(r), \tag{3–12}$$

$$\frac{d}{dt}\,(mr^2\dot{\theta}) = 0. \tag{3–13}$$

The second of these has a geometric interpretation quite apart from the dynamical one of constant angular momentum. We recall that the element of area in polar coordinates is $\frac{1}{2}r^2\,d\theta$. Hence, since Eq. (3–13) may be integrated to yield $mr^2\dot{\theta} = l$, we have

$$\frac{1}{2}\,r^2\,\frac{d\theta}{dt} = \frac{1}{2}\,\frac{l}{m} = \text{constant.} \tag{3–14}$$

But this is the *time rate at which the area of the orbit is swept out by the radius vector*. We see that the rate is constant. This is the areal velocity law expressed by Johannes Kepler in 1609, who obtained it by a study of the motion of Mars.

The angular velocity $\dot{\theta}$ may be eliminated from Eq. (3–12) by means of the integrated form of Eq. (3–13) to yield

$$\frac{d}{dt}\,(m\dot{r}) - \frac{l^2}{mr^3} = F(r). \tag{3–15}$$

Multiplying through by $\dot{r}$, we have

$$\frac{d}{dt}\left(\frac{1}{2}\,m\dot{r}^2\right) - \frac{l^2}{mr^3}\,\frac{dr}{dt} = F(r)\,\frac{dr}{dt}, \tag{3–16}$$

which may be integrated to yield

$$\frac{1}{2}\,m\dot{r}^2 + \frac{l^2}{2mr^2} - \int F(r)\,dr = E. \tag{3-17}$$

This is the *energy equation* for the motion. By noting that the second term is equivalent to $\frac{1}{2}mr^2\dot{\theta}^2$, we identify the first and second terms combined as the kinetic energy, while the third is the potential energy, and E is the total energy. Since $F(r)$ is derivable from a potential $V(r)$, Eq. (3–17) may be written

$$\frac{1}{2}\,m\dot{r}^2 + \frac{l^2}{2mr^2} + V(r) = E. \tag{3-18}$$

Solving Eq. (3–18) for $\dot{r}$, we find

$$\dot{r} = \pm\,\sqrt{2/m[E - V(r) - (l^2/2mr^2)]}. \tag{3-19}$$

The third property of central force motion becomes apparent from this equation; namely, *the velocity of the mass particle depends only upon the radius vector.* In fact,

$$v = \sqrt{2/m[E - V(r)]}, \tag{3-20}$$

where v is the speed in the orbit.

Equations (3–19) and (3–11) formally define r and θ as functions of the time, and hence yield the parametric equations of the orbit. That is, from Eq. (3–19),

$$\int_{r_0}^{r} \frac{dr}{\sqrt{2/m[E - V(r) - (l^2/2mr^2)]}} = t - t_0, \tag{3-21}$$

and, with r as a function of t from this, Eq. (3–11) yields

$$\int_{t_0}^{t} \frac{l}{m}\,\frac{dt}{r^2} = \theta - \theta_0, \tag{3-22}$$

which gives θ as a function of t.

The equation of the orbit in polar coordinates can be found directly from Eq. (3–19). We write

$$\dot{r} = \frac{dr}{d\theta}\,\dot{\theta} = \frac{l}{mr^2}\,\frac{dr}{d\theta},$$

so that Eq. (3–19) becomes

$$\frac{dr}{d\theta} = \frac{mr^2}{l}\,\sqrt{2/m[E - V(r) - (l^2/2mr^2)]}. \tag{3-23}$$

Integrating, we have

$$\frac{l}{m} \int_{r_0}^{r} \frac{dr}{r^2 \sqrt{2/m[E - V(r) - (l^2/2mr^2)]}} = \theta - \theta_0. \qquad (3\text{-}24)$$

This yields the equation of the orbit in polar coordinates.

The integral in Eq. (3–24) can be put in a more standard form by changing the variable of integration. Let $u = 1/r$, $du = (-1/r^2)\,dr$. Then Eq. (3–24) becomes

$$\frac{l}{\sqrt{2m}} \int_{u_0}^{u} \frac{-du}{\sqrt{E - V(1/u) - (l^2/2m)u^2}} = \theta - \theta_0. \qquad (3\text{-}25)$$

Particular interest attaches to the case in which the central force varies as a power of the distance, such as $F(r) = \alpha r^n$, where α and n are constants. In such cases

$$V(r) = -\int F(r)\,dr = -\frac{\alpha r^{n+1}}{n+1}, \qquad (3\text{-}26)$$

and hence $V(1/u) = -[\alpha/(n+1)]u^{-n-1}$. Substituting this into Eq. (3–25), we have

$$\frac{l}{\sqrt{2m}} \int_{u_0}^{u} \frac{-du}{\sqrt{E + (\alpha u^{-n-1}/n + 1) - (l^2/2m)u^2}} = \theta - \theta_0, \qquad (3\text{-}27)$$

except when $n = -1$. In this case a logarithm in u replaces the power of u in $V(1/u)$. The integral in Eq. (3–27) is in the form

$$\int \{a + bu^2 + cu^{-n-1}\}^{-1/2}\,du,$$

and it may be seen from a table of integrals that trigonometric functions will result from it as long as the radicand is no higher than the second degree in u. This means that

$$-n - 1 = 0, 1, \text{ or } 2$$

or

$$n = -1, -2, -3.$$

But $n = -1$ was excluded above. Furthermore, we observe that when $n = 1$, the integral becomes

$$\int (c + au^2 + bu^4)^{-1/2} u\,du, \qquad (3\text{-}28)$$

or, with $v = u^2$ and $dv = 2u\,du$,

$$\tfrac{1}{2}\int (c + av + bv^2)^{-1/2}\, dv, \qquad (3\text{–}29)$$

which is integrable in terms of circular functions.

We conclude that motion under a central force varying as r^n, where

$$n = +1, -2, -3, \qquad (3\text{–}30)$$

results in an equation for the orbit which may be expressed in terms of trigonometric functions. It may be shown also that when $n = +5, +3$, $0, -4, -5, -7$, the integral on the left in Eq. (3–27) may be evaluated in terms of elliptic functions.

3–2 Inverse square forces. A most important type of central force motion arises in the case of two mutually attracting masses m_1 and m_2. Newton's law of gravitation states that they will attract each other according to the equation

$$F(r) = -\frac{Gm_1m_2}{r^2}, \qquad (3\text{–}31)$$

where r is their distance apart and G is a constant which, in the cgs system, is $6.67 \times 10^{-8}\ \mathrm{gm^{-1}\,cm^3\,sec^{-2}}$. If one mass is placed at the origin and is considered fixed, the other moves according to the laws of motion discussed in Section 3–1, with $n = -2$. Before applying the results found in Section 3–1, let us consider the two masses moving in space under their mutual attraction.

In Fig. 3–3 the position vectors of the two are shown as $\mathbf{r}_1$ and $\mathbf{r}_2$ referred to a fixed origin. The equations of motion are

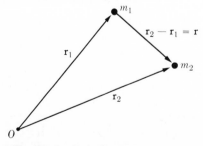

$$m_1\ddot{\mathbf{r}}_1 = +\frac{Gm_1m_2\mathbf{r}}{r^3}, \qquad (3\text{–}32)$$

$$m_2\ddot{\mathbf{r}}_2 = -\frac{Gm_1m_2\mathbf{r}}{r^3}, \qquad (3\text{–}33)$$

where $\mathbf{r} = \mathbf{r}_2 - \mathbf{r}_1$ is the vector from m_1 to m_2. Adding Eqs. (3–32) and (3–33), we have

FIG. 3–3. Relative position vectors in the two-body problem.

$$m_1\ddot{\mathbf{r}}_1 + m_2\ddot{\mathbf{r}}_2 = 0, \qquad (3\text{–}34)$$

and integration yields

$$m_1\dot{\mathbf{r}}_1 + m_2\dot{\mathbf{r}}_2 = \mathbf{c}_1$$

and

$$m_1\mathbf{r}_1 + m_2\mathbf{r}_2 = \mathbf{c}_1 t + \mathbf{c}_2. \tag{3-35}$$

Since the center of mass $_{\wedge}$ *of* m_1 and m_2 is defined by Eq. (1-71) as $\mathbf{R} = (m_1\mathbf{r}_1 + m_2\mathbf{r}_2)/(m_1 + m_2)$, we may write Eq. (3-35) as

$$(m_1 + m_2)\mathbf{R} = \mathbf{c}_1 t + \mathbf{c}_2, \tag{3-36}$$

and conclude that the *center of mass of the system moves uniformly with the time*, a result that conforms with the analysis of particle systems discussed in Section 1-12. Therefore we may treat the rotational motion of the particles about the center of mass as though the latter were at rest.

Let $\mathbf{r}_1'$ and $\mathbf{r}_2'$ denote the position vectors of the two masses m_1 and m_2 relative to the center of mass $\mathbf{R}$. Then $\mathbf{r}_1 = \mathbf{r}_1' + \mathbf{R}$, and $\mathbf{r}_2 = \mathbf{r}_2' + \mathbf{R}$, and $m_1\mathbf{r}_1' + m_2\mathbf{r}_2' = 0$. Using these relations together with $\ddot{\mathbf{R}} = 0$ and Eqs. (3-32) and (3-33), we find

$$m_1\ddot{\mathbf{r}}_1' = -\frac{Gm_1(m_1 + m_2)}{r^3}\,\mathbf{r}_1',$$

$$m_2\ddot{\mathbf{r}}_2' = -\frac{Gm_2(m_1 + m_2)}{r^3}\,\mathbf{r}_2',$$

or, writing $G(m_1 + m_2) = \mu$,

$$\ddot{\mathbf{r}}_1' = -\frac{\mu}{r^3}\,\mathbf{r}_1', \tag{3-37}$$

$$\ddot{\mathbf{r}}_2' = -\frac{\mu}{r^3}\,\mathbf{r}_2'. \tag{3-38}$$

These are the equations of motion of m_1 and m_2 relative to the center of mass. By subtraction,

$$\ddot{\mathbf{r}}_2' - \ddot{\mathbf{r}}_1' = -\frac{\mu}{r^3}\,(\mathbf{r}_2' - \mathbf{r}_1')$$

or

$$\ddot{\mathbf{r}} = -\frac{\mu}{r^3}\,\mathbf{r} \tag{3-39}$$

is the equation of motion of m_2 relative to m_1.

A similar procedure will show that by appropriate choice of μ any central force problem involving two bodies may be reduced to the equivalent relative motion of one about the other. We shall now consider the relative motion of one mass about the other.

With one mass considered stationary at the origin, we may apply Eqs. (3–12) and (3–13) directly to obtain the scalar equations of relative motion equivalent to the vector Eq. (3–39), namely,

$$\ddot{r} - r\dot{\theta}^2 = -\frac{\mu}{r^2} \quad \text{and} \quad r^2\dot{\theta} = k, \tag{3–40}$$

where k is a constant which contains the mass factor and is proportional to the angular momentum.

We find that the energy equation (3–18) in this instance yields

$$\dot{r} = \pm\sqrt{2[E - (k^2/2r^2) + (\mu/r)]}. \tag{3–41}$$

where E is the total energy per unit mass.

From this a number of properties of the motion can be deduced. To show these we shall employ an energy diagram such as that discussed in Section 1–9. Note the similarity between Eqs. (3–41) and (1–50), where the velocity in straight line motion was expressed in terms of the total energy E and the potential energy V. As evident from Eq. (3–41), the radial velocity $\dot{r}$ is real only when $E - (k^2/2r^2) + (\mu/r) \geq 0$. Hence motion is restricted to those values of r for which this inequality holds.

In order to analyze the ensuing motion by means of an energy diagram, we define a fictitious potential energy by

$$V'(r) = -\frac{\mu}{r} + \frac{k^2}{2r^2}. \tag{3–42}$$

We call this a fictitious potential because it includes not only the true potential $-\mu/r$ due to the force field but also the term $k^2/2r^2$. Referring to Eqs. (3–12), (3–15), and (3–18), we observe that this arises from the term $mr\dot{\theta}^2$ in Eq. (3–12). This is called the *centrifugal force* acting on the particle. It is a fictitious force arising from the curvilinear motion.

We now plot $V'(r)$ against r in an energy diagram, as in Fig. 3–4. The behavior of the mass point in the radial coordinate will be similar to that under a potential $V'(r)$ in rectilinear motion. Dotted curves show the *centrifugal barrier*, $k^2/2r^2$, and the true potential, $-\mu/r$. The heavy line curve is the sum of these two. The velocity $\dot{r}$ of the particle at any value of r is proportional to the difference between a constant energy level E and the heavy curve. This follows from Eq. (3–41). At any value of r, the value of $\dot{r}$ may be positive or negative.

The type of motion arising for various values of the constant total energy E becomes evident from a study of Fig. 3–4.

(a) $E > 0$. When the total energy is positive, the particle comes in from an infinite distance at the right, stops at the value of r where the $V'(r)$ curve is intersected by the E-line, reverses direction, and then returns to larger and larger values of r.

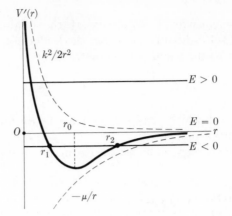

F$_{\text{IG}}$. 3–4. Energy diagram for motion under an inverse square force.

(b) $E = 0$. The motion is much the same as in (a), but the velocities are considerably less. As $r \to \infty$, $\dot{r} \to 0$ and $\dot{\theta} \to 0$, so that the particle is at rest at infinity. In both (a) and (b) the maximum velocity occurs at $r = r_0$, where $V'(r)$ has a minimum.

(c) $E < 0$. When E is negative, the particle oscillates between a minimum radius vector r_1 and a maximum r_2. At these values of r, the derivative $\dot{r} = 0$. Hence, by Eq. (3–41), r_1 and r_2 are the roots of the equation

$$2Er^2 + 2\mu r - k^2 = 0. \tag{3–43}$$

Furthermore, the period of the motion in r is

$$P = 2 \int_{r_1}^{r_2} \frac{r \, dr}{\sqrt{2Er^2 + 2\mu r - k^2}}. \tag{3–44}$$

We recall in carrying out this integration that E is negative. At the lowest values of $E < 0$, r_1 and r_2 coincide, and the closed path becomes a circle of radius r_0. The total energy for motion in the circular orbit is $-\mu^2/2k^2$, while the radius of this orbit is $r_0 = -\mu/2E$.

To find the equation of the orbit in polar coordinates, we use Eq. (3–27) with $n = -2$, $\alpha = -\mu$, $l = k$, and $m = 1$. These values are obtained by direct comparison of Eq. (3–40) with Eqs. (3–12) and (3–13). We find

$$k \int_{u_0}^{u} \frac{-du}{\sqrt{2E + 2\mu u - k^2 u^2}} = \theta - \theta_0, \tag{3–45}$$

and upon integration,

$$\sin^{-1} \left\{ \frac{k^2 u - \mu}{\sqrt{\mu^2 + 2Ek^2}} \right\} - \sin^{-1} \left\{ \frac{k^2 u_0 - \mu}{\sqrt{\mu^2 + 2Ek^2}} \right\} = \theta_0 - \theta. \tag{3–46}$$

Now suppose we arbitrarily choose $\theta_0 = 0$ when the radius vector r is the smallest or when u is the greatest. At this point (r_1 in Fig. 3–4) the radial velocity $\dot{r} = 0$, and by Eq. (3–41) with $u = 1/r$,

$$u = u_0 = \frac{\mu + \sqrt{\mu^2 + 2Ek^2}}{k^2}. \qquad (3\text{–}47)$$

With this value of u_0 in the second term of Eq. (3–46), we have

$$\sin^{-1}\left[\frac{k^2 u - \mu}{\sqrt{\mu^2 + 2Ek^2}}\right] = \frac{\pi}{2} - \theta.$$

Solving for u, we find

$$u = \frac{\mu}{k^2} + \frac{\sqrt{\mu^2 + 2Ek^2}}{k^2}\cos\theta. \qquad (3\text{–}48)$$

We recall from analytic geometry that the equation of a conic section in polar coordinates with one focus at the pole is

$$r = \frac{ep}{1 + e\cos(\theta - \theta_0)}, \qquad (3\text{–}49)$$

where for convenience we may set $\theta_0 = 0$. Inverting this, we have

$$\frac{1}{r} = u = \frac{1 + e\cos\theta}{ep} = \frac{1}{ep} + \frac{1}{p}\cos\theta. \qquad (3\text{–}50)$$

Comparison with Eq. (3–48) shows that the orbit of one mass particle about the other, resulting from an inverse square force, will be a conic section* in which

$$\frac{\sqrt{\mu^2 + 2Ek^2}}{k^2} = \frac{1}{p}, \qquad (3\text{–}51)$$

$$\frac{\mu}{k^2} = \frac{1}{ep}. \qquad (3\text{–}52)$$

From Eq. (3–52), $1/p = \mu e/k^2$, and hence Eq. (3–51) becomes

$$\sqrt{\mu^2 + 2Ek^2} = \mu e$$

or

$$e = \sqrt{1 + (2Ek^2/\mu^2)}. \qquad (3\text{–}53)$$

---

* Johannes Kepler, in 1609, deduced from his studies of Mars that the planetary orbits were ellipses with the sun at one focus.

If $E = 0$, the eccentricity $e = 1$, and the orbit is a parabola; if $E > 0$, the $e > 1$, and the orbit is a hyperbola; if $E < 0$, the $e < 1$, and the orbit is an ellipse. Thus the paths in space are related to the total energy of the system.

Suppose the mass m is moving in an ellipse of major axis $2a$. This will be the sum $r_1 + r_2$, which we obtain from Eq. (3–43), and hence we find

$$E = -\frac{\mu}{2a} \qquad (3\text{–}54)$$

for the total energy as a function of the length of the major axis. With this value for E substituted in Eq. (3–41), and with the transverse speed $r\dot\theta = k/r$, we find that the relative speed in the orbit is given by

$$v^2 = \dot{r}^2 + r^2\dot\theta^2 = \mu\left[\frac{2}{r} - \frac{1}{a}\right]. \qquad (3\text{–}55)$$

The period P for motion in an elliptic orbit can be found from Eq. (3–44). Substituting $E = -\mu/2a$, we have

$$P = 2\int_{r_1}^{r_2} \frac{r\,dr}{\sqrt{-(\mu/a)r^2 + 2\mu r - k^2}} = \frac{2\pi}{\sqrt{\mu}}\,a^{3/2}. \qquad (3\text{–}56)$$

This is Kepler's Third Law of planetary motion, the so-called harmonic law. It may be deduced equally well from the areal velocity law, $\frac{1}{2}r^2\dot\theta = \frac{1}{2}k$.

3–3 Stability of circular orbits. The energy diagram, Fig. 3–4, shows that, for the lowest possible total energy E, motion under an inverse square force takes place in a circle of radius r_0. That is, the radii r_1 and r_2 for elliptic motion coincide. This will be true for all central forces such that the function $V'(r)$, the fictitious potential, has a minimum. Suppose that the force law is $F(r) = -ar^n$, where a is a positive constant. Then, in place of Eq. (3–42), in the special case of an inverse square force, we would have for $V'(r)$

$$V'(r) = \frac{ar^{n+1}}{n+1} + \frac{l^2}{2mr^2}, \qquad (3\text{–}57)$$

as is evident from Eq. (3–19). This will have a minimum at some value $r = r_0$ provided $(dV'/dr)_{r_0} = 0$ and $(d^2V'/dr^2)_{r_0} > 0$. From the first, we find

$$ar_0^n - \frac{l^2}{mr_0^3} = 0,$$

which yields

$$r_0^{n+3} = \frac{l^2}{ma} ; \qquad (3\text{–}58)$$

while from the second,

$$nar_0^{n-1} + \frac{3l^2}{mr_0^4} > 0,$$

or, by using the value of r_0 from Eq. (3–58),

$$(n + 3)ar_0^{n-1} > 0. \qquad (3\text{–}59)$$

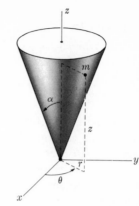

FIG. 3–5. Motion of a mass particle on a cone.

In order that Eq. (3–59) hold, n is restricted to values greater than -3.

We may expect, therefore, that central forces of attraction of the form $F(r) = -ar^n$ for $n > -3$ can produce motion in a circular orbit.

If a particle moving in a circular orbit of radius r_0 under a central force is disturbed slightly from this path, will it return to the circular path, or possibly oscillate about it? Or will the particle, if disturbed, deviate from the circular path more and more with increasing time? If the former situation prevails, the circular orbit is said to be *stable*. If the particle recedes farther and farther from the circular path, the orbit is *unstable*. We shall discuss a simplified method of deciding whether a circular orbit is stable or unstable.

As an example, let a particle of mass m be constrained to slide without friction under gravity on the inside of a cone of half angle α. Figure 3–5 shows the particle, whose cylindrical coordinates are (r, θ, z). The Lagrangian function for the motion is

$$L = \tfrac{1}{2}m[\dot{r}^2 + r^2\dot{\theta}^2 + \dot{z}^2] - mgz.$$

But since the particle stays on the surface of the cone at all times, $z = r \cot \alpha$. We have, therefore, two degrees of freedom, the remaining generalized coordinates being r and θ. Hence

$$L = \tfrac{1}{2}m[\dot{r}^2 \csc^2 \alpha + r^2\dot{\theta}^2] - mgr \cot \alpha. \qquad (3\text{–}60)$$

From Eq. (3–60) we derive Lagrange's equations of motion,

$$\frac{d}{dt}(m\dot{r} \csc^2 \alpha) - mr\dot{\theta}^2 + mg \cot \alpha = 0, \qquad (3\text{–}61)$$

$$\frac{d}{dt}(mr^2\dot{\theta}) = 0. \qquad (3\text{–}62)$$

These simplify to

$$\ddot{r} - r \sin^2 \alpha \, \dot{\theta}^2 + g \sin \alpha \cos \alpha = 0, \qquad (3\text{--}63)$$

$$r^2 \dot{\theta} = \frac{l}{m} = k \qquad \text{(constant)}. \qquad (3\text{--}64)$$

Observe that the last term in Eq. 3–60, $mgr \cot \alpha$, is a potential energy proportional to the radial distance from the z-axis. This gives rise to the force $-g \sin \alpha \cos \alpha$ which is directed toward the z-axis. At any instant, therefore, there is a central force directed toward that point on the z-axis on the same horizontal line with the particle.

Suppose we assume that the particle has been projected initially in such a direction and with such an energy that it moves in a horizontal circle on the cone. Let r_0 be the radius of this orbit. Then Eq. (3–64) yields the circular angular velocity,

$$\dot{\theta}_0 = \frac{k}{r_0^2}. \qquad (3\text{--}65)$$

Substituting this into Eq. (3–63), we have, at $r = r_0$,

$$r_0^3 = \frac{k^2}{g} \tan \alpha \qquad (3\text{--}66)$$

because $\ddot{r}_0 = 0$. The reader may verify this result by noting that the horizontal orbit results when the component of gravity downward along an element of the cone just balances the component of the centrifugal force upward along the element.

Let the particle be disturbed slightly from its circular orbit. We wish to study its subsequent motion to see if the orbit is stable. To do this let $r = r_0 + x$ and $\theta = \theta_0 + \psi$, where x and ψ are small changes or perturbations in r_0 and $\dot{\theta}_0$ respectively. We substitute these for r and θ in Eqs. (3–63) and (3–64) and *neglect all terms involving products and powers higher than the first in x and ψ*. The resulting equations are

$$\ddot{r}_0 - r_0 \sin^2 \alpha \, \dot{\theta}_0^2 + g \sin \alpha \cos \alpha$$
$$+ \, \ddot{x} - 2 \sin^2 \alpha \, r_0 \dot{\theta}_0 \dot{\psi} - x \sin^2 \alpha \, \dot{\theta}_0^2 = 0, \qquad (3\text{--}67)$$

$$r_0^2 \dot{\theta}_0 + 2 r_0 x \dot{\theta}_0 + r_0^2 \dot{\psi} = k. \qquad (3\text{--}68)$$

But the first three terms of Eq. (3–67) add to zero, since r_0 satisfies Eq. (3–63). Furthermore, by Eq. (3–64), the first term in Eq. (3–68) is k.

Hence these equations simplify to

$$\ddot{x} - \sin^2 \alpha \, (2r_0\dot{\psi}\dot{\theta}_0 + x\dot{\theta}_0^2) = 0,$$

$$2x\dot{\theta}_0 + r_0\dot{\psi} = 0.$$

Elimination of $\dot{\psi}$ between them leaves

$$\ddot{x} + (3\sin^2 \alpha \, \dot{\theta}_0^2)x = 0. \tag{3–69}$$

This is a linear differential equation with constant coefficients which defines the perturbation $x(t)$. The theory of such equations* indicates that when the coefficient of x is positive the solution $x(t)$ is bounded and is in fact a linear combination of a sine and a cosine. In the present case,

$$x = c_1 \sin (3\sin^2 \alpha \, \dot{\theta}_0^2)^{1/2}t + c_2 \cos (3\sin^2 \alpha \, \dot{\theta}_0^2)^{1/2}t,$$

where c_1 and c_2 are constants. We conclude that when the particle is disturbed from the circle, it oscillates about the circular orbit with small amplitude and with frequency $\omega = \sqrt{3} \sin \alpha \, \dot{\theta}_0$ radians per unit time. Therefore, the motion in the circular orbit is stable.

The method we have used in this example can be applied in the general case represented by Eqs. (3–12) and (3–13) when $F(r)$ is an appropriate force of attraction. We shall take this force to be $-mf(r)$, where $f(r) > 0$ for all r. Then, from Eqs. (3–12) and (3–13),

$$\ddot{r} - r\dot{\theta}^2 = -f(r), \tag{3–70}$$

$$r^2\dot{\theta} = \frac{l}{m} = k. \tag{3–71}$$

Let r_0 be the radius of the circular orbit in which the particle is assumed to be moving. Let $r = r_0 + x$ and $\theta = \theta_0 + \psi$, where, as in our first example, x and $\dot{\psi}$ are small perturbations in r and θ respectively. For the circular orbit

$$r_0\dot{\theta}_0^2 = f(r_0), \qquad r_0^2\dot{\theta}_0 = k,$$

and hence

$$r_0^3 = \frac{k^2}{f(r_0)}. \tag{3–72}$$

---

*See, for example, W. T. Martin and E. Reissner, *Elementary Differential Equations*. Reading, Massachusetts: Addison-Wesley Publishing Company, Inc., 1956, pp. 84–85.

For the perturbed orbit, upon eliminating $\dot{\theta}^2$ from Eq. (3–70) by means of Eq. (3–71), we have

$$\ddot{x} - k^2(r_0 + x)^{-3} = -f(r_0 + x). \qquad (3\text{–}73)$$

Now we assume that $f(r)$ can be expanded into a Taylor's series about the value $r = r_0$. We find

$$f(r) = f(r_0) + (r - r_0)f'(r_0) + \frac{(r - r_0)^2}{2!}\, f''(r_0) + \cdots$$

$$= f(r_0) + xf'(r_0) + \cdots . \qquad (3\text{–}74)$$

Also,

$$(r_0 + x)^{-3} = r_0^{-3}\left(1 + \frac{x}{r_0}\right)^{-3} = r_0^{-3}\left(1 - \frac{3x}{r_0} + \cdots\right). \qquad (3\text{–}75)$$

Substituting from Eqs. (3–74) and (3–75) into Eq. (3–73), and retaining only linear terms in x, we have

$$\ddot{x} - k^2 r_0^{-3}\left(1 - \frac{3x}{r_0}\right) = -f(r_0) - xf'(r_0),$$

but by Eq. (3–72) we can simplify this to

$$\ddot{x} + \left[\frac{3f(r_0)}{r_0} + f'(r_0)\right]x = 0. \qquad (3\text{–}76)$$

Let

$$\alpha^2 = \left[\frac{3f(r_0)}{r_0} + f'(r_0)\right].$$

Then

if $\alpha^2 > 0$, $x = c_1 \sin \alpha t + c_2 \cos \alpha t$;

if $\alpha^2 = 0$, $x = c_1 t + c_2$;

if $\alpha^2 < 0$, $x = c_1 \sinh \alpha t + c_2 \cosh \alpha t$.

We see that when $\alpha^2 > 0$, periodic motion in x of frequency α radians per unit time ensues. In these circumstances the circular orbit is stable. We have, therefore, linearized the problem for small perturbations, and we find as a general condition for the stability of a circular orbit in a central force field

$$\frac{r_0 f'(r_0)}{f(r_0)} > -3, \qquad (3\text{–}77)$$

where $f'(r_0)$ is the derivative of $f(r)$ with respect to r evaluated at r_0.

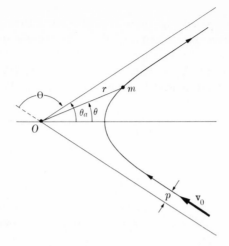

Fig. 3–6. Orbit under a central force of repulsion.

3–4 Repulsive forces: scattering. Suppose that a particle of mass m is propelled into a force field centered at O (Fig. 3–6) in which it is repelled. A deflection of the particle will take place as shown. If the force center had not been active, the particle would have passed by O at a distance p. The quantity p is called the *impact parameter*. For the present we assume that O is fixed and that the force field diminishes to zero at large distances from O.

Let the initial speed of the particle be v_0. Then it is clear that (1) the initial kinetic energy $\frac{1}{2}mv_0^2$ is the total energy E of the system and remains constant because the force field is conservative; (2) the initial moment of momentum about the origin is $l = mv_0p$ and is constant during the motion because the force is a central one.

For definiteness, let the force field produced by O be an inverse square field; that is, let $F(r) = \alpha r^{-2}$, where $\alpha > 0$. Then the orbit will be given by Eq. (3–27) with $n = -2$. We find

$$u = -\frac{m\alpha}{l^2} + \frac{m}{l^2}\sqrt{\alpha^2 + (2El^2/m)}\cos\theta, \qquad (3\text{–}78)$$

where, as in Eq. (3–46), we have chosen the polar axis so that θ is measured from the line where u has its maximum, or r its minimum, value.

Equation (3–78) represents a conic section. We relate the parameters to those in the standard form $r = eq/(1 - e\cos\theta)$ by the equations

$$eq = -\frac{l^2}{m\alpha},$$

$$e = \sqrt{1 + (2El^2/m\alpha^2)}, \qquad (3\text{–}79)$$

where e is the eccentricity of the conic. We note that $e > 1.0$, and hence the orbit is a hyperbola. The parameter q is the distance from focus to directrix of the conic and does not concern us here.

Since $l = mv_0p$ and $E = \frac{1}{2}mv_0^2$, we may express the equation of the conic in terms of the dynamical parameters α, E, p. We find

$$r = \frac{-(2Ep^2/\alpha)}{1 - \sqrt{1 + (4E^2p^2/\alpha^2)}\,\cos\theta}, \qquad (3\text{--}80)$$

or

$$r = \frac{-(2Ep^2/\alpha)}{1 - e\cos\theta}. \qquad (3\text{--}81)$$

In Eq. (3–81) it is apparent that as $\cos\theta \to 1/e$ the radius vector $r \to \infty$. The orbit, therefore, has an asymptote at the value of θ given by

$$\theta_a = \cos^{-1}\left(\frac{1}{e}\right). \qquad (3\text{--}82)$$

The angle between asymptotes is then $2\theta_a$.

Generally it is customary to measure the deflection angle between the initial direction of the particle motion and the final direction. This angle, designated by Θ in Fig. 3–6, is called the *scattering angle*. From the figure it is clear that $\Theta = \pi - 2\theta_a$. By using Eqs. (3–79), (3–80), and (3–82), we may express the angle θ_a in terms of the dynamical parameters E, p, α. We find

$$\tan\theta_a = \frac{2Ep}{\alpha}. \qquad (3\text{--}83)$$

For the scattering angle Θ, therefore,

$$\cot\frac{\Theta}{2} = \cot\left(\frac{\pi}{2} - \theta_a\right) = \tan\theta_a = \frac{2Ep}{\alpha}. \qquad (3\text{--}84)$$

Suppose that a beam of particles moves toward the scattering center O, their original paths being parallel to the particle path shown in Fig. 3–6. Each particle is characterized by a different value of p. What we wish to compute is a measure of the number of particles deflected into a given direction. For example, consider a beam of charged particles propelled into a thin metallic foil. They emerge in different directions, scattered by the atomic nuclei of the foil. The nuclei serve as centers of the force field, one nucleus for each particle. A knowledge of the angular distribution of the emerging particles leads to a knowledge of the field characteristics of the nuclei in the foil.*

---

* See, for example, R. S. Shankland, *Atomic and Nuclear Physics*. New York: Macmillan Company, 1955, pp. 59 ff.

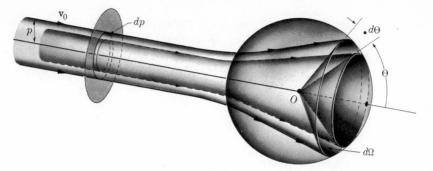

FIG. 3–7. Flux density of particles due to scattering.

The number of particles per unit time passing unit area normal to the beam is called the *intensity*, or flux density, and will be denoted by I. The total flux, therefore, through a ring of width dp (Fig. 3–7) at distance p from the axis of symmetry will be

$$2\pi I p \, dp. \tag{3–85}$$

These particles will be deflected into a ring of angular width $d\Theta$ on the spherical surface surrounding O. The solid angle subtended at O by this surface ring will be

$$d\Omega = 2\pi \sin \Theta \, d\Theta. \tag{3–86}$$

Now we define the *differential scattering cross section*, $\sigma(\Omega)$, for a given direction by the ratio

$$\sigma(\Omega) \, d\Omega = \frac{\text{number of particles scattered into solid angle } d\Omega \text{ per unit time}}{\text{incident intensity}}.$$

From Eqs. (3–85) and (3–86), therefore, we may write

$$2\pi I p \, dp = -2\pi \sigma(\Theta) I \sin \Theta \, d\Theta,$$

the minus sign implying that as p increases, Θ decreases. Since p is a function of Θ by Eq. (3–84), we may write

$$\sigma(\Theta) = -\frac{p \, dp}{\sin \Theta \, d\Theta}. \tag{3–87}$$

If we wish the *total scattering cross section*, we integrate Eq. (3–87) over the complete solid angle about O and obtain

$$\sigma = 2\pi \int_0^\pi \sigma(\Theta) \sin \Theta \, d\Theta. \tag{3–88}$$

If the force field in which the particles move does not vanish even at large distances, σ will be infinite. If the force field is zero beyond a certain distance, σ will be finite. To illustrate the first case, let the force field be an inverse square field so that the scattering angle is given by Eq. (3–84). Then

$$p = \frac{\alpha \cot \frac{1}{2}\Theta}{2E},$$ (3–89)

and, by Eq. (3–87),

$$\sigma(\Theta) = \frac{1}{4}\left(\frac{\alpha}{2E}\right)^2 \csc^4\left(\frac{\Theta}{2}\right).$$ (3–90)

Then the total scattering cross section is

$$\sigma = 2\pi \int_0^\pi \frac{1}{4}\left(\frac{\alpha}{2E}\right)^2 \cdot 2\sin^{-3}\left(\frac{\Theta}{2}\right)\cos\left(\frac{\Theta}{2}\right) d\left(\frac{\Theta}{2}\right).$$ (3–91)

Integration of Eq. (3–91) yields

$$\sigma = -\frac{\pi}{2}\left(\frac{\alpha}{2E}\right)^2 \csc^2\frac{\Theta}{2}\bigg]_0^\pi,$$ (3–92)

which indicates that σ becomes infinite when $\Theta = 0$.

If the force field is not infinite in extent, contrary to the case with the inverse square field, the total scattering cross section remains finite. Suppose that the force field vanishes beyond a critical distance $r = r_0$ from the force center. Then all particles with impact parameter $p > r_0$ will be undeflected in passing by the center of force. By Eqs. (3–87) and (3–88) we may write

$$\sigma = 2\pi \int_{\Theta_0}^\pi \sigma(\Theta)\sin\Theta\,d\Theta = -2\pi \int_{p=r_0}^{p=0} p\,dp,$$ (3–93)

where Θ_0 is the deflection angle experienced by a particle whose impact parameter is the greatest, namely r_0. Thus in this case, $\sigma = \pi r_0^2$. Problem 3–13 will illustrate a simple case in which the potential energy $V = -V_0$ (constant) for $r \leq r_0$ and $V = 0$ for $r > r_0$. In this instance a deflecting force is exerted on the particle only at the boundaries of the region in which V vanishes.

We have regarded O in our discussion as a fixed point. In an actual scattering experiment, however, two movable bodies are involved. The recoil of the second body must be taken into account in any laboratory measurement of scattering angles. What we have calculated above is the angle $\pi - \Theta$ between the initial and final position vectors of the incident particle as seen from the scattering center at O. If O moves

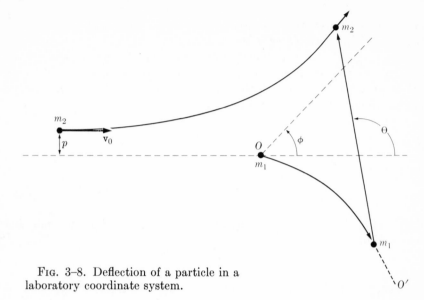

FIG. 3–8. Deflection of a particle in a laboratory coordinate system.

during the collision, this angle is quite different from the angle between the incident and final directions *relative to a fixed laboratory system of coordinates*. This is illustrated in Fig. 3–8. The particle originally at O will move so that after the collision it will recede along an asymptote as indicated by O' in the figure. In the laboratory system of coordinates we can measure the angle ϕ, while the analysis given in the preceding paragraphs yields the angle Θ. We will now find a relationship between these two.

Let the incident particle in Fig. 3–8 have a mass m_2 and an initial velocity $\mathbf{v}_0$ directed toward the right. Let m_1 be the mass of the particle initially at O, and let it be at rest. Furthermore, let $\mathbf{r}_1$ and $\mathbf{r}_2$ denote the position vectors of the two masses relative to some origin which is fixed in the laboratory. Then by the analysis of the two-body problem given in Section 3–2, we would have

$$m_1\dot{\mathbf{r}}_1 + m_2\dot{\mathbf{r}}_2 = \mathbf{c}_1 \qquad \text{(a constant),}$$

and by use of the initial conditions we find $\mathbf{c}_1 = m_2\mathbf{v}_0$. Hence, in the laboratory system of coordinates,

$$m_1\mathbf{v}_1 + m_2\mathbf{v}_2 = m_2\mathbf{v}_0. \qquad (3\text{–}94)$$

But the center of mass $\mathbf{R} = (m_1\mathbf{r}_1 + m_2\mathbf{r}_2)/(m_1 + m_2)$, and hence its velocity is

$$\dot{\mathbf{R}} = \mathbf{v}_c = \frac{m_1\mathbf{v}_1 + m_2\mathbf{v}_2}{m_1 + m_2} = \frac{m_2\mathbf{v}_0}{m_1 + m_2}. \qquad (3\text{–}95)$$

Thus we conclude that the center of mass continues to move in the *same direction as that given by the initial velocity vector.*

Since the center of mass always lies on the line joining m_1 and m_2, the point at m_2 as seen from the center of mass would appear to be on a line making the angle Θ with the direction of $\mathbf{v}_c$. Relative to $\mathbf{R}$, the two masses would have position vectors

$$\rho_1 = \mathbf{r}_1 - \mathbf{R}, \qquad \rho_2 = \mathbf{r}_2 - \mathbf{R},$$

and hence velocities

$$\dot{\boldsymbol{\rho}}_1 = \mathbf{v}_1 - \mathbf{v}_c, \qquad \dot{\boldsymbol{\rho}}_2 = \mathbf{v}_2 - \mathbf{v}_c. \qquad (3\text{--}96)$$

Multiplying these by m_1 and m_2, respectively, and adding, we find that the total momentum

$$m_1\dot{\boldsymbol{\rho}}_1 + m_2\dot{\boldsymbol{\rho}}_2 = 0,$$

and hence that the momentum vectors as seen from the center of mass are always in opposite directions. The velocity vectors must, therefore, lie along the line joining the particles. This relation holds as the particles recede along their respective final paths.

From these results we may form a vector diagram that yields a relation between the angle Θ and the angle ϕ, for ϕ is the angle which the final velocity vector $\mathbf{v}_2$ makes with the initial vector $\mathbf{v}_0$, and Θ is the angle which the final vector $\dot{\boldsymbol{\rho}}_2$ makes with $\mathbf{v}_0$. The diagram in Fig. 3–9 makes this clear. The second of Eqs. (3–96) together with Eq. (3–95) yields

$$\mathbf{v}_2 = \dot{\boldsymbol{\rho}}_2 + \mathbf{v}_c = \dot{\boldsymbol{\rho}}_2 + \frac{m_2}{m_1 + m_2}\,\mathbf{v}_0.$$

From this parallelogram we find

$$\tan \phi = \frac{\dot{\rho}_2 \sin \Theta}{\dot{\rho}_2 \cos \Theta + v_c}, \quad (3\text{--}97)$$

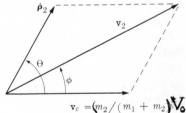

$$v_c = (m_2/(m_1 + m_2))\mathbf{V}_0$$

FIG. 3–9. Relation between deflection angles in two coordinate systems.

where $\dot{\rho}_2$ is the final magnitude of the velocity vector $\dot{\boldsymbol{\rho}}_2$. This may be put into more usable form. Since $\rho_2 = (m_1\mathbf{r})/(m_1 + m_2)$, we have $\dot{\rho}_2 = (m_1\mathbf{v})/(m_1 + m_2)$, where $\mathbf{v}$ is the relative velocity of m_2 with respect to m_1. Hence, if v_f is the final magnitude of this relative velocity, and since $v_c = (m_2 v_0)/(m_1 + m_2)$, we have

$$\tan \phi = \frac{\sin \Theta}{\cos \Theta + (m_2 v_0 / m_1 v_f)}. \qquad (3\text{--}98)$$

If there is no energy loss in the collision, $v_f = v_0$, and Eq. (3–98) is in-dependent of the velocities. Suppose this is the case, and suppose also that $m_1 \gg m_2$. Then $\phi \to \Theta$ and we have the case of a fixed center of force. An interesting result also arises if $m_1 = m_2$. Then

$$\tan \phi = \frac{\sin \Theta}{1 + \cos \Theta} = \tan\left(\frac{\Theta}{2}\right). \qquad (3\text{–}99)$$

The cross section for scattering in terms of Θ may be expressed readily in terms of ϕ. The number of particles within a given solid angle must be the same no matter which system of reference we use. Hence

$$2\pi I\sigma(\Theta) \sin \Theta \, d\Theta = 2\pi I\sigma_L(\phi) \sin \phi \, d\phi, \qquad (3\text{–}100)$$

from which we have

$$\sigma_L(\phi) = \sigma(\Theta) \frac{\sin \Theta \, d\Theta}{\sin \phi \, d\phi}, \qquad (3\text{–}101)$$

where $\sigma_L(\phi)$ is the cross section in the laboratory system of coordinates and where $d\Theta/d\phi$ can be calculated from Eq. (3–98).

While the total kinetic energy remains the same during such a close approach of two masses, the speeds of the particles *in the laboratory system* do change. Mass m_1 was initially at rest in this system, while m_2 had a speed v_0. As the approach took place, m_1 acquired a velocity and hence a kinetic energy. The mass m_2 must have lost an equal amount in order that the total energy remain constant. We can calculate this amount directly. Referring to Fig. 3–9, we see that

$$\dot{\rho}_2^2 = v_2^2 + v_c^2 - 2v_c v_2 \cos \phi. \qquad (3\text{–}102)$$

But after the scattering has taken place, under the assumption of an elastic collision, the relative velocity will be $\dot{\rho}_2 = m_1 v_0/(m_1 + m_2)$, and, since $v_c = m_2 v_0/(m_1 + m_2)$, we have from Eq. (3–102)

$$\left(\frac{v_2}{v_0}\right)^2 - 2\left(\frac{v_2}{v_0}\right)\frac{m_2}{M}\cos\phi - \left(\frac{m_1 - m_2}{M}\right) = 0, \qquad (3\text{–}103)$$

where $M = m_1 + m_2$. From Eq. (3–103) we may find both the ratio of the speed of m_2 after scattering to the speed before scattering and the ratio of the kinetic energy of m_2 after collision to that before collision.

In case $m_1 = m_2$, Eq. (3–103) yields $v_2 = v_0 \cos \phi$, and the loss in kinetic energy by the incident particle m_2 will be

$$\Delta E = E_i - E_f = \tfrac{1}{2} m_2 v_0^2 \sin^2 \phi. \qquad (3\text{–}104)$$

It is interesting that when $\phi = 90°$ the mass m_2 loses all its kinetic energy.

Experiments on the scattering of particles played an important part in the accumulation of knowledge about the atom. The scattering of alpha particles by thin metallic foils led Rutherford* to advance a theory of scattering in which the differential scattering cross section $\sigma(\Theta)$ is that given in Eq. (3–90). Further experiments by Geiger and Marsden† confirmed Rutherford's formula for $\sigma(\Theta)$ over a wide range of the angle Θ and hence showed that the atomic nucleus, in this case gold or silver, acted as a center of force producing very closely an inverse square field. In these experiments the nuclei serving as force centers are so massive compared with the masses of the alpha particles being scattered that they remain relatively stationary. The laboratory system of coordinates coincides closely with the fixed system.

The energy transfer in multiple scattering, such as that exhibited in Eq. (3–104), has important application in the atomic pile. In order that fission be produced in an atom of U^{235}, for example, slow neutrons are most efficient. The energies possessed by the neutrons produced by this fission process, however, are too high to cause fission effectively in other atoms of U^{235}. Therefore a moderator is used to slow them down to thermal energies so that a chain reaction can take place. The most important process in slowing down the neutrons is elastic scattering by other nuclei. Graphite frequently is used for the moderator.‡

3–5 The virial theorem. In concluding the work on central force motion, we shall consider a statistical result of considerable importance. Let $\mathbf{r}_j$ denote the position vector of a mass particle m_j relative to an origin O. Let us define the second moment of the particle about O by $m_j\mathbf{r}_j \cdot \mathbf{r}_j$. If there are n particles altogether, we have for the total second moment of the system

$$S = \sum_{j=1}^{n} m_j\mathbf{r}_j \cdot \mathbf{r}_j. \tag{3–105}$$

Differentiating this twice with respect to the time yields

$$\frac{d^2S}{dt^2} = \sum_{j=1}^{n} 2\dot{\mathbf{r}}_j \cdot \mathbf{p}_j + \sum_{j=1}^{n} 2\mathbf{r}_j \cdot \dot{\mathbf{p}}_j, \tag{3–106}$$

where $\mathbf{p}_j = m_j(d\mathbf{r}_j/dt)$ is the momentum of the jth particle. The first

---

* E. Rutherford, *Phil. Mag.*, **21**, 669 (1911).

† H. Geiger and E. Marsden, *Phil. Mag.*, **25**, 604 (1913).

‡ See, for example, R. S. Shankland, *Atomic and Nuclear Physics*. New York: Macmillan Company, 1955, pp. 411 ff.

summation in Eq. (3–106), however, is four times the kinetic energy of the system. Furthermore, $\dot{\mathbf{p}}_j = \mathbf{F}_j$, the resultant force on the jth particle. Hence

$$\frac{d^2S}{dt^2} = 4T + 2\sum_{j=1}^{n} \mathbf{r}_j \cdot \mathbf{F}_j. \tag{3–107}$$

Now we calculate the time average of (d^2S/dt^2) over the interval $(0,\tau)$ in the usual way as the integral

$$\frac{1}{\tau} \int_0^\tau \frac{d^2S}{dt^2}\, dt = \overline{4T} + \overline{2\sum_{j=1}^{n} \mathbf{r}_j \cdot \mathbf{F}_j}, \tag{3–108}$$

the bars standing for time averages of the quantities on the right side of the equation. From this equation we have

$$\frac{1}{\tau}\left[\left(\frac{dS}{dt}\right)_\tau - \left(\frac{dS}{dt}\right)_0\right] = \overline{4T} + \overline{2\sum_{j=1}^{n} \mathbf{r}_j \cdot \mathbf{F}_j}. \tag{3–109}$$

We assume that the velocities of the particles and their coordinates never become infinite. Then there must be an upper bound to the function (dS/dt), and by choosing τ large enough, the left side of Eq. (3–109) can be made as small as we please. Hence, we obtain

$$\overline{T} = -\tfrac{1}{2}\overline{\sum_{j=1}^{n} \mathbf{r}_j \cdot \mathbf{F}_j}, \tag{3–110}$$

which is called the *virial theorem*. The right side was called the *virial* by Clausius.

Let us apply this theorem to a single particle moving in central force motion. Let $\mathbf{F} = -ar^n \mathbf{u}_r$, where a is a positive constant. Then the virial is

$$\frac{1}{2}\,(\mathbf{r} \cdot ar^n \mathbf{u}_r) = \frac{1}{2}\,ar^{n+1} = \frac{n+1}{2}\,V, \tag{3–111}$$

where V is the potential energy. By Eq. (3–110)

$$\overline{T} = \frac{n+1}{2}\,\overline{V}. \tag{3–112}$$

If $n = -2$, the case of the inverse square force

$$\overline{T} = -\tfrac{1}{2}\overline{V}. \tag{3–113}$$

Hence the kinetic energy is, on the average, one half the average potential energy.

The virial theorem assumes considerable importance in the kinetic theory of gases. By its use one finds, for example, that the pressure of a gas may be expressed in terms of the time average of the squares of the molecular velocities. One may also derive the well-known relation $pV = nkT$ (where p is the pressure, V is the volume, T is the absolute temperature, n is the number of molecules in V, and k is Boltzmann's constant). For discussion of these applications, we refer the reader to other sources on the kinetic theory.*

---

* See, for example, L. B. Loeb, *The Kinetic Theory of Gases*, New York: McGraw-Hill Book Company, Inc., 1927. A brief account is given by R. B. Lindsay, *Physical Mechanics*. New York: D. Van Nostrand Company, Inc., 1933.

PROBLEMS

3–1. A particle of mass m moves under an attractive force whose components are $X = -\alpha x$, $Y = -\alpha y$. (a) Write the Lagrangian equations of motion. Compare them with those derived from the vector differential equation of motion. (b) By an energy diagram analysis, study the motion of the particle, compute the period for the motion, and find the polar equation of the orbit. (c) Are the periods in r and θ the same for this motion? (Section 3–1)

3–2. (a) Deduce from the analysis in Section 3–2 the differential equations in r_1 and r_2 for the individual masses in the two-body problem. (b) Show directly from the differential equations that the period of circular motion is proportional to $a^{3/2}$, where a is the radius of the orbit of one mass relative to the other. (Section 3–2)

3–3. (Section 3–1) By letting $1/r = u$, show that the equations $mr^2\dot\theta = l$ and $d(m\dot r)/dt - (l^2/mr^3) = F(r)$ may be combined to yield for the orbit under a central force the differential equation

$$\frac{d^2u}{d\theta^2} + u = -\frac{mF(1/u)}{l^2u^2}. \tag{3–114}$$

3–4. A particle describes the path $r = a(1 + \cos\theta)$ under the action of a central force directed toward the origin of coordinates. By use of Eq. (3–114) find the law of central force. (Section 3–1)

3–5. A particle is projected from the point $(r_0,0)$ with a velocity v_0 perpendicular to the x-axis. It is acted upon by a force $-(m/r^3)\mathbf{u}_r$, where $\mathbf{u}_r$ is a unit vector along the radius vector. Find the equation of its path, studying all possible cases that arise. (Section 3–1)

3–6. Discuss the stability of small radial perturbations from the circular orbit under an inverse square force whose fictitious potential is shown in Fig. 3–4. How does the frequency of these radial oscillations compare with the angular frequency in the orbit? (Section 3–3)

3–7. A particle describes a circular path under a law of force $F(r) = -\alpha r^{-2}e^{-\beta r}$, where $\alpha > 0$ and $\beta > 0$. Investigate the stability of small radial perturbations from the circular orbit. (Section 3–3)

3–8. A particle of mass m slides under gravity on the inside of a smooth paraboloid of revolution whose axis is vertical. (a) Write the Lagrangian equations of motion in cylindrical coordinates. (b) For what angular velocity will the particle move in a circular orbit? (c) Show that a slight disturbance of the particle from this circular orbit will cause the particle to oscillate about the circle, and (d) find the period of this perturbed motion. (Section 3–3)

3–9. The velocity of escape of a mass in a central force field is that velocity which would just send the particle to an infinite distance and leave it there with zero velocity, or we may define it as the velocity acquired in falling from zero velocity at an infinite value of r to a given point. (a) What is the velocity of escape at distance a from the sun? (b) How does this compare with the velocity in a circular orbit of radius a about the sun? (Section 3–2)

3–10. A small satellite of mass m, negligible compared to that of the earth, is projected with a speed v parallel to the earth's surface at a height of 320 km.

Assuming that the mass of the earth is 5.98×10^{27} gm, that its radius is 6.38×10^8 cm, and that the constant of gravitation is 6.67×10^{-8} cgs units, (a) calculate the value of v required to put the satellite into a circular orbit. (b) What is the escape velocity of the satellite? If the satellite projected at a height of 320 km, as above, is observed later at a height of 1000 km when farthest from the earth's surface, (c) what is the eccentricity of its orbit (d) what was its velocity of projection, and (e) what is the total energy of the satellite in its elliptical orbit? (Section 3–2)

3–11. Suppose a particle of mass m moves about the origin under the force law $F(r) = -(\alpha/r^2) + (\beta/r^3)$, where β is small compared to α, and both are positive constants. (a) Show that the resulting motion takes place in a curve whose equation has the form $r = \text{constant}/(1 + e \cos k\theta)$. This may be regarded as an orbit with a precessing axis of symmetry. (b) Determine the rate of precession as a function of k and sketch the resulting orbit. (Sections 3–1 and 3–2)

3–12. A beam of particles of energy E and initial velocity v is projected into the field of a force center which repels them according to the law $F(r) = \alpha r^{-3}(\alpha > 0)$. Compute the differential cross section for scattering. (Section 3–4)

3–13. A beam of particles of energy E is incident on a force center for which the potential is given by the function $V = 0$ for $r > r_0$ and $V = -V_0$ for $r \leq r_0$. (a) Plot the energy diagram for this force center. (b) Find the paths of incident and scattered particles. (c) What happens when the impact parameter p is greater than r_0? (d) Show that the ratio of the velocity inside the force field to that outside is $n = \sqrt{(E + V_0)/E}$, where E is the total energy of the particle. (e) Show that the total deviation of a particle of impact parameter p in passing through the field is $\Theta = 2\{\sin^{-1}(p/r_0) - \sin^{-1}(p/nr_0)\}$. Hence, (f) find the differential cross section for scattering to be

$$\sigma(\Theta) = \frac{n^2 r_0^2 (\cos \tfrac{1}{2}\Theta - n)(n \cos \tfrac{1}{2}\Theta - 1)}{4 \cos \tfrac{1}{2}\Theta (1 + n^2 - 2n \cos \tfrac{1}{2}\Theta)^2}.$$

(g) Calculate the total cross section σ to show that it is finite. (Section 3–4)

3–14. A particle moves under the force law $F(r) = -kr(k > 0)$. (a) Show that the average kinetic energy equals the average potential energy. (b) Does this result agree with that of Problem 2–6? (Section 3–5)

3–15. Find an expression for the average kinetic energy of a particle moving in a force field given by $F(r) = -\alpha r^{-2}e^{-\beta r}$ ($\alpha > 0$, $\beta > 0$). (Section 3–5)

3–16. An electron moves in an axially symmetric magnetic field which changes with the time as in the betatron. The position of the electron is given at any time t by the cylindrical coordinates (r, θ, z), where the axis of symmetry of the system is the z-axis. The magnetic induction $\mathbf{B} = \text{curl } \mathbf{A}$, where $\mathbf{A}$ is the vector potential with components $A_r = 0$, $A_\theta(r,z,t)$, $A_z = 0$. The mass of the electron is $m = m_0[1 - v^2/c^2]^{-1/2}$, c being the velocity of light, v being the speed of the electron. No electrostatic field is present.

The components of curl $\mathbf{A}$ in cylindrical coordinates are

$$\left(\frac{1}{r}\frac{\partial A_z}{\partial \theta} - \frac{\partial A_\theta}{\partial z}\right), \quad \left(\frac{\partial A_r}{\partial z} - \frac{\partial A_z}{\partial r}\right), \quad \left(\frac{1}{r}\frac{\partial(rA_\theta)}{\partial r} - \frac{1}{r}\frac{\partial A_r}{\partial \theta}\right).$$

(a) If the force on the electron is $\mathbf{F} = e(\mathbf{v} \times \mathbf{B}) - e(\partial \mathbf{A}/\partial t)$, write the vector equation of motion and from it the equations of motion in cylindrical coordinates. It is convenient to leave the equations in terms of the relativistic mass, m, and its derivative, dm/dt.

(b) Using the Lagrangian $L = m_0 c^2 [1 - (1 - v^2/c^2)^{1/2}] + e r \dot{\theta} A_\theta$, write the Lagrangian equations of motion in (r, θ, z) and compare with the equations found in (a) above.

(c) From the results of (a) or (b), write the equations of motion for a circular orbit of radius a.

(d) If $A_\theta = \alpha t + \beta$ $(\alpha > 0)$, compute from (c) the period of the circular motion. Show that as $t \to \infty$, this period $P \to (2\pi a)/c$.

(e) If in the neighborhood of the circular orbit $B_z = B(a/r)^n$, show that the angular frequency ω in the circular orbit is given by $\omega = -(eB/m)$, where m is the relativistic mass.

(f) Set $r = a + \rho$, $\dot{\theta} = \omega + \dot{\phi}$, and measure z from the plane of the circular orbit. Here ρ and $\dot{\phi}$ are small perturbations in a and ω. With B_z as given in (e), and on the assumption that $(\partial B_z/\partial r) = (\partial B_r/\partial z)$, investigate the stability of the circular motion in the neighborhood of the circular orbit. Neglect squares and products of ρ, $\dot{\phi}$, etc. That is: (1) Show that the perturbation frequency in the radial direction is $\omega_\rho = [(e^2 B^2/m^2)(1 - n)]^{1/2}$, and hence $n < 1$ for stability. (The perturbations are assumed to be slow so that terms of the type $\dot{\rho} dm/dt$ may be neglected.) (2) By neglecting time effects in $A_\theta(r,z,t)$ and letting $dm/dt = 0$, show that the perturbation frequency in the z-direction is $\omega_z = [n\omega^2]^{1/2}$, and hence for stability $n > 0$. (3) Hence, show that $\omega_\rho^2 + \omega_z^2 = \omega^2$ and that complete stability demands $0 < n < 1$.

(g) If Φ is the total magnetic flux linking the circular orbit of radius a, show that circular motion requires that $d\Phi/dt$ equals twice the area of the circle times the z-component of the time rate of change of the magnetic induction $\mathbf{B}$ at the orbit. (Stokes' theorem is useful here.)

CHAPTER 4

DYNAMICS OF A RIGID BODY

General theorems relating to systems of particles in motion were discussed in Sections 1–12 and 1–13. If, in such a system, the positions of the particles relative to one another do not change with the time, the system is called a *rigid body*. In this chapter we shall discuss the basic concepts of rigid-body motion and apply them to a torque-free system, to the motion of a symmetrical top, and to the motion of a spinning projectile.

4–1 Rigid-body motion. Consider three noncollinear points of a rigid body. If the coordinates of these three are specified relative to fixed coordinate axes, the position of the body is fixed in space. If these three points are denoted by $\mathbf{r}_1$, $\mathbf{r}_2$, $\mathbf{r}_3$ relative to an origin O, not all the nine components of these three vectors are independent. Since the body is rigid, there are relations $|\mathbf{r}_2 - \mathbf{r}_1| = $ constant, $|\mathbf{r}_3 - \mathbf{r}_1| = $ constant, $|\mathbf{r}_3 - \mathbf{r}_2| = $ constant, which express the fact that the distances between the points are invariant. Hence there remain only six independent coordinates in three-space required to specify uniquely the position and orientation of the body. We may, for example, give the cartesian coordinates of the center of mass together with three angles that orient the body relative to three axes of fixed direction passing through the center of mass. These six independent scalar quantities are the components of $\mathbf{R}$ and $\mathbf{L}_c$ obtainable by solving the fundamental vector equations of motion,

$$M\ddot{\mathbf{R}} = \mathbf{F}, \qquad \frac{d\mathbf{L}_c}{dt} = \mathbf{N}_c,$$

that is, by Eq. (1–77) and Newton's Second Law for rotational motion together with appropriate initial conditions. It is clear by Eq. (1–84) that the second of these may be replaced by

$$\frac{d\mathbf{L}_0}{dt} = \mathbf{N}_0,$$

where $\mathbf{L}_0$ and $\mathbf{N}_0$ are the angular momentum and torque, respectively, about any fixed point O.

Let a force $\mathbf{F}$ (Fig. 4–1) act at a point of the rigid body whose position is $\mathbf{r}$ relative to a fixed arbitrary point O in the body. The result, in general, will be a translation of the body in space and a rotation of the body about O. Clearly the translation will be unaffected if we introduce forces $\mathbf{F}$ and $-\mathbf{F}$ at O. A pair of noncollinear forces such as $\mathbf{F}$ and $-\mathbf{F}$ acting at two points in the rigid body is known as a *couple*. Its moment about

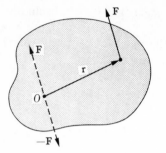

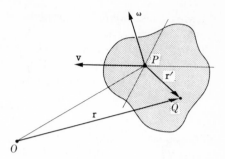

FIG. 4–1. Couple acting on a rigid body.

FIG. 4–2. Rotational and translational velocities of a rigid body.

any point in the body is the same and equal to $\mathbf{r} \times \mathbf{F}$ in the present case. By introducing equal and opposite forces at O, we have formed an equivalent system of forces under which the motion of the body will be the same as if only $\mathbf{F}$ were present. But we have now a force $\mathbf{F}$ at O combined with a couple whose moment is $\mathbf{r} \times \mathbf{F}$ about O. What we have shown here may be extended to an entire system of forces. We have, then, the fundamental theorem that *any system of n forces acting on a rigid body may be reduced to a single resultant force $\sum_{j=1}^{n} \mathbf{F}_j$ acting at an arbitrary point together with a total moment $\sum_{j=1}^{n} \mathbf{r}_j \times \mathbf{F}_j$ about the point.*

Let $\mathbf{F}_0 = \sum_{j=1}^{n} \mathbf{F}_j$ be the resultant of the forces considered as acting at O, and let $\mathbf{N}_0 = \sum_{j=1}^{n} \mathbf{r}_j \times \mathbf{F}_j$ be their total moment about O. In general $\mathbf{F}_0$ and $\mathbf{N}_0$ will not be collinear. As O is moved about in the body, $\mathbf{F}_0$ will not change, but $\mathbf{N}_0$ will vary because of its dependence upon $\mathbf{r}_j$. Let O be moved to O', whose position vector relative to O is $\mathbf{a}$. Then an equivalent force system would be $\mathbf{F}_0$ at O' together with a couple $-\mathbf{a} \times \mathbf{F}_0$, and the resulting total moment about O' would be $\mathbf{N}_{0'} = \mathbf{N}_0 - (\mathbf{a} \times \mathbf{F}_0)$. This change in moment with change in position of O in the rigid body is of importance, for example, in the analysis of the motion of a projectile under gravity and under the aerodynamic forces due to the atmosphere.

We shall now show that in the motion of a rigid body there is a locus of points that are instantaneously at rest. This locus is called the *instantaneous axis of rotation*. Let the motion be described by the velocity $\mathbf{v}$ of some point P together with an angular velocity $\boldsymbol{\omega}$ which describes the instantaneous rotation of the body about an axis through P. Let the position vector of any other point Q in the body be designated by $\mathbf{r}$ relative to an origin O fixed in space, as shown in Fig. 4–2. Then by Eq. (1–103), the instantaneous velocity of Q relative to the fixed point O will be

$$\dot{\mathbf{r}} = \mathbf{v} + \boldsymbol{\omega} \times \mathbf{r}'. \qquad (4\text{–}1)$$

We seek those points in the body, if any, such that $\dot{\mathbf{r}} = 0$, excluding the trivial case where $\boldsymbol{\omega} = 0$.

Case I. Suppose that $\mathbf{v} = 0$, so that the motion is entirely rotational about an axis through P. Then $\dot{\mathbf{r}}$ will be zero if $\boldsymbol{\omega} \times \mathbf{r}' = 0$. But this means that $\mathbf{r}'$ is coincident with $\boldsymbol{\omega}$, and hence we may write

$$\mathbf{r}' = k\boldsymbol{\omega}. \tag{4-2}$$

This is a straight line through P.

Case II. If $\mathbf{v} \neq 0$, we have, for $\dot{\mathbf{r}} = 0$,

$$\boldsymbol{\omega} \times \mathbf{r}' = -\mathbf{v}, \tag{4-3}$$

which implies that $\mathbf{v}$ is perpendicular to both $\boldsymbol{\omega}$ and $\mathbf{r}'$ since it is perpendicular to their plane. Hence we may write $\mathbf{r}'$ as a linear function of $\boldsymbol{\omega}$ and a vector perpendicular to the plane of $\boldsymbol{\omega}$ and $\mathbf{v}$, say $\boldsymbol{\omega} \times \mathbf{v}$ (see Fig. 4–3),

$$\mathbf{r}' = a\boldsymbol{\omega} + b(\boldsymbol{\omega} \times \mathbf{v}). \tag{4-4}$$

Then, by Eq. (4–3),

$$\begin{aligned} -\mathbf{v} = \boldsymbol{\omega} \times \mathbf{r}' &= a\boldsymbol{\omega} \times \boldsymbol{\omega} + b\boldsymbol{\omega} \times (\boldsymbol{\omega} \times \mathbf{v}) \\ &= b[(\boldsymbol{\omega}\cdot\mathbf{v})\boldsymbol{\omega} - (\boldsymbol{\omega}\cdot\boldsymbol{\omega})\mathbf{v}] \\ &= -\omega^2 b\mathbf{v}, \end{aligned} \tag{4-5}$$

and we find that $b = 1/\omega^2$, so that

$$b(\boldsymbol{\omega} \times \mathbf{v}) = \frac{1}{\omega^2}(\boldsymbol{\omega} \times \mathbf{v}) = \left(\frac{v}{\omega}\right)\mathbf{u}_r, \tag{4-6}$$

where $\mathbf{u}_r$ is a unit vector in the direction of $\boldsymbol{\omega} \times \mathbf{v}$.

From Eqs. (4–4) and (4–6) it follows that

$$\mathbf{r}' = a\boldsymbol{\omega} + \left(\frac{v}{\omega}\right)\mathbf{u}_r. \tag{4-7}$$

This is a locus of points (Fig. 4–4) parallel to the vector $\boldsymbol{\omega}$ and at a distance (v/ω) from it. This locus is *the instantaneous axis of rotation.*

As an example, consider a disk rolling down an inclined plane, as shown in Fig. 4–5. The angular velocity vector $\boldsymbol{\omega}$ through its center is perpendicular to the paper and toward the reader. The vectors $\mathbf{v}$ and $\mathbf{r}'$ remain in the plane of the motion. By the preceding analysis, the instantaneous axis of rotation is also perpendicular to the paper, parallel to $\boldsymbol{\omega}$, and passes through the point of contact R. The distance of the instantaneous axis of rotation from the vector $\boldsymbol{\omega}$ is v/ω, which is the radius of the disk.

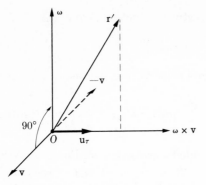

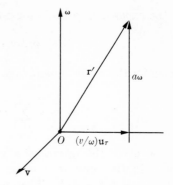

FIG. 4–3. Vector relationship between $\mathbf{v}$, $\boldsymbol{\omega}$, $\boldsymbol{\omega} \times \mathbf{v}$, and $\mathbf{r}'$.

FIG. 4–4. Instantaneous axis of rotation.

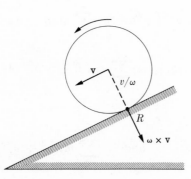

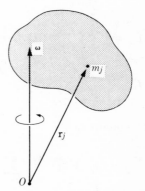

FIG. 4–5. Wheel rolling on an inclined plane.

FIG. 4–6. Rotating rigid body.

4–2 Moments and products of inertia. We found in Section 1–12 that the motion of a system of particles may be resolved into a translation of the center of mass and a rotation about that center, a result known to Euler in 1749. In studying the motion of a rigid body in this section, we shall concentrate our attention entirely upon rotation about a fixed point.

Let a rigidly connected system of masses rotate with angular velocity $\boldsymbol{\omega}$ about an axis passing through O (Fig. 4–6). The angular velocity vector $\boldsymbol{\omega}$ is not fixed in magnitude or in direction but is localized through O. At any instant the linear velocity of a particle at $\mathbf{r}_j$, relative to O, will be $\boldsymbol{\omega} \times \mathbf{r}_j$. Its angular momentum is

$$\mathbf{L} = \mathbf{r}_j \times m_j \mathbf{v}_j = m_j[\mathbf{r}_j \times (\boldsymbol{\omega} \times \mathbf{r}_j)]. \tag{4–8}$$

By the expansion formula for a triple vector product, we have

$$\mathbf{L} = m_j[(\mathbf{r}_j \cdot \mathbf{r}_j)\boldsymbol{\omega} - (\mathbf{r}_j \cdot \boldsymbol{\omega})\mathbf{r}_j]. \tag{4–9}$$

Hence for the whole assemblage of points constituting the body,

$$\mathbf{L} = \boldsymbol{\omega} \sum_{j=1}^{n} m_j r_j^2 - \sum_{j=1}^{n} m_j(\mathbf{r}_j \cdot \boldsymbol{\omega})\mathbf{r}_j. \tag{4–10}$$

Now place the origin of a right-handed cartesian coordinate system at O. In this system $\mathbf{r} = x\mathbf{i} + y\mathbf{j} + z\mathbf{k}$, $\boldsymbol{\omega} = \omega_x\mathbf{i} + \omega_y\mathbf{j} + \omega_z\mathbf{k}$, and $\mathbf{L} = L_x\mathbf{i} + L_y\mathbf{j} + L_z\mathbf{k}$. Then we have, from Eq. (4–10),

$$L_x = \omega_x \sum_{j=1}^{n} m_j(y_j^2 + z_j^2) - \omega_y \sum_{j=1}^{n} m_j x_j y_j - \omega_z \sum_{j=1}^{n} m_j x_j z_j, \tag{4–11}$$

$$L_y = -\omega_x \sum_{j=1}^{n} m_j y_j x_j + \omega_y \sum_{j=1}^{n} m_j(x_j^2 + z_j^2) - \omega_z \sum_{j=1}^{n} m_j y_j z_j, \tag{4–12}$$

$$L_z = -\omega_x \sum_{j=1}^{n} m_j z_j x_j - \omega_y \sum_{j=1}^{n} m_j z_j y_j + \omega_z \sum_{j=1}^{n} m_j(x_j^2 + y_j^2). \tag{4–13}$$

The quantities

$$\sum_{j=1}^{n} m_j(y_j^2 + z_j^2), \qquad \sum_{j=1}^{n} m_j(x_j^2 + z_j^2), \qquad \text{and} \qquad \sum_{j=1}^{n} m_j(x_j^2 + y_j^2)$$

are defined to be the *moments of inertia* of the system about the x-, y-, and z-axes respectively. We shall designate them by I_{xx}, I_{yy}, and I_{zz}. They play a role in rotational motion similar to that of the mass in translational motion.

The other summations are called *products of inertia*. We shall designate them by

$$I_{xy} = \sum_{j=1}^{n} m_j x_j y_j, \qquad I_{yz} = \sum_{j=1}^{n} m_j y_j z_j, \qquad I_{zx} = \sum_{j=1}^{n} m_j z_j x_j. \tag{4–14}$$

Thus we have the following fundamental relations between the angular momentum components and the moments and products of inertia:

$$\begin{aligned} L_x &= I_{xx}\omega_x - I_{xy}\omega_y - I_{xz}\omega_z, \\ L_y &= -I_{yx}\omega_x + I_{yy}\omega_y - I_{yz}\omega_z, \\ L_z &= -I_{zx}\omega_x - I_{zy}\omega_y + I_{zz}\omega_z. \end{aligned} \tag{4–15}$$

It is important to observe that, in general, $\mathbf{L}$ and $\boldsymbol{\omega}$ are not collinear vectors. Furthermore, if $\mathbf{L}$ is used directly in Newton's Second Law, $(d\mathbf{L}/dt) = \mathbf{N}$, not only do the components of $\boldsymbol{\omega}$ change with the time but so do the moments and products of inertia. These have been defined with respect to fixed axes. As the system of particles rotates, and hence as the orientation changes, these moments and products vary. We shall see later how this situation may be avoided by computing the moments and products of inertia with respect to appropriate axes fixed in the rigid system and rotating with it. The array of nine quantities

$$
\begin{array}{ccc}
I_{xx} & -I_{xy} & -I_{xz} \\
-I_{yx} & I_{yy} & -I_{yz} \\
-I_{zx} & -I_{zy} & I_{zz}
\end{array}
$$

is called a *tensor*, and here, in particular, the *momental* or *inertial tensor* of the system. We shall refer to these quantities collectively as the *inertial parameters* of the system.

Suppose the system of particles is a bounded, continuous, solid medium of density ρ at any point. Then we modify the definitions of the inertial parameters I_{xx}, I_{xy}, and so forth, by writing the summations as integrals over the space considered. That is,

$$
I_{xx} = \int_V (y^2 + z^2)\rho \, dv, \quad I_{yy} = \int_V (z^2 + x^2)\rho \, dv, \quad I_{zz} = \int_V (x^2 + y^2)\rho \, dv,
$$

$$
(4\text{--}16)
$$

with similar integrals for the products of inertia.

4–3 Computation of inertial moments. Since specification of the inertial parameters is a prerequisite to the study of the motion of the rigid body, we shall consider their evaluation. The methods of elementary calculus enable us to compute moments of inertia about any arbitrary axes in a rigid body. The calculations are usually quite straightforward *if the axes are chosen to conform to the symmetry axes of the body.* We shall restrict ourselves to the regular solids, or combinations of regular solids, for which the integrals such as those of Eq. (4–16) are more or less readily evaluated. Furthermore, we assume that the reader is familiar with the parallel-axis theorem by which the moment of inertia about any axis can be found if the mass and the moment of inertia about a parallel axis through the center of mass are known.

Let λ, μ, ν be the direction cosines of a line l in space (Fig. 4–7) which passes through the origin of a fixed cartesian system of coordinates. Let $\mathbf{r}_j$ be the position vector of a mass point m_j, and let d_j be the perpendicular distance from m_j to the line. By definition, the moment of inertia about the line l is

$$I_l = \sum_{j=1}^{n} m_j d_j^2, \qquad (4\text{-}17)$$

where n particles comprise the system.

Since the unit vector in the direction of l is $\mathbf{u}_l = \lambda \mathbf{i} + \mu \mathbf{j} + \nu \mathbf{k}$, we may write $d_j^2 = [\mathbf{r}_j \times \mathbf{u}_l]^2$, and hence

$$I_l = \sum_{j=1}^{n} m_j[\mathbf{r}_j \times \mathbf{u}_l]^2, \qquad (4\text{-}18)$$

but

$$\mathbf{r}_j \times \mathbf{u}_l = \begin{vmatrix} \mathbf{i} & \mathbf{j} & \mathbf{k} \\ x_j & y_j & z_j \\ \lambda & \mu & \nu \end{vmatrix} \qquad (4\text{-}19)$$

and the square of the magnitude of this vector is

$$(y_j\nu - z_j\mu)^2 + (z_j\lambda - x_j\nu)^2 + (x_j\mu - y_j\lambda)^2. \qquad (4\text{-}20)$$

Grouping coefficients of λ^2, μ^2, ν^2, and so forth, and using the definitions of moments and products of inertia, we obtain

$$I_l = \lambda^2 I_{xx} + \mu^2 I_{yy} + \nu^2 I_{zz} - 2\mu\lambda I_{xy} - 2\lambda\nu I_{xz} - 2\mu\nu I_{yz}. \qquad (4\text{-}21)$$

From this relation we may calculate the moment of inertia about any line through O if the inertial parameters with respect to the coordinate axes are known. These are readily calculated if the coordinate axes are chosen so as to coincide with the symmetry axes of the body.

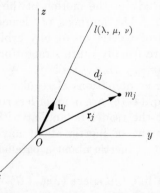

FIG. 4–7. Moment of inertia of a mass particle.

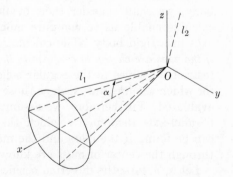

FIG. 4–8. Axes for moments of inertia of a cone.

As an example of the application of Eq. (4–21), we shall calculate the moments of inertia about an element of a cone and a line perpendicular to it at the vertex. Choose the x-axis to be the symmetry axis of the cone whose semivertical angle is α (Fig. 4–8). By direct integration we find $I_{xx} = (3/10)ML^2 \sin^2 \alpha$, where L is the slant height of the cone and M is its mass. Similarly,

$$I_{yy} = I_{zz} = (3/5)ML^2(\cos^2 \alpha + 1/4 \sin^2 \alpha).$$

Our choice of axes makes all the products of inertia vanish.

The element l_1 of the cone in the xz-plane has direction cosines

$$\lambda = \cos \alpha, \qquad \mu = 0, \qquad \nu = \sin \alpha. \tag{4–22}$$

Hence Eq. (4–21) yields

$$
\begin{aligned}
I_{l_1} &= I_{xx} \cos^2 \alpha + I_{zz} \sin^2 \alpha \\
&= (3/10)ML^2 \sin^2 \alpha \cos^2 \alpha + (3/5)ML^2(\cos^2 \alpha + 1/4 \sin^2 \alpha) \sin^2 \alpha \\
&= (3/4)ML^2 \sin^2 \alpha[\cos^2 \alpha + 1/5] \tag{4–23}
\end{aligned}
$$

for the moment of inertia about an element of the cone.

Similarly for the moment of inertia about a line l_2 in the xz-plane perpendicular to the element l_1, we have

$$\lambda = -\sin \alpha, \qquad \mu = 0, \qquad \nu = \cos \alpha. \tag{4–24}$$

From this,

$$I_{l_2} = ML^2[(3/4) \sin^4 \alpha - (21/20) \sin^2 \alpha + 3/5]. \tag{4–25}$$

4–4 Principal axes. It is clear from Eq. (4–21) that as we allow λ, μ, ν to vary, we find moments of inertia about all lines through the origin O. Suppose we write for one of these lines $\lambda = \xi/\rho$, $\mu = \eta/\rho$, $\nu = \zeta/\rho$ and substitute into Eq. (4–21). Here ξ, η, ζ are the coordinates of a point on the line and ρ is the distance of the point from the origin. There results

$$I_{xx}\xi^2 + I_{yy}\eta^2 + I_{zz}\zeta^2 - 2\xi\eta I_{xy} - 2\xi\zeta I_{xz} - 2\eta\zeta I_{yz} = \rho^2 I_l. \tag{4–26}$$

This equation, a familiar one from solid analytic geometry, represents a quadric surface provided we set $\rho^2 I_l = 1$. For a given set of quantities $I_{xx}, I_{yy}, I_{zz}, I_{xy}, I_{xz}, I_{yz}$ one can construct a quadric surface with center at the origin such that the distance from O to a point P on the surface is related to the moment of inertia about the line OP by the relation $\rho = 1/\sqrt{I_l}$. For any physical body, I_l cannot be zero. Hence none of the values of ρ can be infinite, and the surface must be a closed surface, that is, an ellipsoid. It is called the *momental ellipsoid* or *inertial ellipsoid* for the rigid body.

We know that an ellipsoid has three axes of symmetry. Had we chosen the cartesian coordinate system so as to eliminate the cross-product terms in Eq. (4–26), the equation of the momental ellipsoid would have been in the symmetric form

$$I_1 x^2 + I_2 y^2 + I_3 z^2 = 1, \tag{4–27}$$

where I_1, I_2, I_3 are the moments of inertia about the coordinate axes which now coincide with the axes of symmetry. These are the *principal moments of inertia* of the body, and the new axes are called the *principal axes* of the ellipsoid.

The problem of finding the directions of the principal axes of inertia in a given situation is one of rotating the coordinate system so as to eliminate the products of inertia. Suppose this has been done so that the **i, j, k** unit vectors used in deriving Eqs. (4–11), (4–12), and (4–13) coincide with the principal axes of inertia. Suppose the body is rotating about the x-axis so that $\boldsymbol{\omega} = \omega_x \mathbf{i} (\omega_y = \omega_z = 0)$. Then, since the products of inertia vanish, we see by Eq. (4–15) that $L_x = I_{xx}\omega_x$, and hence $\mathbf{L} = I_{xx}\omega_x \mathbf{i}$. The angular momentum vector and the angular velocity vector coincide in direction. In a similar way one may show that if the body rotates about the **j**- or **k**-axes, the angular momenta are $\mathbf{L} = \omega_y I_{yy}\mathbf{j}$ and $\mathbf{L} = \omega_z I_{zz}\mathbf{k}$ respectively. Hence, in general, if the body is rotating about a principal axis, $\mathbf{L} = I\boldsymbol{\omega}$, where I is a proportionality constant to be determined.

Let us assume that we have selected *arbitrarily* a set of xyz-axes and have computed the inertial parameters with respect to them. Then in order that **L** and $\boldsymbol{\omega}$ be collinear, we must have, from Eq. (4–15),

$$\begin{aligned}
L_x &= I_{xx}\omega_x - I_{xy}\omega_y - I_{xz}\omega_z = I\omega_x, \\
L_y &= -I_{yx}\omega_x + I_{yy}\omega_y - I_{yz}\omega_z = I\omega_y, \\
L_z &= -I_{zx}\omega_x - I_{zy}\omega_y + I_{zz}\omega_z = I\omega_z,
\end{aligned} \tag{4–28}$$

or

$$\begin{aligned}
(I_{xx} - I)\omega_x - I_{xy}\omega_y - I_{xz}\omega_z &= 0, \\
-I_{yx}\omega_x + (I_{yy} - I)\omega_y - I_{yz}\omega_z &= 0, \\
-I_{zx}\omega_x - I_{zy}\omega_y + (I_{zz} - I)\omega_z &= 0.
\end{aligned} \tag{4–29}$$

These equations will have a nontrivial solution for the ratios $\omega_x : \omega_y : \omega_z$ if

$$\begin{vmatrix} (I_{xx} - I) & -I_{xy} & -I_{xz} \\ -I_{yx} & (I_{yy} - I) & -I_{yz} \\ -I_{zx} & -I_{zy} & (I_{zz} - I) \end{vmatrix} = 0. \tag{4–30}$$

This is a cubic equation in I, whose three roots we shall denote by I_1, I_2, and I_3. These are the principal moments of inertia. It may be shown that I_1, I_2, and I_3 are always real.*

The direction of the principal axis associated with each of these moments of inertia may now be found from Eqs. (4–29). The components ω_x, ω_y, and ω_z define a direction with respect to the coordinate axes, namely, that of the angular velocity vector. Since, for rotation about a principal axis, the angular velocity vector coincides with this axis, the set of numbers ω_x, ω_y, ω_z which satisfy Eqs. (4–29) are the direction numbers of the axis. For example, to find the direction of the principal axis corresponding to I_1, we have

$$(I_{xx} - I_1)\omega_x^{(1)} - I_{xy}\omega_y^{(1)} - I_{xz}\omega_z^{(1)} = 0,$$

$$-I_{yx}\omega_x^{(1)} + (I_{yy} - I_1)\omega_y^{(1)} - I_{yz}\omega_z^{(1)} = 0,$$

$$-I_{zx}\omega_x^{(1)} - I_{zy}\omega_y^{(1)} + (I_{zz} - I_1)\omega_z^{(1)} = 0,$$

where $\omega_x^{(1)}$, $\omega_y^{(1)}$, $\omega_z^{(1)}$ are the direction numbers of this axis. These equations can be solved for the ratios $\omega_x^{(1)} : \omega_y^{(1)} : \omega_z^{(1)}$, and the axis associated with I_1 is thereby defined relative to the original coordinate system. In a similar way, by using I_2 and I_3 in Eqs. (4–29), we may find the ratios $\omega_x^{(2)} : \omega_y^{(2)} : \omega_z^{(2)}$ and $\omega_x^{(3)} : \omega_y^{(3)} : \omega_z^{(3)}$ for the axes associated with I_2 and I_3 respectively.

An example will serve to illustrate the method. Figure 4–9 shows a homogeneous solid cube of edge a and density ρ situated with its edges along the axes of a cartesian coordinate system. By direct integration

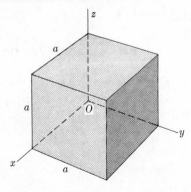

Fig. 4–9. Homogeneous solid cube.

---

* See, for example, A. G. Webster, *The Dynamics of Particles and of Rigid, Elastic, and Fluid Bodies.* New York: Hafner Publishing Company, 1949, pp. 567 ff.

we find the moments and products of inertia to be

$$I_{xx} = I_{yy} = I_{zz} = \frac{2}{3}\,Ma^2,$$

$$I_{xy} = I_{yz} = I_{zx} = \frac{Ma^2}{4},$$

where M is the mass of the cube. Then, from Eq. (4–30), we have

$$\begin{vmatrix} \left(\dfrac{2}{3}\,Ma^2 - I\right) & -\dfrac{Ma^2}{4} & -\dfrac{Ma^2}{4} \\[2mm] -\dfrac{Ma^2}{4} & \left(\dfrac{2}{3}\,Ma^2 - I\right) & -\dfrac{Ma^2}{4} \\[2mm] -\dfrac{Ma^2}{4} & -\dfrac{Ma^2}{4} & \left(\dfrac{2}{3}\,Ma^2 - I\right) \end{vmatrix} = 0. \quad (4\text{–}31)$$

For convenience, set $\lambda = (2/3)Ma^2 - I$, $\beta = -Ma^2/4$, so that Eq. (4–31) becomes

$$\begin{vmatrix} \lambda & \beta & \beta \\ \beta & \lambda & \beta \\ \beta & \beta & \lambda \end{vmatrix} = \begin{vmatrix} \lambda & \beta & \beta \\ \beta - \lambda & \lambda - \beta & 0 \\ \beta & \beta & \lambda \end{vmatrix} = 0, \quad (4\text{–}32)$$

from which we find

$$(\lambda - \beta)^2(\lambda + 2\beta) = 0. \quad (4\text{–}33)$$

The three roots of Eq. (4–33) are

$$I_1 = \frac{11}{12}\,Ma^2, \quad I_2 = \frac{11}{12}\,Ma^2, \quad I_3 = \frac{1}{6}\,Ma^2. \quad (4\text{–}34)$$

These are the principal moments of inertia for the block. Note that there is a degeneracy in the sense that two of these are the same. This means that the momental ellipsoid at O is a prolate spheroid with its longest axis along the direction in which the moment of inertia is I_3.

To find the direction of the principal axis (3), associated with I_3, we write Eqs. (4–29) in the form

$$\left(\frac{2}{3}\,Ma^2 - \frac{1}{6}\,Ma^2\right)\omega_x^{(3)} - \frac{Ma^2}{4}\,\omega_y^{(3)} - \frac{Ma^2}{4}\,\omega_z^{(3)} = 0,$$

$$-\frac{Ma^2}{4}\,\omega_x^{(3)} + \left(\frac{2}{3}\,Ma^2 - \frac{1}{6}\,Ma^2\right)\omega_y^{(3)} - \frac{Ma^2}{4}\,\omega_z^{(3)} = 0, \quad (4\text{–}35)$$

$$-\frac{Ma^2}{4}\,\omega_x^{(3)} - \frac{Ma^2}{4}\,\omega_y^{(3)} + \left(\frac{2}{3}\,Ma^2 - \frac{1}{6}\,Ma^2\right)\omega_z^{(3)} = 0,$$

which simplify to

$$2 \left(\frac{\omega_x}{\omega_z}\right)_3 - \left(\frac{\omega_y}{\omega_z}\right)_3 = 1,$$

$$- \left(\frac{\omega_x}{\omega_z}\right)_3 + 2 \left(\frac{\omega_y}{\omega_z}\right)_3 = 1,$$

$$\left(\frac{\omega_x}{\omega_z}\right)_3 + \left(\frac{\omega_y}{\omega_z}\right)_3 = 2.$$

From the first two of these we find the direction ratios

$$\omega_x^{(3)} : \omega_y^{(3)} : \omega_z^{(3)} = 1{:}1{:}1. \tag{4–36}$$

Thus the principal axis associated with I_3 passes through O and coincides with the body diagonal of the cube.

We may try using $I_1 = (11/12)Ma^2$ in Eqs. (4–29) in a similar way to obtain the principal axis associated with I_1. But we find upon simplifying equations analogous to Eqs. (4–35) that, because of the double root which appeared in Eq. (4–33) by virtue of the symmetry of the cube, there remains only one independent relation, namely,

$$\omega_x^{(1)} + \omega_y^{(1)} + \omega_z^{(1)} = 0.$$

Hence we may choose axes (1) and (2) to be any two mutually perpendicular lines through O and perpendicular to axis (3). For example, we may choose axis (1), associated with I_1, to lie in the xy-plane and have direction ratios

$$\omega_x^{(1)} : \omega_y^{(1)} : \omega_z^{(1)} = 1{:}{-}1{:}0.$$

Then axis (2), associated with I_2, would be designated by the ratios

$$\omega_x^{(2)} : \omega_y^{(2)} : \omega_z^{(2)} = -1{:}{-}1{:}2.$$

When the cube is rotating about axis (3), the angular momentum vector lies along this axis and has the value $\mathbf{L}_3 = (1/6)Ma^2\boldsymbol{\omega}$, where $\boldsymbol{\omega}$ is the angular velocity. Similar statements may be made with regard to axes (1) and (2).

Any rigid body has three mutually perpendicular axes that serve as the principal axes of inertia for the body. The general treatment of transformations to reduce the momental ellipsoid to its symmetric form is an interesting part of analysis, but we shall not go into the topic in this book.*

---

* See, for example, A. G. Webster, *Dynamics of Particles and of Rigid, Elastic, and Fluid Bodies.* New York: Hafner Publishing Company, 1949, pp. 567 ff.

4–5 Euler's equations of motion. The preceding sections have dealt with the inertial properties of a rigid body. We turn now to the dynamics of its rotational motion about a fixed point. We have seen in Section 1–12, however, that if we choose the center of mass as the origin of reference, the same theory will hold even if the origin is being translated.

In general, if we refer the angular momentum **L** and the angular velocity **ω** to a fixed coordinate system, a computation of $d\mathbf{L}/dt$ involves the time rate of change of the inertial parameters as well as the rate of change of **ω**. However, if we choose the principal axes of the body as the reference system, the moments of inertia with respect to these axes are fixed. Since Newton's Second Law for rotational motion is valid only for a fixed system, we must make due allowance for the rotation of the new system in our analysis. The basic equations are those of Section 1–14.

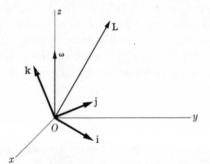

Fig. 4–10. Angular velocity and momentum in rotating system.

Let **i**, **j**, **k** (Fig. 4–10) be a triad of unit vectors *along the principal axes* (1), (2), (3) of the rigid body. For simplicity we picture the angular velocity vector along Oz. The analysis that follows, however, is independent of this assumption.

The xyz-system is fixed in space but, as the body rotates, **i**, **j**, **k** partake of the rotation. Furthermore, in general, **ω** changes with the time. Let **N** be the torque. Then, from Newton's Second Law, in the xyz-system

$$\frac{d\mathbf{L}}{dt} = \dot{L}_1\mathbf{i} + \dot{L}_2\mathbf{j} + \dot{L}_3\mathbf{k} + \boldsymbol{\omega} \times \mathbf{L} = \mathbf{N} \tag{4–37}$$

by analogy to Eqs. (1–104) and (1–105). Here L_1, L_2, L_3 are the components of **L** *in the rotating system* of axes. Similarly, we have for the angular velocity

$$\boldsymbol{\omega} = \omega_1\mathbf{i} + \omega_2\mathbf{j} + \omega_3\mathbf{k}, \tag{4–38}$$

so that

$$\boldsymbol{\omega} \times \mathbf{L} = \begin{vmatrix} \mathbf{i} & \mathbf{j} & \mathbf{k} \\ \omega_1 & \omega_2 & \omega_3 \\ L_1 & L_2 & L_3 \end{vmatrix}. \tag{4–39}$$

Hence we may write

$$\frac{d\mathbf{L}}{dt} = (\dot{L}_1 + \omega_2 L_3 - \omega_3 L_2)\mathbf{i}$$
$$+ (\dot{L}_2 + \omega_3 L_1 - \omega_1 L_3)\mathbf{j}$$
$$+ (\dot{L}_3 + \omega_1 L_2 - \omega_2 L_1)\mathbf{k}$$
$$= N_1\mathbf{i} + N_2\mathbf{j} + N_3\mathbf{k}. \tag{4-40}$$

But, since $\mathbf{L}$ and $\boldsymbol{\omega}$ are proportional for the principal axes, $L_1 = I_1\omega_1$, $L_2 = I_2\omega_2$, $L_3 = I_3\omega_3$, and $\dot{L}_1 = I_1\dot{\omega}_1$, $\dot{L}_2 = I_2\dot{\omega}_2$, $\dot{L}_3 = I_3\dot{\omega}_3$. Substituting for the components of $\dot{\mathbf{L}}$ and $\mathbf{L}$, we have

$$I_1\dot{\omega}_1 + \omega_2\omega_3(I_3 - I_2) = N_1,$$
$$I_2\dot{\omega}_2 + \omega_3\omega_1(I_1 - I_3) = N_2, \tag{4-41}$$
$$I_3\dot{\omega}_3 + \omega_1\omega_2(I_2 - I_1) = N_3.$$

These are the *Euler equations of motion*. The principal restriction on their use is that the origin of coordinates be fixed, or, if in translational motion, that the center of mass be taken as O. It is well to emphasize that ω_1, ω_2, ω_3 are not angular velocity components in the ordinary sense of being derivatives of some spatial coordinates which describe the position of the body at time t.

While Euler's equations have been derived on the assumption that $\mathbf{i}, \mathbf{j}, \mathbf{k}$ are fixed in the body, there are occasions when this condition may be relaxed with profit. If, for example, the body has rotational symmetry so that two of its moments of inertia are the same, we may wish to fix only one of the triad vectors, say $\mathbf{k}$, in the body and allow the others to rotate in a plane perpendicular to $\mathbf{k}$ but at a different velocity from the body axes. In this more general case, if we denote the angular velocity of the triad $\mathbf{i}, \mathbf{j}, \mathbf{k}$ by

$$\boldsymbol{\alpha} = \alpha_1\mathbf{i} + \alpha_2\mathbf{j} + \alpha_3\mathbf{k},$$

we have

$$\frac{d\mathbf{L}}{dt} = \dot{L}_1\mathbf{i} + \dot{L}_2\mathbf{j} + \dot{L}_3\mathbf{k} + (\boldsymbol{\alpha} \times \mathbf{L}) = N. \tag{4-42}$$

Hence, in terms of components,

$$I_1\dot{\omega}_1 + \alpha_2\omega_3 I_3 - \alpha_3\omega_2 I_2 = N_1,$$
$$I_2\dot{\omega}_2 + \alpha_3\omega_1 I_1 - \alpha_1\omega_3 I_3 = N_2, \tag{4-43}$$
$$I_3\dot{\omega}_3 + \alpha_1\omega_2 I_2 - \alpha_2\omega_1 I_1 = N_3.$$

These are obviously similar to Eq. (4–41) and reduce to the latter when $\boldsymbol{\alpha} = \boldsymbol{\omega}$.

As an application of Euler's equations, consider a uniform bar of cylindrical cross section, mounted as shown in Fig. 4–11(a), rotating about a horizontal shaft. The supports for the shaft are mounted on a turntable that revolves about a vertical axis. We shall consider the mass of the shaft to be negligible compared to the mass of the bar. Let the angular speed of the bar about the horizontal axis be constant and equal to s. Let Ω denote the constant angular speed of rotation of the turntable.

By inspection we choose the principal axes of the bar as shown by (1), (2), and (3) in Fig. 4–11(b). We choose the triad of unit vectors $\mathbf{i}$, $\mathbf{j}$, $\mathbf{k}$ to be along the principal axes and, as the bar rotates, these rotate with it. We denote the moments of inertia about the principal axes by I_1, I_2, and I_3. By virtue of the symmetry and shape of the bar, $I_2 = I_3$ and these are larger than I_1.

At any instant let the bar make an angle α with a horizontal y-axis in its plane of rotation, as shown in Fig. 4–11(b). As the turntable rotates, the z-axis remains vertical while the y-axis moves into the plane of the paper. The x-axis points toward the reader, and we may represent the angular velocities at any instant by the vectors $\boldsymbol{\Omega}$ and $\mathbf{s}$, as shown in Fig. 4–11(c).

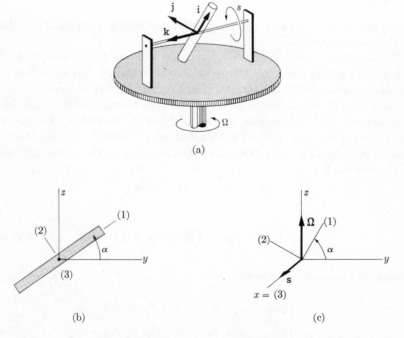

Fig. 4–11. Rotating bar on revolving turntable.

By direct projection of Ω and $\mathbf{s}$ on the principal axes of the bar, we find the angular velocity components

$$\omega_1 = \Omega \sin \alpha,$$
$$\omega_2 = \Omega \cos \alpha,   \text{(4–44)}$$
$$\omega_3 = s,$$

where Ω and s are constant. From these equations we obtain the accelerations

$$\dot{\omega}_1 = \Omega \cos \alpha \dot{\alpha} = \Omega s \cos \alpha,$$
$$\dot{\omega}_2 = -\Omega \sin \alpha \dot{\alpha} = -\Omega s \sin \alpha,   \text{(4–45)}$$
$$\dot{\omega}_3 = 0,$$

since $\dot{\alpha} = s$. Hence, by Eqs. (4–41), Euler's equations are

$$I_1 \Omega s \cos \alpha + \Omega s \cos \alpha (I_3 - I_2) = N_1,$$
$$-I_2 \Omega s \sin \alpha + \Omega s \sin \alpha (I_1 - I_3) = N_2,   \text{(4–46)}$$
$$\Omega^2 \sin \alpha \cos \alpha (I_2 - I_1) = N_3.$$

These simplify to

$$I_1 \Omega s \cos \alpha = N_1,$$
$$(I_1 - 2I_2)\Omega s \sin \alpha = N_2,   \text{(4–47)}$$
$$(I_2 - I_1)\Omega^2 \sin \alpha \cos \alpha = N_3.$$

Hence it is apparent that the torque components relative to the principal axes are periodic functions. If Ω is very small compared to s, we note that N_3 is the smallest of these torques.

We are more interested, however, in the resulting moments about the x-, y-, and z-axes shown in Fig. 4–11(c). They are

$$N_x = N_3$$
$$N_y = N_1 \cos \alpha - N_2 \sin \alpha,   \text{(4–48)}$$
$$N_z = N_1 \sin \alpha + N_2 \cos \alpha.$$

Substituting from Eqs. (4–47) into Eqs. (4–48) and simplifying, we have

$$N_x = \tfrac{1}{2}(I_2 - I_1)\Omega^2 \sin 2\alpha,   \text{(4–49)}$$
$$N_y = I_3 \Omega s + (I_1 - I_2)\Omega s \cos 2\alpha,   \text{(4–50)}$$
$$N_z = (I_1 - I_2)\Omega s \sin 2\alpha.   \text{(4–51)}$$

Note that these are all periodic functions with period one half that of the rotation of the bar. The physical interpretation of these equations is the following. The term $I_3\Omega s$ in Eq. (4–50) represents a constant moment tending to depress the positive x-axis, i.e., the $\mathbf{k}$ direction of the rotational axis. Since $I_1 < I_2$, the second term in Eq. (4–50) represents an uplifting moment on the positive x-axis when $\cos 2\alpha > 0$ and a depressing moment when $\cos 2\alpha < 0$. This action results in a periodic thrust downward on the left bearing in Fig. 4–11(a). Similarly, Eq. (4–51) represents a moment tending to rotate the shaft in a periodic way horizontally, and consequently can be used to calculate the side thrust on the bearings. Lastly, Eq. (4–49) represents the torque about the shaft axis itself. We call the moments N_x, N_y, N_z the *rolling*, *pitching*, and *yawing* moments of the system.

4–6 Rotational kinetic energy of a rigid body. Let the jth particle of a rigid body have a position vector $\mathbf{r}_j$ with respect to a fixed origin and system of axes. Then its linear velocity due to the rotation is $\mathbf{v}_j = \boldsymbol{\omega} \times \mathbf{r}_j$, and we may write for the kinetic energy

$$T = \frac{1}{2} \sum_{j=1}^{n} m_j(\boldsymbol{\omega} \times \mathbf{r}_j) \cdot (\boldsymbol{\omega} \times \mathbf{r}_j). \qquad (4\text{–}52)$$

Expanding the scalar product and using the definitions of moments and products of inertia, we have

$$T = \frac{1}{2}[I_{xx}\omega_x^2 + I_{yy}\omega_y^2 + I_{zz}\omega_z^2 - 2I_{yz}\omega_y\omega_z - 2I_{zx}\omega_z\omega_x - 2I_{xy}\omega_x\omega_y]. \qquad (4\text{–}53)$$

Thus we see that T is a quadratic form in the angular velocity components. Furthermore, since

$$|\boldsymbol{\omega} \times \mathbf{r}_j| = \omega r_j \sin \theta_j = \omega\, d_j,$$

where θ_j is the angle between $\mathbf{r}_j$ and $\boldsymbol{\omega}$, Eq. (4–52) may be written as

$$T = \frac{1}{2}\, \omega^2 \sum_{j=1}^{n} m_j d_j^2 = \frac{1}{2}\, I\omega^2.$$

Here I is the moment of inertia about the instantaneous direction of the vector $\boldsymbol{\omega}$.

By a transformation of axes to the principal axes in the body, Eq. (4–53) becomes

$$T = \frac{1}{2}[I_1\omega_1^2 + I_2\omega_2^2 + I_3\omega_3^2]. \qquad (4\text{–}54)$$

This is a convenient form for discussions of rigid-body motion because

I_1, I_2, I_3 are constants. Since $\mathbf{L} = I_1\omega_1\mathbf{i} + I_2\omega_2\mathbf{j} + I_3\omega_3\mathbf{k}$, in terms of a coordinate system coincident with the principal axes such as that in Fig. 4–10, we observe that the kinetic energy may be written

$$T = \tfrac{1}{2}\mathbf{L}\cdot\boldsymbol{\omega}. \qquad (4\text{--}55)$$

One further relation of fundamental importance may be deduced from Euler's equations (4–41). Multiply the first of these by ω_1, the second by ω_2, the third by ω_3, and add. There results

$$\frac{d}{dt}\left\{\frac{1}{2}\left(I_1\omega_1^2 + I_2\omega_2^2 + I_3\omega_3^2\right)\right\} = N_1\omega_1 + N_2\omega_2 + N_3\omega_3. \qquad (4\text{--}56)$$

The left side of Eq. (4–56) is the time rate of change of the kinetic energy. The right side is the rate of working of the applied torque. Thus we are led to the theorem: *the time rate of change of the kinetic energy equals the rate of working of the applied torque.*

4–7 Euler's angles. In the preceding discussion, the angular velocities ω_1, ω_2, ω_3 are not quantities that, when integrated with respect to the time, describe the orientation of the rigid body in space. Nor do the components of $\boldsymbol{\omega}$ in a fixed (x_0, y_0, z_0) system yield, when integrated, angles that are satisfactory as coordinates. To meet the need for such a set of coordinates, we introduce Euler's angles. These do not refer to mutually perpendicular directions, but they are adequate to express the orientation of the rigid body at any time. Figure 4–12 serves to define these angles. The principal axes of the body are shown as (1), (2), (3); Ox_0, Oy_0, Oz_0 are axes fixed in space. We shall assume first that axis (3) is a symmetry axis of the body, and hence that $I_1 = I_2 \neq I_3$. The line ON, where the equatorial plane containing the (1)- (2)-axes intersects the (x_0, y_0) plane, is called the line of *nodes*.

Euler's angles are those desig- nated by ϕ, ψ, θ in Fig. 4–12. An- gular velocity vectors associated with these angles are indicated by the arrows. The angles ϕ, ψ, θ serve as generalized coordinates for a Lagrangian approach to the equa- tions of motion.

We now relate the angular veloc- ities $\dot{\phi}$, $\dot{\psi}$, $\dot{\theta}$ to ω_1, ω_2, ω_3. By in- spection, we find

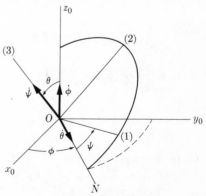

Fig. 4–12. Euler's angles.

$$\omega_1 = \dot{\theta}\cos\psi + \dot{\phi}\sin\theta\sin\psi,$$

$$\omega_2 = -\dot{\theta}\sin\psi + \dot{\phi}\sin\theta\cos\psi, \qquad (4\text{--}57)$$

$$\omega_3 = \dot{\phi}\cos\theta + \dot{\psi}.$$

Furthermore, in terms of Euler's angles, the kinetic energy, Eq. (4–54), becomes

$$T = \tfrac{1}{2}[I\{\dot{\theta}^2 + \dot{\phi}^2\sin^2\theta\} + I_3\{\dot{\psi} + \dot{\phi}\cos\theta\}^2]. \qquad (4\text{--}58)$$

From Eq. (4–58) we may obtain the Lagrangian equations of motion for the rigid body. We have

$$\frac{\partial T}{\partial \dot{\theta}} = I\dot{\theta},$$

$$\frac{\partial T}{\partial \dot{\phi}} = I\dot{\phi}\sin^2\theta + I_3(\dot{\psi} + \dot{\phi}\cos\theta)\cos\theta,$$

$$\frac{\partial T}{\partial \dot{\psi}} = I_3(\dot{\psi} + \dot{\phi}\cos\theta),$$

$$\frac{\partial T}{\partial \theta} = I\dot{\phi}^2\sin\theta\cos\theta - I_3\dot{\phi}(\dot{\psi} + \dot{\phi}\cos\theta)\sin\theta,$$

$$\frac{\partial T}{\partial \phi} = 0,$$

$$\frac{\partial T}{\partial \psi} = 0.$$

Hence, by Eq. (2–53), the equations of motion are

$$\frac{d}{dt}(I\dot{\theta}) - I\dot{\phi}^2\sin\theta\cos\theta + I_3\dot{\phi}(\dot{\psi} + \dot{\phi}\cos\theta)\sin\theta = N_\theta, \quad (4\text{--}59)$$

$$\frac{d}{dt}[I\dot{\phi}\sin^2\theta + I_3(\dot{\psi} + \dot{\phi}\cos\theta)\cos\theta] = N_\phi, \qquad (4\text{--}60)$$

$$\frac{d}{dt}[I_3(\dot{\psi} + \dot{\phi}\cos\theta)] = N_\psi, \qquad (4\text{--}61)$$

where we have assumed $I \neq I_3$. In Eqs. (4–59), (4–60), and (4–61) the quantities N_θ, N_ϕ, and N_ψ are the generalized torques corresponding to the coordinates θ, ϕ, ψ. Note that the quantities to be differentiated with respect to the time in the Lagrangian equations are the angular momentum components associated with the generalized coordinates, namely,

$$L_\theta = I\dot\theta,$$

$$L_\phi = I\dot\phi \sin^2 \theta + I_3(\dot\psi + \dot\phi \cos \theta) \cos \theta, \qquad (4\text{–}62)$$

$$L_\psi = I_3(\dot\psi + \dot\phi \cos \theta),$$

where $I = I_1 = I_2$ is the moment of inertia about an axis in the (1)-(2)-plane. These may be derived by projecting the components $L_1 = I_1\omega_1$, $L_2 = I_2\omega_2$, and $L_3 = I_3\omega_3$ onto the line of nodes, the z_0-axis and the (3)-axis respectively, and using Eqs. (4–57).

The torque components appearing on the right in Eqs. (4–59), (4–60), and (4–61) are likewise obtainable from the components N_1, N_2, N_3 by projection. We have

$$N_\theta = N_1 \cos \psi - N_2 \sin \psi,$$

$$N_\phi = (N_1 \sin \psi + N_2 \cos \psi) \sin \theta + N_3 \cos \theta, \qquad (4\text{–}63)$$

$$N_\psi = N_3.$$

Consider the Lagrangian equation for ψ, namely,

$$\frac{d}{dt}\left(\frac{\partial T}{\partial \dot\psi}\right) - \left(\frac{\partial T}{\partial \psi}\right) = N_\psi.$$

Since T is a function of ω_1, ω_2, and ω_3 [by Eq. (4–54)], and ω_1, ω_2, ω_3 are in turn functions of θ, ϕ, ψ [by Eqs. (4–57)], we may write

$$\frac{\partial T}{\partial \dot\psi} = \frac{\partial T}{\partial \omega_3} = I_3\omega_3,$$

$$\frac{\partial T}{\partial \psi} = \frac{\partial T}{\partial \omega_1}\frac{\partial \omega_1}{\partial \psi} + \frac{\partial T}{\partial \omega_2}\frac{\partial \omega_2}{\partial \psi} + \frac{\partial T}{\partial \omega_3}\frac{\partial \omega_3}{\partial \psi}.$$

But

$$\frac{\partial \omega_1}{\partial \psi} = -\dot\theta \sin \psi + \dot\phi \sin \theta \cos \psi = \omega_2,$$

$$\frac{\partial \omega_2}{\partial \psi} = -\dot\theta \cos \psi - \dot\phi \sin \theta \sin \psi = -\omega_1,$$

$$\frac{\partial \omega_3}{\partial \psi} = 0.$$

Hence

$$\frac{\partial T}{\partial \psi} = I_1\omega_1\omega_2 - I_2\omega_2\omega_1 = (I_1 - I_2)\omega_1\omega_2.$$

Therefore the Lagrangian equation for ψ becomes

$$I_3\dot{\omega}_3 + (I_2 - I_1)\omega_1\omega_2 = N_\psi = N_3.$$

This is precisely the third of the Euler equations exhibited in Eqs. (4–41). It is the only one that can be deduced directly by the Lagrangian method. To show further the equivalence between Euler's equations and the Lagrangian equations in θ, ϕ, ψ, we proceed in the following way. Since $I_1 = I_2 = I \neq I_3$, we have from Eqs. (4–41),

$$I\dot{\omega}_1 + (I_3 - I)\omega_2\omega_3 = N_1,$$

$$I\dot{\omega}_2 + (I - I_3)\omega_3\omega_1 = N_2.$$

We multiply the first of these by $\cos\psi$, the second by $\sin\psi$, and subtract to obtain, after some simplification and by using the first of Eqs. (4–63),

$$I[\dot{\omega}_1 \cos\psi - \dot{\omega}_2 \sin\psi - \omega_3(\omega_2 \cos\psi + \omega_1 \sin\psi)]$$

$$+ I_3\omega_3(\omega_2 \cos\psi + \omega_1 \sin\psi) = N_\theta. \tag{4–64}$$

But from Eqs. (4–57),

$$\omega_2 \cos\psi + \omega_1 \sin\psi = \dot{\phi} \sin\theta,$$

$$\dot{\omega}_1 \cos\psi - \dot{\omega}_2 \sin\psi = \ddot{\theta} + \dot{\phi}\dot{\psi}\sin\theta,$$

$$\omega_3 = \dot{\psi} + \dot{\phi} \cos\theta.$$

Hence Eq. (4–64) becomes

$$I\ddot{\theta} - I\dot{\phi}^2 \sin\theta \cos\theta + I_3\dot{\phi}(\dot{\psi} + \dot{\phi} \cos\theta) \sin\theta = N_\theta,$$

which is the Lagrangian equation (4–59). In a similar way, we can show that Eq. (4–60) is also derivable from Euler's equations. Hence the Lagrangian equations in θ, ϕ, ψ are simply the Euler equations transformed into a more useful coordinate system.

In the general case where $I_1 \neq I_2 \neq I_3$, the expression for the kinetic energy becomes more complex. Again, using Eqs. (4–57) together with Eq. (4–54), we find

$$T = \tfrac{1}{2}\{(I_1 - I_2)(\dot{\theta} \cos\psi + \dot{\phi} \sin\theta \sin\psi)^2 + I_2(\dot{\theta}^2 + \dot{\phi}^2 \sin^2\theta)$$

$$+ I_3(\dot{\phi} \cos\theta + \dot{\psi})^2\}. \tag{4–65}$$

From Eq. (4–65) we derive the general Lagrangian equations for θ, ϕ, ψ,

$$\frac{d}{dt}\{(I_1 - I_2)(\dot\theta \cos\psi + \dot\phi \sin\theta \sin\psi)\cos\psi + I_2\dot\theta\}$$
$$- (I_1 - I_2)(\dot\theta \cos\psi + \dot\phi \sin\theta \sin\psi)\dot\phi \cos\theta \sin\psi$$
$$- I_2\dot\phi^2 \sin\theta \cos\theta + I_3(\dot\phi \cos\theta + \dot\psi)\dot\phi \sin\theta = N_\theta, \quad (4\text{–}66)$$

$$\frac{d}{dt}\{(I_1 - I_2)(\dot\theta \cos\psi + \dot\phi \sin\theta \sin\psi)\sin\theta \sin\psi + I_2\dot\phi \sin^2\theta$$
$$+ I_3(\dot\phi \cos\theta + \dot\psi)\cos\theta\} = N_\phi, \quad (4\text{–}67)$$

$$\frac{d}{dt}\{I_3(\dot\phi \cos\theta + \dot\psi)\}$$
$$+ (I_1 - I_2)(\dot\theta \cos\psi + \dot\phi \sin\theta \sin\psi)(\dot\theta \sin\psi - \dot\phi \sin\theta \cos\psi) = N_\psi.$$
$$(4\text{–}68)$$

It is apparent that when $I_1 = I_2$ these equations reduce, respectively, to Eqs. (4–59), (4–60), and (4–61).

As an illustration, let us consider again the rotating bar shown in Fig. 4–11(a). We take fixed axes Ox_0, Oy_0, Oz_0 as shown in Fig. 4–13. Then the Eulerian angle θ is 90° and does not change with the time. Furthermore $\dot\psi = s$, and $\dot\phi = \Omega$, and both are constants. With these restrictions on θ, $\dot\theta$, $\dot\psi$, and $\dot\phi$, Eqs. (4–66), (4–67), and (4–68) become, respectively,

$$N_\theta = I_3 s\Omega + (I_1 - I_2)\Omega s \cos 2\psi,$$
$$N_\phi = (I_1 - I_2)\Omega s \sin 2\psi,$$
$$N_\psi = -\tfrac{1}{2}(I_1 - I_2)\Omega^2 \sin 2\psi.$$

These are identical with Eqs. (4–50), (4–51), and (4–49), which we deduced directly from Euler's equations.

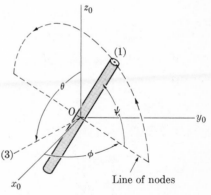

FIG. 4–13. Rotating bar.

4–8 Motion of a torque-free system. Suppose that a symmetric rigid body is rotating about a fixed point but that the resultant torque acting upon it is zero. The external torques acting upon the earth, for example, are so weak that its *rotational* motion can be considered to a first approximation as relatively torque-free.

An immediate consequence of the absence of external torques is that the angular momentum vector is constant in space and time. This follows from Newton's Second Law for rotational motion, Eq. (1–27). The line defined by this vector is called *the invariable line*. It is shown by the direction of **L** in Fig. 4–14. A further consequence of the freedom from torque is that the kinetic energy is constant, as evident from Eq. (4–56).

We observe also from Eq. (4–55) that, since T is constant, $\mathbf{L} \cdot \boldsymbol{\omega}$ remains so. This implies that during the motion $\boldsymbol{\omega}$ must change in such a way that its projection on **L** is always the same. Hence the tip of $\boldsymbol{\omega}$ describes a plane that is called *the invariable plane*. The origin O is the fixed point in the rigid body, and all forces acting on the system have no torque about O.

An analytical treatment of Euler's equations for torque-free motion in the general case where $I_1 \neq I_2 \neq I_3$ is quite complicated and involves finding ω_1, ω_2, ω_3, or θ, ϕ, ψ, as functions of the time by the use of elliptic integrals.* We shall discuss here, however, only the case where axial symmetry allows a simplification and direct integration of the Euler equations (4–41).

We assume that the axis of symmetry is the (3)-axis, so that $I_1 = I_2 \neq I_3$. As before, we shall designate by $I(= I_1 \text{ or } I_2)$ the moment of inertia about either the (1)- or (2)-axis.

Euler's equations then become

$$I\dot{\omega}_1 + \omega_2\omega_3(I_3 - I) = 0,$$
$$I\dot{\omega}_2 + \omega_3\omega_1(I - I_3) = 0, \qquad (4\text{–}69)$$
$$I_3\dot{\omega}_3 = 0.$$

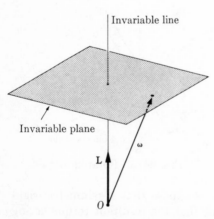

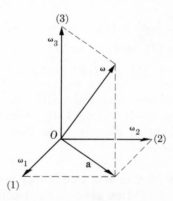

FIG. 4–14. Invariable line and plane.   FIG. 4–15. Angular velocity in free rotation.

---

* For a sketch of this solution, see J. L. Synge and B. A. Griffith, *Principles of Mechanics*. New York: McGraw-Hill Book Company, Inc., 1942, pp. 408 ff. See also E. T. Whittaker, *Analytical Dynamics*. Cambridge, England: Cambridge University Press, 1937, pp. 144 ff.

We note immediately that ω_3 is constant in time. Furthermore, we may write the first two of Eqs. (4–69) in the form

$$\dot{\omega}_1 + \omega_2 \left\{ \left(\frac{I_3}{I} - 1 \right) \omega_3 \right\} = 0 \quad \text{and} \quad \dot{\omega}_2 - \omega_1 \left\{ \left(\frac{I_3}{I} - 1 \right) \omega_3 \right\} = 0.$$
$$(4\text{--}70)$$

Let $k = (I_3/I - 1)\omega_3$, which is constant. We then differentiate the first of Eqs. (4–70) and substitute for $\dot{\omega}_2$ its value from the second equation to obtain

$$\ddot{\omega}_1 + k\dot{\omega}_2 = \ddot{\omega}_1 + k^2\omega_1 = 0. \qquad (4\text{--}71)$$

This has the solution $\omega_1 = a \sin (kt + b)$; and, since $\omega_2 = -(1/k)\dot{\omega}_1$, we have $\omega_2 = -a \cos(kt + b)$. But these expressions for ω_1 and ω_2 are the parametric equations for a circle of radius a in the plane of the (1)- (2)-axes. The projection of the $\boldsymbol{\omega}$ vector on this equatorial plane rotates about the (3)-axis with an angular speed k radians per unit time. Since $\omega_1^2 + \omega_2^2 = a^2$, it is evident that $|\boldsymbol{\omega}| = \sqrt{\omega_1^2 + \omega_2^2 + \omega_3^2}$ is constant during the motion.

Figure 4–15 illustrates the relative position of the $\boldsymbol{\omega}$ vector in the (1)- (2)- (3)-system. It should be noted that $\boldsymbol{\omega}$ does not in general coincide with the axis of mass symmetry. If it does, the problem becomes essentially trivial, the motion being a steady spin about the axis of symmetry.

As an illustration of rigid-body motion of the type discussed above, consider the rotation of the earth. Its axis of figure departs slightly from its axis of rotation. We would expect to find, as the period of rotation of $\boldsymbol{\omega}$ about ω_3,

$$P = \frac{2\pi}{k} = \frac{2\pi}{\omega_3} \left[\frac{I}{I_3 - I} \right].$$

To a first approximation, $I/(I_3 - I)$ is equal to 300, the inverse of the earth's oblateness. The angular velocity $\omega_3 = 2\pi$ radians per day. Hence $P \sim 300$ days. This periodic motion of the $\boldsymbol{\omega}$ vector about the earth's axis of symmetry is known observationally as the *variation of latitude*. The fact that the earth is not a perfectly rigid body accounts for the difference between the observed period of about 433 days and the 300-day period computed above.

The angular momentum vector in this case of axial symmetry becomes

$$\mathbf{L} = I(\omega_1\mathbf{i} + \omega_2\mathbf{j}) + I_3\omega_3\mathbf{k}, \qquad (4\text{--}72)$$

and hence is in the plane of ω_3 and $\boldsymbol{\omega}$. Its position relative to $\boldsymbol{\omega}$ depends upon the values of I_3 and I.

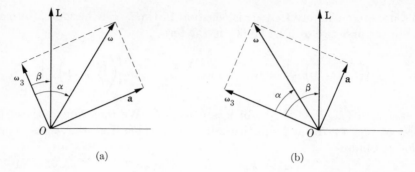

FIG. 4–16. Angular velocity and momentum for (a) oblate spheroid, (b) prolate spheroid.

In Fig. 4–16(a), let the angle between ω_3 and ω be α; that between ω_3 and $\mathbf{L}$ is β. Let $\mathbf{a}$ be the projection of ω on the (1)- (2)-plane, as shown in Fig. 4–15. Then

$$\tan \beta = \frac{\mathbf{L} \cdot (\mathbf{a}/a)}{L_3} = \frac{Ia}{I_3 \omega_3} = \frac{I}{I_3} \tan \alpha, \qquad (4\text{–}73)$$

where $a = \sqrt{\omega_1^2 + \omega_2^2}$. If $I < I_3$, we see that $\beta < \alpha$, and $\mathbf{L}$ lies between ω_3 and ω, as in Fig. 4–16(a). This would be the case for an oblate spheroid such as the earth. If $I > I_3$, then $\beta > \alpha$, and L lies farther from ω_3 than does ω, as in Fig. 4–16(b). A prolate spheroid illustrates this case.

Motion of the type discussed here may be represented geometrically by the rolling of one cone on another, as illustrated in Fig. 4–17. The cone of semivertical angle $\alpha - \beta$ is considered fixed in space, its axis being along $\mathbf{L}$. This is called the *space cone*. The second cone, whose axis is along ω_3, rolls on the space cone in such a way that their common element is ω. The cone centered on ω_3 is the *body cone* and is considered fixed in the body. To an observer fixed in space, ω would appear to trace out the space cone; to an observer on the body, ω would appear to trace out the body cone. In either event, ω_3, $\mathbf{L}$, and ω remain coplanar as one cone rolls on the other. The situation pictured in Fig. 4–17 is that in which $I_3 > I$. This method of describing the motion of a rigid body is due to Poinsot (1834). A more detailed description of it may be found in any of the references listed at the end of this book.

To complete the discussion of motion under no torque, we shall find the Eulerian angles ϕ, ψ, θ from the values of ω_1, ω_2, and ω_3. For convenience we choose the invariable line to be the z-axis of the fixed coordinate system, as shown in Fig. 4–18. Then, by direct projection,

$$\begin{aligned}
L_1 &= I\omega_1 = L \sin \theta \sin \psi, \\
L_2 &= I\omega_2 = L \sin \theta \cos \psi, \\
L_3 &= I_3\omega_3 = L \cos \theta,
\end{aligned} \qquad (4\text{–}74)$$

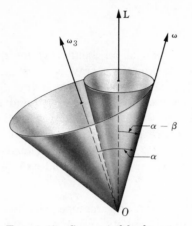

Fig. 4–17. Space and body cones.

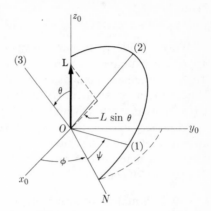

Fig. 4–18. Eulerian angles for motion under no torque.

where

$$L^2 = I^2(\omega_1^2 + \omega_2^2) + I_3\omega_3^2 = I^2a^2 + I_3^2\omega_3^2.$$

The quantity L is the constant magnitude of the angular momentum vector. From the last of these equations, we find

$$\cos \theta = \frac{I_3\omega_3}{L} = \text{constant.} \tag{4–75}$$

From the first two and the solution of Eq. (4–71),

$$\tan \psi = +\frac{\omega_1}{\omega_2} = -\tan (kt + b),$$

so that

$$\psi = -(kt + b) \quad \text{or} \quad 180° - (kt + b). \tag{4–76}$$

Which of these angles we take depends on the fact that, by the first of Eqs. (4–74), $\sin \psi$ must have the same sign as ω_1, hence the same sign as a. If we choose a to be positive, then $\psi = 180° - (kt + b)$; if a is negative, $\psi = -(kt + b)$.

Finally, from the first two of Eqs. (4–57), we have

$$\dot{\phi} \sin \theta = \omega_1 \sin \psi + \omega_2 \cos \psi.$$

Therefore

$$\dot{\phi} = \frac{a \sin (kt + b) \sin \psi - a \cos (kt + b) \cos \psi}{\sin \theta}$$

$$= \frac{a}{\sqrt{1 - (I_3\omega_3/L)^2}}$$

$$= \dot{\phi}_0 \quad \text{(a constant).} \tag{4–77}$$

And, hence,

$$\phi = \dot{\phi}_0 t + \text{constant}.$$

We conclude from our study of the motion of an axially symmetric rigid body under no torque that: (a) the kinetic energy is constant; (b) the angular momentum is constant; (c) the axis of symmetry (3) maintains a constant angle θ with respect to $\mathbf{L}$ but precesses around $\mathbf{L}$ at a constant rate given by Eq. (4–77); (d) the axis (1) moves in the equatorial plane of the body in the negative ψ direction at a uniform rate, completing one cycle in time $2\pi\{[(I_3 - I)/I]\omega_3\}^{-1/2}$; (e) the magnitude of $\boldsymbol{\omega}$ remains constant but its direction changes, $\boldsymbol{\omega}$, $\mathbf{L}$, and axis (3) being always coplanar.

4–9 The motion of a top under gravity. A top or gyroscope consists of an axially symmetrical rigid body spinning about its axis of symmetry. Some point on the axis of spin is fixed. We assume this to be different from the center of mass. The torque acting on the top is due to the force of gravity acting through the center of mass of the body. At any given instant, let the orientation of the top be given by Euler's angles.

In Fig. 4–19, ON is the line of nodes, and l is the distance from the fixed point O to the center of gravity of the top. The torque on the top is $mgl \sin \theta$, and this tends to cause a rotation about the line of nodes. The spin velocity of the top about its axis is $\dot{\psi}$. Axes (1) and (2), therefore, are attached to the top and rotate at this speed about (3).

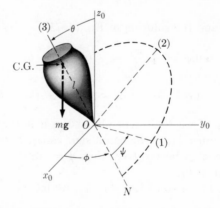

Fig. 4–19. Top spinning under gravity.

If I is the moment of inertia about any axis in the (1)- (2)-plane and I_3 is the moment of inertia about axis (3), the equations of motion are Eqs. (4–59), (4–60), and (4–61) with $N_\theta = mgl \sin \theta$, $N_\phi = 0$, $N_\psi = 0$. We observe at once that, since $d/dt[I_3(\dot{\psi} + \dot{\phi} \cos \theta)] = 0$,

$$\dot{\psi} + \dot{\phi} \cos \theta = \omega_3 = \text{constant}. \tag{4–78}$$

Then, by Eq. (4–60),

$$\frac{d}{dt} [I\dot\phi \sin^2 \theta + I_3\omega_3 \cos \theta] = \frac{d}{dt} (L_\phi) = 0, \qquad (4\text{–}79)$$

where L_ϕ is the component of angular momentum along the z-axis. Hence, L_ϕ is constant in time. Therefore, we may write

$$\dot\phi = \frac{L_\phi - I_3\omega_3 \cos \theta}{I \sin^2 \theta}, \qquad (4\text{–}80)$$

which shows that $\dot\phi$ is a function only of θ.

Substituting from Eqs. (4–78) and (4–80) into Eq. (4–59), we obtain the differential equation for θ,

$$I\ddot\theta - \left\{\frac{L_\phi - I_3\omega_3 \cos \theta}{I \sin^3 \theta}\right\} \{L_\phi \cos \theta - I_3\omega_3\} - mgl \sin \theta = 0. \qquad (4\text{–}81)$$

In principle we may solve Eq. (4–81) for θ as a function of the time. Then from the value of θ so found, Eqs. (4–80) and (4–78) yield the angles ϕ and ψ respectively as functions of time. In certain circumstances, when θ is small and remains so, Eq. (4–81) can be simplified by an approximate linearization. But, in general, the detailed integration of Eq. (4–81) involves elliptic integrals.* A qualitative knowledge of the motion may be obtained by other means.

We return to a consideration of the energy of the top. The potential energy at any instant is $mgl \cos \theta$, so that, from Eqs. (4–58) and (4–80), we have

$$\frac{1}{2} \left[I\left\{\dot\theta^2 + \left(\frac{L_\phi - I_3\omega_3 \cos \theta}{I \sin^2 \theta}\right)^2 \sin^2 \theta\right\} + I_3\omega_3^2 \right] + mgl \cos \theta = E, \qquad (4\text{–}82)$$

and hence,

$$\dot\theta = \sqrt{\frac{2}{I}\left\{E - mgl \cos \theta - \frac{1}{2} I_3\omega_3^2 - \frac{1}{2} \frac{(L_\phi - I_3\omega_3 \cos \theta)^2}{I \sin^2 \theta}\right\}}. \qquad (4\text{–}83)$$

This is a first integral of Eq. (4–81).

Let

$$V'(\theta) = mgl \cos \theta + \frac{1}{2} I_3\omega_3^2 + \frac{1}{2} \frac{(L_\phi - I_3\omega_3 \cos \theta)^2}{I \sin^2 \theta}$$

---

* For a detailed integration of these equations, see W. D. MacMillan, *Theoretical Mechanics*, Vol. 3 ("Dynamics of Rigid Bodies"). New York: McGraw-Hill Book Company, Inc., 1936, pp. 216 ff.

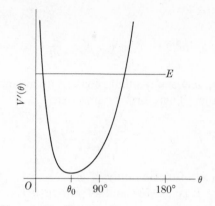

FIG. 4–20. Energy diagram for the top.

be a fictitious potential, whose terms have the following physical significance: Term 1 is the gravitational potential energy, decreasing as θ increases. Its maximum is at $\theta = 0$. Term 2 is the kinetic energy of spin, plus a contribution from the precessional energy, and is constant. Term 3 is analogous to the energy involved in the centrifugal force contribution to particle dynamics. This term is infinite at $\theta = 0$ and $\theta = \pi$.

If we then plot $V'(\theta)$ against θ, as in Fig. 4–20, we have an energy diagram of the kind discussed in Chapter 1. For a given total and constant energy E, depending upon the initial conditions, motion will be limited to the range in θ for which $\dot{\theta}$ is real, that is, where $E - V'(\theta) \geq 0$. The energy diagram exhibits a single minimum at $\theta = \theta_0$, which may be found by setting $(dV'/d\theta) = 0$. If we do this, we find θ_0 to be given by

$$\dot{\phi}[I_3\dot{\psi} + (I_3 - I)\dot{\phi} \cos \theta_0] = mgl. \qquad (4\text{–}84)$$

The motion of the top, then, in the θ direction is an oscillation about θ_0. This is called *nutation*, and the period can be computed for a given energy E from the relation

$$P = 2\int_{\theta_1}^{\theta_2} \frac{d\theta}{\sqrt{(2/I)[E - V'(\theta)]}}, \qquad (4\text{–}85)$$

where θ_1 and θ_2 are the roots of the equation $E - V'(\theta) = 0$.

If the total energy is just at the minimum of $V'(\theta)$, the angle θ remains fixed at θ_0, and a steady precession results. This is evident because in these circumstances, by Eq. (4–80),

$$\dot{\phi} = \frac{L_\phi - I_3\omega_3 \cos \theta_0}{I \sin^2 \theta_0} = \text{constant}. \qquad (4\text{–}86)$$

In the general case where θ oscillates in time, $\dot{\phi}$ will also oscillate in time.

When the spin velocity, $\dot{\psi}$, of the top is very large compared with $\dot{\phi}$, Eq. (4–84) indicates that $\dot{\phi} I_3 \dot{\psi} \cong mgl$, so that

$$\dot{\phi} \cong \frac{mgl}{I_3 \dot{\psi}}. \tag{4–87}$$

This is the usual precessional velocity quoted in elementary discussions of the top. It is implied that the term $I_3 \dot{\psi}$ is so nearly the total angular momentum of the system that the **L** vector coincides approximately with the axis of symmetry of the top.

Equation (4–84) shows that, in general, there will be two values of steady precession since this equation is quadratic in $\dot{\phi}$. Since $\dot{\phi}$ must be real, in any actual motion the discriminant of this quadratic equation must be positive. That is, for a given θ_0, any initial value assigned to $\dot{\psi}$ must satisfy the inequality,

$$I_3^2 \dot{\psi}^2 + 4mgl(I_3 - I)\cos\theta_0 \geq 0. \tag{4–88}$$

Furthermore, while $\dot{\phi}$ may be zero initially, it cannot remain so for a finite spin velocity $\dot{\psi}$; hence to obtain a uniform precession, the top must always receive an initial push to start it precessing. The two values of $\dot{\phi}$ obtained in the general case are known as the fast and the slow precession.

We consider now the case of the rapidly spinning top started in such a way that at $t = 0$, $\theta = \theta_1$, $\dot{\phi} = 0$, and $\dot{\theta} = 0$. We assume that the rotational energy about axis (3) is much greater than any possible maximum change in the potential energy. That is,

$$\tfrac{1}{2} I_3 \omega_3^2 \gg 2mgl. \tag{4–89}$$

With the initial conditions as given, there results

$$L_\phi = I_3 \omega_3 \cos\theta_1, \tag{4–90}$$

and hence at any time,

$$\dot{\phi} = \frac{I_3 \omega_3(\cos\theta_1 - \cos\theta)}{I \sin^2\theta}. \tag{4–91}$$

Furthermore, since $\dot{\theta}$ must vanish at $\theta = \theta_1$, $E = mgl\cos\theta_1 + \tfrac{1}{2}I_3\omega_3^2$, by Eq. (4–83). Thus, at any later time t,

$$\dot{\theta} = \sqrt{(2/I)\{mgl(\cos\theta_1 - \cos\theta) - \tfrac{1}{2}(I_3^2\omega_3^2/I\sin^2\theta)(\cos\theta_1 - \cos\theta)^2\}},$$

or

$$\dot{\theta} = \frac{1}{\sin\theta}\sqrt{(2/I)(\cos\theta_1 - \cos\theta)\{mgl(\sin^2\theta) - (I_3^2\omega_3^2/2I)(\cos\theta_1 - \cos\theta)\}}. \tag{4–92}$$

Now we assume that $\sin^2 \theta$, in the brace, may be approximated by its value initially, that is, $\sin^2 \theta_1$, since it is multiplied by a factor which is much less than $(1/2)I_3\omega_3^2$. Then, writing

$$\alpha = \frac{2mglI}{I_3^2\omega_3^2} \sin^2 \theta_1 \quad \text{and} \quad (\cos \theta_1 - \cos \theta) = x,$$

we have, from Eq. (4-92),

$$\frac{dx}{dt} = \frac{I_3\omega_3}{I} \sqrt{x(\alpha - x)}, \tag{4-93}$$

which may be integrated directly to yield

$$x = \frac{\alpha}{2}\left[1 - \cos\left(\frac{I_3\omega_3}{I}\right)t\right]. \tag{4-94}$$

This equation tells us two things. First, the angular frequency of nutation is $(I_3\omega_3)/I$ and hence is greater, the greater the initial spin. Secondly, the range in the value of x is given by $\alpha = 2mgl(I \sin^2 \theta_1)/(I_3^2\omega_3^2)$, which decreases rapidly with increasing spin.

Returning to Eq. (4-91), we see that

$$\dot{\phi} = \frac{I_3\omega_3}{I} \frac{x}{\sin^2 \theta_1} = \frac{mgl}{I_3\omega_3}\left(1 - \cos \frac{I_3\omega_3}{I}t\right). \tag{4-95}$$

Thus the precession is not uniform but has a periodic variation of the same frequency as the nutation. If we compute the time average of $\dot{\phi}$ over one cycle, we find

$$\dot{\phi}_{\text{av}} = \frac{mgl}{I_3\omega_3}, \tag{4-96}$$

so that the precession becomes less pronounced as the spin is increased.

The picture we have obtained of the motion of the top started from rest with its axis at an angle θ_1 from the vertical may be summarized as follows: (a) immediately upon being released the center of mass falls under gravity; (b) the change in θ so produced gives the axis a precessional velocity $\dot{\phi}$ which is directly proportional to the vertical drop x in the center of mass; (c) these two effects combine to produce a nutational velocity $\dot{\theta}$; (d) the greater the initial spin, the higher the nutational frequency and the smaller the range in the nutation angle.

A top, started in the manner indicated with a very high spin velocity, may appear to precess steadily with no evident nutation. This is illusory. Actually, the friction in the pivot damps out the very high frequency wobble so that it is not apparent. The top must always fall as it is released, and then it begins to precess.

4–10 Motion of a spinning projectile. We shall consider in this section the motion of an axially symmetric projectile, such as an artillery shell, in the earth's atmosphere. The forces acting on it are the aerodynamic force due to the air resistance together with the torques created by this resistance. We shall not discuss this force and torque system in detail.* Basically, the effects of the atmosphere on the projectile result in a *drag*, which tends to retard its motion in the trajectory, a *moment*, which creates an overturning tendency, and a *lift* on the shell. For our purposes we shall assume that the aerodynamic force on the shell acts at a point on the axis of the shell somewhat ahead of the center of mass. This point is called the *center of pressure*. The force, indicated in Fig. 4–21 by the vector **F**, not only retards the shell but creates a torque about the center of mass which tends to deflect the shell axis from the trajectory. Hence, by the analysis given in Section 1–12, we may consider the motion of the center of mass in the fixed (x_0, y_0, z_0) system independently of the rotation of the shell about its center of mass.

Let O be the center of mass and have coordinates x_0, y_0, z_0 in the fixed system. The axial moment of inertia of the shell is I_3, the transverse moment of inertia is I, both calculated with respect to the mass center. The mass of the shell is m. We take Eulerian angles ϕ, ψ, θ as shown in Fig. 4–22 to define the orientation of the shell with respect to a set of cartesian axes (x,y,z) parallel to (x_0,y_0,z_0) but through O. Principal axis (3) coincides with the axis of symmetry of the shell, and we assume that the latter is spinning about it with angular speed $\dot{\psi}$. Then by Eqs. (1–87) and (4–58) we have for the kinetic energy

$$T = \tfrac{1}{2}m[\dot{x}_0^2 + \dot{y}_0^2 + \dot{z}_0^2] + \tfrac{1}{2}[I(\dot{\theta}^2 + \dot{\phi}^2 \sin^2 \theta) + I_3(\dot{\psi} + \dot{\phi} \cos \theta)^2], \quad (4\text{–}97)$$

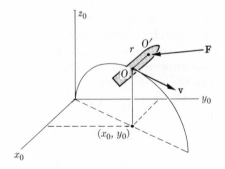

FIG. 4–21. Projectile moving in space.   FIG. 4–22. Eulerian angles for rotating projectile.

* See, for example, K. L. Nielsen and J. L. Synge, *Quarterly of Applied Mathematics*, Vol. 4, pp. 201 ff. (1946), for a discussion of this problem.

and for the potential energy, $V = mgz_0$. Hence the equations of motion are

$$m\ddot{x}_0 = X,$$

$$m\ddot{y}_0 = Y, \qquad\qquad (4\text{-}98)$$

$$m\ddot{z}_0 = Z - mg,$$

$$\frac{d}{dt}[I\dot{\theta}] - I\dot{\phi}^2 \sin\theta\cos\theta + I_3\dot{\phi}(\dot{\psi} + \dot{\phi}\cos\theta)\sin\theta = N_\theta,$$

$$\frac{d}{dt}[I\dot{\phi}\sin^2\theta + I_3(\dot{\psi} + \dot{\phi}\cos\theta)\cos\theta] = N_\phi, \qquad\qquad (4\text{-}99)$$

$$\frac{d}{dt}[I_3(\dot{\psi} + \dot{\phi}\cos\theta)] = N_\psi,$$

where X, Y, Z are the nonconservative aerodynamic forces considered as acting at O, and N_θ, N_ϕ, N_ψ are the torque components resulting from the fact that the aerodynamic force acts through the point O', a distance r from O (see Fig. 4-21).

We shall assume for our discussion here that the force $\mathbf{F}$ is coplanar with the velocity vector $\mathbf{v}$ and the shell axis (3). Then the rotational motion about O will be similar to that of the top since the torque due to $\mathbf{F}$ will be perpendicular to the plane of $\mathbf{v}$ and (3), that is, in the θ direction. Furthermore, we shall assume that the force is proportional to the square of the speed of the projectile in its path and has the direction opposite to $\mathbf{v}$. We have then

$$\mathbf{F} = -Kv^2\mathbf{u}_v, \qquad\qquad (4\text{-}100)$$

where K is a function of the air density and the diameter of the shell and contains an aerodynamic coefficient that has been determined experimetally. The vector $\mathbf{u}_v$ is the unit vector in the direction of the velocity of O, and hence is tangent to the trajectory at all points.

Under the above assumptions, the force components are

$$X = -Kv\dot{x}_0,$$

$$Y = -Kv\dot{y}_0, \qquad\qquad (4\text{-}101)$$

$$Z = -Kv\dot{z}_0.$$

Let θ_0 be the angle between the z-axis (Fig. 4-23) and the velocity vector at any time; hence it is the angle from the z-axis to the tangent to the path. Then the torque components in the θ, ϕ, ψ directions will be

$$N_\theta = -Kv^2 r \sin (\theta_0 - \theta),$$

$$N_\phi = 0, \qquad (4\text{-}102)$$

$$N_\psi = 0.$$

The motion of the mass center O
will then be given by

$$m\ddot{x}_0 = -Kv\dot{x}_0,$$

$$m\ddot{y}_0 = -Kv\dot{y}_0, \qquad (4\text{-}103)$$

$$m\ddot{z}_0 = -Kv\dot{z}_0 - mg.$$

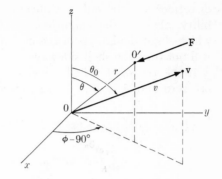

Fig. 4–23. Force-velocity relationships for the projectile.

Since K is a function of the air
density, which in turn depends upon
the height of O above the earth's surface, these equations are very complex
and must be solved by numerical integration when the appropriate aerodynamic coefficients and functional relationships are known.   However,
we may draw certain qualitative conclusions about the motion by writing
Eqs. (4–103) in terms of the speed v and the angles θ_0 and ϕ. From Fig.
4–23 we see that

$$\dot{x}_0 = v \sin \theta_0 \sin \phi,$$

$$\dot{y}_0 = -v \sin \theta_0 \cos \phi, \qquad (4\text{-}104)$$

$$\dot{z}_0 = v \cos \theta_0.$$

If these are differentiated with respect to the time and the results sub-
stituted in Eqs. (4–103), we may eliminate in turn $\dot{\phi}$, $\dot{\theta}_0$, or $\dot{v}$ and obtain

$$\dot{v} = -\frac{Kv^2}{m} - g \cos \theta_0,$$

$$\dot{\theta}_0 = \frac{g \sin \theta_0}{v}, \qquad (4\text{-}105)$$

$$\dot{\phi} = 0.$$

The first of Eqs. (4–105) yields the speed in the trajectory; the second
states that θ_0 increases with the time so that the trajectory is concave
downward; the third implies that ϕ is constant in time and, hence, that
the trajectory is a plane curve.

Let us return now to Eqs. (4–99) and apply the values for the torque,
Eqs. (4–102). We shall assume that the axis of the shell does not deviate
much from the tangent to the path. In other words, the angle $(\theta_0 - \theta)$
is small, and first order deviations in angle and in velocity in the θ or ϕ

directions are the only significant ones. We seek the condition for stability, that is, the conditions relating to axial spin and torque under
which slight deviations of the instantaneous axis of spin from the vector **v**
will not turn the shell sideways.

If the axis of the shell coincides with the velocity vector **v**, all torques
are zero and $\theta = \theta_0$. In this circumstance we have from Eqs. (4–99),

$$\frac{d}{dt}(I\dot{\theta}_0) - I\dot{\phi}_0^2 \sin\theta_0 \cos\theta_0 + I_3\dot{\phi}_0(\dot{\psi} + \dot{\phi}_0 \cos\theta_0)\sin\theta_0 = 0, \quad (4\text{–}106)$$

$$\frac{d \cos\theta_0}{dt}[I\dot{\phi}_0 \sin^2\theta_0 + I_3(\dot{\psi} + \dot{\phi}_0 \cos\theta_0)] = 0, \quad (4\text{–}107)$$

$$\frac{d}{dt}[I_3(\dot{\psi} + \dot{\phi}_0 \cos\theta_0)] = 0. \quad (4\text{–}108)$$

Hence, from the last of these,

$$I_3(\dot{\psi} + \dot{\phi}_0 \cos\theta_0) = L_\psi = a \qquad \text{(constant)},$$

where L_ψ is the component of the angular momentum about axis (3).
Then from Eq. (4–107),

$$I\dot{\phi}_0 \sin^2\theta_0 + a\cos\theta_0 = L_\phi = b \qquad \text{(constant)},$$

where L_ϕ is the angular momentum about the z-axis. Hence

$$\dot{\phi}_0 = \frac{b - a\cos\theta_0}{I \sin^2\theta_0}. \quad (4\text{–}109)$$

Both L_ϕ and L_ψ are conserved under the conditions we have assumed.

To the approximation we are using here, by the last of Eqs. (4–105),
$\dot{\phi}_0 = 0$. Hence $b = a\cos\theta_0$. And from Eq. (4–106) we find that $\dot{\theta}_0 =$
constant or $\ddot{\theta}_0 = 0$.

Now let $\theta - \theta_0 = \alpha$ be a small angular deviation of the axis of spin
from the tangent to the path. Let $\dot{\phi} = \dot{\phi}_0 + \dot{\beta}$, where $\dot{\beta}$ is the perturbation in the angular velocity about the vertical. Then, since $\cos\theta =$
$\cos\theta_0 - \alpha\sin\theta_0$ and $\sin\theta = \alpha\cos\theta_0 + \sin\theta_0$ to a first approximation
in β, we have by use of the second of Eqs. (4–99) together with Eq. (4–109),

$$\dot{\beta} = \frac{a\alpha}{I \sin\theta_0} = \frac{I_3\dot{\psi}\alpha}{I \sin\theta_0}. \quad (4\text{–}110)$$

Unless the spin is unduly large, $\dot{\beta}$ will be small when α is small. Furthermore, if $\alpha > 0$ so that the nose of the shell dips below the trajectory,
$\dot{\beta} > 0$ for positive spin and the projectile has a tendency to turn left

as seen from behind. If $\alpha < 0$ so that the nose points upward with respect to the path of the mass center, $\dot\beta < 0$ and the projectile has a tendency to deviate to the right.

From the first of Eqs. (4–99) together with Eqs. (4–106), (4–109), and (4–110), we may find an equation for the determination of α. We have

$$I\ddot\theta - I\dot\phi^2 \sin\theta \cos\theta + \dot\phi a \sin\theta = Kv^2 r\alpha,$$

$$I\ddot\theta_0 - I\dot\phi_0^2 \sin\theta_0 \cos\theta_0 + \dot\phi_0 a \sin\theta_0 = 0,$$

so that, subtracting and using $\dot\phi_0 = 0$,

$$I\ddot\alpha - I\dot\beta^2 (\sin\theta_0 \cos\theta_0 + \alpha\cos^2\theta_0 - \alpha\sin^2\theta_0)$$
$$+ \dot\beta a(\alpha\cos\theta_0 + \sin\theta_0) = Kv^2 r\alpha,$$

or, if we neglect terms of higher order than the first in $\dot\beta$ and α,

$$I\ddot\alpha + \dot\beta a \sin\theta_0 - Kv^2 r\alpha = 0. \tag{4–111}$$

But $\dot\beta \sin\theta_0 = (a\alpha)/I$; hence we have

$$\ddot\alpha + \alpha\left\{\frac{a^2}{I^2} - \frac{Kv^2 r}{I}\right\} = 0. \tag{4–112}$$

The angular perturbation α will be periodic, and hence the shell will be stable if

$$\frac{a^2}{I^2} > \frac{Kv^2 r}{I},$$

or, since $a = I_3\dot\psi$, if

$$\dot\psi^2 > \frac{Kv^2 rI}{I_3^2}. \tag{4–113}$$

As indicated in the introductory paragraph of this section, we may anticipate in reality a far more complicated state of motion than we have analyzed here. Not only does the air resistance tend to overturn the shell; it retards its spin as well. If $\dot\psi$ diminishes, then the angular deviation with respect to the horizontal changes also. These complications, which introduce nonlinearities into the equations of motion, are usually treated by tabular and numerical techniques that form part of the study of exterior ballistics.*

---

* See, for example, E. J. McShane, J. L. Kelley, and F. V. Reno, *Exterior Ballistics*. Denver, Colorado: University of Denver Press, 1953.

4–11 Motion of a rocket. As a final example of rigid-body motion, we shall study the motion of a rocket in the short time interval during which its fuel is being consumed. This time is of the order of 0.1 to 2.0 seconds for a small rocket. During the time of propellant action, the aerodynamic drag is of minor importance compared with the force due to the rocket motor. The angular orientation of the missile, however, is important because the propellant force acts along the axis of the projectile and not along the tangent to the trajectory. We consider first the rocket as a particle losing mass.

Let m be the mass of the rocket and its unburned fuel at time t. Its velocity at this time relative to a fixed coordinate system will be taken as $\mathbf{v}$. In a time interval Δt, a small amount of mass Δm will be ejected and the resultant change in linear momentum provides the thrust to drive the rocket forward. Suppose $\mathbf{v}_1$ is the velocity of the ejected mass Δm relative to the fixed coordinate system. Then, ignoring for the moment the action of gravity on the rocket, we find that the conservation of linear momentum requires that

$$(m - \Delta m)(\mathbf{v} + \Delta \mathbf{v}) + \mathbf{v}_1 \, \Delta m - m\mathbf{v} = 0. \qquad (4\text{--}114)$$

Here $\Delta \mathbf{v}$ is the change in velocity in the interval Δt, and Δm is the ejected mass.

If we let $\mathbf{v}_e$ be the velocity of the exhaust gases as they leave the rocket, *relative to the rocket*, we have

$$\mathbf{v}_e = \mathbf{v}_1 - \mathbf{v}. \qquad (4\text{--}115)$$

Then Eq. (4–114) becomes

$$m \, \Delta \mathbf{v} + \mathbf{v}_e \, \Delta m - \Delta \mathbf{v} \, \Delta m = 0.$$

Dividing by Δt and proceeding to the limit as $\Delta t \to 0$, we obtain

$$m \, \frac{d\mathbf{v}}{dt} + \mathbf{v}_e \, \frac{dm}{dt} = 0. \qquad (4\text{--}116)$$

Hence the rocket moves as though subjected to a force $-\mathbf{v}_e \, dm/dt$. The quantity Δm is the ejected mass; hence $dm/dt > 0$ and, since $\mathbf{v}_e$ is opposite in direction to $\mathbf{v}$, the force $-\mathbf{v}_e \, (dm/dt)$ tends to increase $\mathbf{v}$. It is the *thrust* on the rocket due to the exhaust gases.

Equation (4–116) may be solved easily to obtain $\mathbf{v}$ as a function of m. We write it as

$$\frac{d\mathbf{v}}{dm} = - \frac{\mathbf{v}_e}{m}, \qquad (4\text{--}117)$$

and hence, by direct integration, find

$$\mathbf{v} = -\mathbf{v}_e \log m + \text{constant},$$

where $\mathbf{v}_e$ has been considered constant during the burning of the fuel. If $\mathbf{v}_0$ is the initial velocity of the rocket and M is its initial mass, we have

$$\mathbf{v} = \mathbf{v}_0 + \mathbf{v}_e \log\left(\frac{M}{m}\right). \tag{4–118}$$

When the fuel is exhausted, the velocity will attain the value

$$\mathbf{v}_{\max} = \mathbf{v}_0 + \mathbf{v}_e \log\left(\frac{M}{m_r}\right), \tag{4–119}$$

where m_r is the mass of the rocket alone.

If an external body force $\mathbf{F}$ acts on the rocket, the equation of motion (4–116) becomes

$$m\frac{d\mathbf{v}}{dt} = \mathbf{F} - \mathbf{v}_e\frac{dm}{dt}. \tag{4–120}$$

This would be the case, for example, when gravity acts on the missile. Problem 1–3 illustrates this case.

The discussion above treats the rocket as if it were a particle of variable mass m. We turn now to the more realistic situation in which the rocket is considered as a rigid body. We shall set up the equations of motion for a rocket projectile that has symmetry about its longitudinal axis and that is stabilized in flight by a system of longitudinal fins. Its motion is determined by the thrust provided by the motor, by gravity, and by the restoring torque due to the aerodynamic forces acting on the fins. We shall not consider the flight of the rocket after its fuel is exhausted, since it then behaves as an ordinary projectile.

At any given instant let the rocket be oriented as shown in Fig. 4–24. Its center of mass describes a curve in space while at the same time the axis of the rocket rotates with respect to the tangent to the path. From our general theorems on rigid-body motion (Section 1–12) we know that the motion of the center of mass and the rotation about this point may be studied as if the latter were independent of the former.

Let the following quantities describe the rotational motion:

θ is the angle made with the horizontal axis by the tangent to the trajectory;

ϕ is the angle which the axis of the rocket makes with the horizontal;

δ is the angle between the tangent to the curve and the rocket axis;

$\mathbf{c} = -(\mathbf{v}_e/m)(dm/dt)$ is the acceleration of the rocket due to the motor and *will be considered constant*.

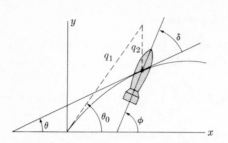

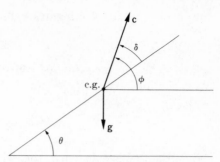

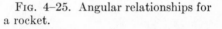

FIG. 4–24. Orientation of a rocket.   FIG. 4–25. Angular relationships for
a rocket.

These quantities are shown in Fig. 4–25. To define the position of
the center of mass, we choose the coordinates q_1 and q_2 shown in Fig.
4–24.

If v is the speed of the rocket along its trajectory at any time, we have
the acceleration along the tangent,

$$\dot{v} = c \cos \delta - g \sin \theta, \tag{4–121}$$

and along the normal,

$$v\dot{\theta} = c \sin \delta - g \cos \theta. \tag{4–122}$$

Furthermore, the restoring torque about the center of mass due to the
forces on the fins is

$$N = -Kv^2 \sin \delta, \tag{4–123}$$

where K contains the air density, the diameter of the projectile, and an
experimentally determined coefficient.* For our purposes, we shall
consider K constant. It has the dimensions of mass. The rotational
motion is then given by

$$I\ddot{\phi} = -Kv^2\delta \tag{4–124}$$

if we make the approximation, valid for small angle of yaw, that
$\sin \delta = \delta$. For purposes of simplification, let us define a constant $\lambda = 2\pi\sqrt{I/K}$ which has the dimensions of length and may be termed the
wavelength of yaw. Then Eq. (4–124) becomes

$$\ddot{\phi} = -\frac{4\pi^2 v^2 \delta}{\lambda^2}. \tag{4–125}$$

---

* For a detailed account of the torque acting on the rocket, see J. B. Rosser,
R. R. Newton, and G. L. Gross, *Mathematical Theory of Rocket Flight*. New
York: McGraw-Hill Book Company, Inc., 1947.

Consider, now, the quantity $v \sin \delta$, which is the projection of the velocity of the center of mass on a line perpendicular to the axis of the rocket. By differentiation with respect to t, we have

$$\dot{v} \sin \delta + v \dot{\delta} \cos \delta = \dot{v} \sin \delta + v(\dot{\phi} - \dot{\theta}) \cos \delta,$$

and substitution from Eqs. (4–121) and (4–122) yields

$$v \dot{\phi} \cos \delta + g \cos (\theta + \delta).$$

Hence

$$\frac{d}{dt} (v \sin \delta) = v \dot{\phi} \cos \delta + g \cos \phi. \qquad (4\text{–}126)$$

Suppose that the trajectory is relatively flat and that δ is small. Then we may replace Eq. (4–126) by the relation

$$\frac{d}{dt} (v\delta) = v \dot{\phi} + g \cos \theta_0, \qquad (4\text{–}127)$$

where θ_0 is the angle made with the horizontal by the initial tangent to the trajectory (Fig. 4–24). Furthermore, Eq. (4–121) becomes

$$\dot{v} = c - g \sin \theta = \alpha, \qquad (4\text{–}128)$$

which we take as a constant. Equations (4–125), (4–127), and (4–128) describe the motion.

These equations are most readily solved by the introduction of a new independent variable τ defined by

$$\tau = v\sqrt{2/\alpha\lambda}. \qquad (4\text{–}129)$$

Since $\dot{\phi} = (d\phi/d\tau)(d\tau/dt)$ and $\dot{v} = \alpha$, we have, in place of Eq. (4–125),

$$\frac{d^2\phi}{d\tau^2} + \pi^2\tau^2\, \delta = 0, \qquad (4\text{–}130)$$

and in place of Eq. (4–127),

$$\frac{d}{d\tau} (\tau\delta) = \tau \frac{d\phi}{d\tau} + \frac{g \cos \theta_0}{\alpha}. \qquad (4\text{–}131)$$

From Eq. (4–130) we have $\tau\delta = -(1/\pi^2\tau)(d^2\phi/d\tau^2)$, and substituting in Eq. (4–131) we obtain

$$\frac{1}{\tau} \frac{d}{d\tau} \left(-\frac{1}{\pi^2\tau} \frac{d^2\phi}{d\tau^2} \right) = \frac{d\phi}{d\tau} + \frac{g \cos \theta_0}{\tau\alpha}. \qquad (4\text{–}132)$$

For convenience let $(d\phi/d\tau) = \phi'$, $(d^2\phi/d\tau^2) = \phi''$, and $\tau^2 = p$. Then Eq. (4–132) becomes

$$\frac{d^2\phi'}{dp^2} + \frac{\pi^2\phi'}{4} = \frac{-\pi^2 g \cos\theta_0}{4\alpha p^{1/2}}. \qquad (4\text{–}133)$$

This is a linear differential equation with constant coefficients that has a complementary function,

$$\phi'_c = A \cos\left(\frac{\pi p}{2}\right) + B \sin\left(\frac{\pi p}{2}\right).$$

The particular integral may be found by the method of variation of parameters so that the complete solution for ϕ' as a function of p is

$$\begin{aligned}
\phi'(p) = {}& c_1 \cos\left(\frac{\pi p}{2}\right) + c_2 \sin\left(\frac{\pi p}{2}\right) \\
& - \frac{2\beta}{\pi} \cos\left(\frac{\pi p}{2}\right) \int p^{-1/2} \sin\left(\frac{\pi p}{2}\right) dp \qquad (4\text{–}134) \\
& + \frac{2\beta}{\pi} \sin\left(\frac{\pi p}{2}\right) \int p^{-1/2} \cos\left(\frac{\pi p}{2}\right) dp,
\end{aligned}$$

where

$$\beta = -\frac{\pi^2 g \cos\theta_0}{4\alpha}.$$

To complete the solution, let us prescribe the initial conditions

$$t = 0, \qquad \dot\phi = \omega_0, \qquad \tau = \tau_0,$$
$$v = v_0, \qquad \delta = \delta_0,$$

and rewrite the integrals in Eq. (4–134) in terms of τ. These may be written as

$$\begin{aligned}
& 2\int_{\tau_0}^{\tau} \sin\left(\frac{\pi s^2}{2}\right) ds, \\
& 2\int_{\tau_0}^{\tau} \cos\left(\frac{\pi s^2}{2}\right) ds, \qquad (4\text{–}135)
\end{aligned}$$

where s is a dummy variable. Combining the trigonometric functions in Eq. (4–134) with those under the integrals (4–135), we have as a solution

$$\begin{aligned}
\phi'(\tau) = {}& c_1 \cos\frac{\pi}{2}(\tau^2 - \tau_0^2) + c_2 \sin\frac{\pi}{2}(\tau^2 - \tau_0^2) \\
& + \frac{\pi g \cos\theta_0}{\alpha} \int_{\tau_0}^{\tau} \sin\frac{\pi}{2}(s^2 - \tau^2)\, ds. \qquad (4\text{–}136)
\end{aligned}$$

Applying the initial conditions, we see that since $\phi' = \dot{\phi}/\dot{\tau}$ and $\dot{\phi}_0 = \omega_0$,

$$\phi'(\tau_0) = c_1 = \omega_0\sqrt{\lambda/2\alpha}. \qquad (4\text{--}137)$$

Differentiating Eq. (4–136) with respect to τ and using the initial conditions together with the fact that by Eq. (4–130) $\phi_0'' = -\pi^2\tau_0^2\delta_0$, we find $c_2 = -\pi\delta_0\tau_0$. With these values of c_1 and c_2 substituted in Eq. (4–136), the function $\phi'(\tau)$ is known. This substituted for $(d\phi/d\tau)$ in Eq. (4–131) allows us to solve for $\tau\delta$ as a function of τ and hence for δ as a function of τ. We shall not solve for these functions explicitly.

Consider, finally, the position of the center of mass as specified by the coordinates (q_1, q_2) in Fig. 4–24. Clearly

$$q_1 = x \sec\theta_0, \qquad\qquad q_2 = x\tan\theta_0 - y,$$

$$\dot{q}_1 = v\cos\theta\sec\theta_0, \qquad \dot{q}_2 = v\sin(\theta_0 - \theta)\sec\theta_0.$$

For a flat trajectory such as we have been considering, we have approximately

$$\dot{q}_1 \cong v, \qquad \dot{q}_2 \cong v(\theta_0 - \theta)\sec\theta_0, \qquad (4\text{--}138)$$

where θ is in radians.

Now we have, by the first of Eqs. (4–138) and by Eq. (4–128),

$$\dot{q}_1 = \frac{dq_1}{dv}\,\dot{v} = \frac{dq_1}{dv}\,\alpha = v.$$

Hence

$$q_1 = \frac{1}{2\alpha}\,(v^2 - v_0^2). \qquad (4\text{--}139)$$

Similarly, we may write

$$\dot{q}_2 = \frac{dq_2}{d\tau}\cdot\frac{d\tau}{dt} = \frac{dq_2}{d\tau}\cdot\alpha\sqrt{\frac{2}{\lambda\alpha}} = \tau\sqrt{\frac{\lambda\alpha}{2}}\,(\theta_0 - \theta)\sec\theta_0,$$

from which we obtain

$$\frac{dq_2}{d\tau} = \frac{\tau\lambda}{2}\,(\theta_0 - \theta)\sec\theta_0. \qquad (4\text{--}140)$$

This may be integrated to yield

$$q_2 = \frac{\lambda\sec\theta_0}{2}\int_{\tau_0}^{\tau} s(\theta_0 - \theta)\,ds, \qquad (4\text{--}141)$$

where θ is considered a function of τ_0 and of s, the dummy variable.

Our analysis of the motion of the rocket in a flat trajectory may be summarized in the following way:

(a) The fundamental differential equation, $(d/dt)(v\delta) = v\phi(v) + g\cos\theta_0$, relating the angle of yaw δ with the speed of the projectile v and the time, has been solved by eliminating the time and by first finding the function $\phi(v)$. This function $\phi(v) = \alpha\sqrt{(2/\alpha\lambda)}\phi'(v)$, where $\phi'(v)$ is given in terms of the initial conditions by Eq. (4–136). The function $\phi'(v)$ is a bounded periodic function of v. Hence $\phi(v)$ is bounded and periodic. This represents the angular velocity of the rocket about a horizontal axis through its center of gravity. Under the assumptions made here, therefore, the yawing motion of the rocket consists of an oscillatory rotation about a horizontal axis through its center of gravity.

(b) The position of the center of gravity in its trajectory is given by the coordinates

$$q_1 = \frac{1}{2\alpha}\,(v^2 - v_0^2), \qquad q_2 = \frac{\lambda\sec\theta_0}{2}\int_{\tau_0}^{\tau} s(\theta_0 - \theta)\,ds,$$

which are defined by means of Fig. (4–24).

To find δ, q_1, and q_2 as functions of the time, we may use the relation, Eq. (4–128),

$$\dot{v} = c - g\sin\theta = \alpha \qquad \text{(constant)},$$

where c is the driving acceleration due to the exhaust gases. Hence both the position and the orientation of the rocket are known at any time during its propelled flight.

PROBLEMS

4–1. Prove that the moment of a couple about any point in a rigid body is the same. (Section 4–1)

4–2. Let the moment of inertia about an axis through the center of mass of a homogeneous solid be I_0. Show that the moment of inertia about any parallel axis is $I = I_0 + Md^2$, where M is the mass of the solid and d is the perpendicular distance between the axes. (Section 4–2)·

4–3. Given a triangular plate of mass m, as shown in Fig. 4–26, (a) show that the moment of inertia of the plate about any line L through vertex A and in the plane of the triangle is the same as the moment of inertia about L of three point masses, each $m/3$, placed at the midpoints of AB, BC, and CA. (b) Show that a similar relationship holds with respect to a line parallel to L but passing through the center of mass of the triangle. (c) Find the principal axes of the plate at the center of mass. (Sections 4–3 and 4–4)

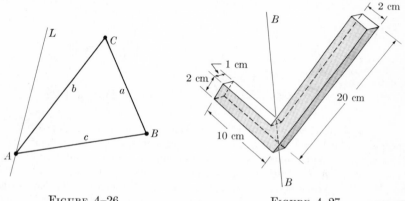

FIGURE 4–26   FIGURE 4–27

4–4. An L-shaped metal plate 1 cm thick has the dimensions shown in Fig. 4–27. (a) Compute in as simple a way as possible moments and products of inertia for this plate. (b) Find from them the directions of the principal axes of the plate. (c) Suppose the plate is rotating about the line BB with an angular speed of 50 radians/sec. Find the direction and magnitude of the angular momentum vector. (Sections 4–3 and 4–4)

4–5. A thin uniform rectangular plate of mass 400 gm originally and dimensions 20 × 40 cm has 2 × 2 cm squares cut out at two diagonally opposite corners. (a) Find the moments and products of inertia about axes through the center of mass, one axis being perpendicular to the plane of the plate, the other two being in the plane of the plate and parallel to its edges. (b) Locate the principal axes through the center of mass and find the principal moments of inertia. (c) Find the total angular momentum vector if the plate spins with angular speed ω about an axis in its plane through the center of mass and parallel to the longer edge of the plate. (Sections 4–3 and 4–4)

4–6. Three equal masses are mounted on rigid weightless rods making angles of 120°, as shown in Fig. 4–28. The system rotates with constant angular velocity $\omega = \dot{\theta}$ about the z-axis, which is perpendicular to the plane of the paper and toward the reader. The direction of rotation is indicated by the arrow. At the same time, the system turns about the x-axis in such a way that the y-axis moves out of the page, as shown. This rotation is with constant angular velocity $\Omega(\ll\omega)$. (a) Establish principal axes for the system, and (b) by means of Euler's equations compute the torques about Ox, Oy, and Oz. (c) Would the same analysis be valid if the origin O were describing a curve in space? (Section 4–5)

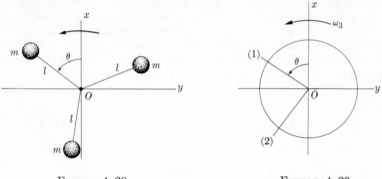

FIGURE 4–28   FIGURE 4–29

4–7. A gyro-wheel mounted in gimbals rotates about the positive z-axis (perpendicular to the paper in Fig. 4–29) with constant angular velocity $\omega_3 = \dot{\theta}$. Its axial moment of inertia is I_3; the moment of inertia about any axis in the (1)- (2)-plane is I. Initially the wheel is vertical, as shown. A weight W is hung on the gyro-axis, Oz, at a distance d from the origin. By Euler's equations, (a) establish in as simple a form as possible the differential equations for ω_x and ω_y in terms of θ and constants. (b) Solve these for ω_x and ω_y and discuss the motion of the system. (c) What motion ensues if ω_y is forced to be zero? (Section 4–5)

4–8. When the motor armature of an electric locomotive is carried around a curve, it experiences a gyroscopic torque in addition to the centrifugal force due to its motion. The shaft of the armature is always perpendicular to the

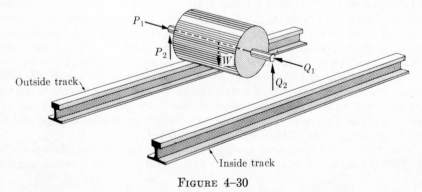

FIGURE 4–30

rails of the track (Fig. 4–30). Let the weight of the armature be $W = 10,000$ lb, its radius of gyration 15 inches, its angular speed of rotation 700 rpm, and the distance between bearings 5 ft. The curve around which the armature is being carried has a radius of 2000 ft, and the locomotive has a speed of 40 mi/hr. If the armature spins on its axis in the same direction that the locomotive's wheels rotate, find the forces P and Q (Fig. 4–30) acting on the bearings during the locomotive's motion around the curve, neglecting frictional forces. (Section 4–5)

4–9. A tuning fork supported vertically has a frequency of vibration Ω, the amplitude of vibration being maintained constant. The fork is turned about the vertical axis at constant angular speed ω, and $\omega \ll \Omega$. The mass of each tine of the fork is m; the amplitude of lateral vibration is a; the moment of inertia of the fork about its vertical axis, when the tines are in the equilibrium position, is I_0. (a) Find an expression for the torque on the vertical axis during rotation of the fork. (b) Suggest a practical application for such a device. (Section 4–5)

4–10. (a) Show by the use of Euler's equations that when a rigid body rotates about its axes of greatest or least moment of inertia, the rotational motion is stable; that is, slight perturbations of the axis of rotation will not cause the body to deviate markedly in its motion. (b) Show also that rotation about the axis of intermediate moment of inertia is unstable. *Hint:* For axis (1), assume ω_1 constant, and ω_2, ω_3 very small, and neglect their product; write the simultaneous equations for ω_2 and ω_3; set $\omega_2 = Ae^{\lambda t}$, $\omega_3 = Be^{\lambda t}$, and find the condition for λ to be imaginary. (Section 4–5)

4–11. (a) Solve Problem 4–7 by using the Eulerian angles ϕ, ψ, θ and Lagrange's equations. (b) Show that the solution so obtained is identical with that found previously from Euler's equations. (Section 4–7)

4–12. A symmetrical disk of axial moment of inertia I_3 and transverse moment of inertia I rotates with angular speed s on a shaft of length l, as shown in Fig. 4–31. The axis of symmetry of the disk makes a small angle α with the shaft. The disk is mounted at the middle of the shaft. By use of Euler's angles, ϕ, ψ, θ, and Lagrange's equations, (a) find the torque on the shaft and the forces exerted on the bearings. (b) Investigate, also, the torques and forces if the entire support system rotates with angular speed Ω about the vertical. (Section 4–7)

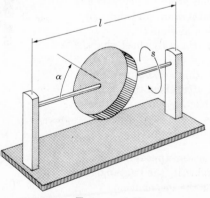

FIGURE 4–31

4–13. A right circular cone spins rapidly in such a way that its vertex remains fixed. The axis of the cone, inclined to the vertical by a constant amount, makes one rotation about the vertical in T seconds. The axis is a cm long and the radius of its base is $a/2$ cm. Deduce an approximate expression for the spin velocity of the cone. (Section 4–8)

4–14. (Section 4–9) A symmetrical top of axial moment of inertia I_3 is started with its axis vertical, that is, $\theta = 0$ and $\dot\theta = 0$. (a) Establish the fictitious potential $V'(\theta)$ for this case. (b) Show that if $\omega_3^2 > (4mglI)/I_3^2$, the angle θ will remain zero. (c) Show also that if ω_3 is less than the value quoted, the top will, after a slight disturbance, oscillate between θ nearly equal to zero and

$$\theta = \cos^{-1}\left[\left(\frac{\omega_3^2 I_3^2}{2mglI}\right) - 1\right].$$

4–15. A symmetrical top of axial moment of inertia I_3 is set in motion at $t = 0$, with $\dot\theta = 0$, $\theta = \pi/2$, and $\dot\phi = (I_3\omega_3)/I$. Investigate the behavior of the top for $t > 0$ if $\omega_3^2 = (2Imgl)/I_3^2$. (Section 4–9)

4–16. A solid right circular cone whose vertex angle is 2α rolls without slipping on a plane inclined at an angle β to the horizontal. The cone has a mass M and a slant height L. (a) Write the Lagrangian equation of motion for the cone, using, as generalized coordinate, the angle θ between its line of contact with the plane and the line of steepest descent. (b) What is the frequency of small oscillations about this equilibrium position? *Hint:* Use the line of contact as the instantaneous axis of rotation.

4–17. A vertical engine is shown schematically in Fig. 4–32. The physical quantities involved are:

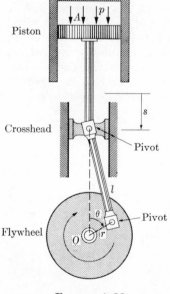

l = length of connecting rod,

r = length of crank,

A = area of piston,

p = pressure on piston head,

n = number of revolutions of flywheel per unit time,

s = distance of crosshead pivot from its highest position at any time t,

θ = angle between crank and line of action of piston at time t,

I = moment of inertia of flywheel, shaft, and crank about O,

m = mass of connecting rod, assumed uniformly distributed along the rod,

M = mass of the piston, rod, and crosshead,

N = torque applied to flywheel.

Assume that $r \ll l$, choose an appropriate generalized coordinate, and write the Lagrangian equation of motion for the mechanism.

FIGURE 4–32

CHAPTER 5

OSCILLATORY MOTION

Oscillatory motion plays an important part in many physical problems. In this chapter we shall discuss motion in which the forces are linear functions of the displacements and the velocities. The oscillations occurring under this restriction will be assumed to take place in the neighborhood of a position of stable equilibrium. Such a position has been identified in Section 2–1 with a minimum of the potential energy. In the case of simple oscillatory motion in one dimension, for example, the potential energy is $V(x) = \frac{1}{2}kx^2$, and an oscillatory motion in the neighborhood of $x = 0$ results when the total energy E is very small. The velocity is $\pm\sqrt{(2/m)(E - V)}$ in this case. Hence for small E and small $V(x)$, the resulting velocity will be small. The force in this example is $F(x) = -(dV/dx) = -kx$, and we observe that it is a linear function of the displacement.

5–1 The equations of motion. Let us assume a system described at time t by the generalized coordinates $q_1, q_2, \ldots, q_n$ where these are measured from a stable equilibrium position. This means that when $q_1, q_2, \ldots, q_n$ are zero the generalized forces $Q_i = -(\partial V/\partial q_i)_0 = 0$.

We assume, first, that the system is conservative with a potential energy function $V(q_1, q_2, \ldots, q_n)$. Expanding V into a Taylor's series about the equilibrium configuration, we have, to terms of the second degree,

$$V(q_1 \cdots q_n) = V_0 + \sum_{i=1}^{n} \left(\frac{\partial V}{\partial q_i}\right)_0 q_i + \frac{1}{2} \sum_{i=1}^{n} \sum_{j=1}^{n} \left(\frac{\partial^2 V}{\partial q_i \partial q_j}\right)_0 q_i q_j + \cdots. \tag{5-1}$$

No generality will be lost by taking $V_0 = 0$. Furthermore, the second sum vanishes, since $(\partial V/\partial q_i)_0 = 0$ for all i. Hence we are left with

$$V = \frac{1}{2} \sum_{i=1}^{n} \sum_{j=1}^{n} \left(\frac{\partial^2 V}{\partial q_i \partial q_j}\right)_0 q_i q_j. \tag{5-2}$$

The second partial derivatives, however, are evaluated at the equilibrium position and hence are constants. We shall denote them by k_{ij}. Furthermore, since the order of differentiation is immaterial under our assumptions, $k_{ij} = k_{ji}$. The expression, Eq. (5–2), for V is called a *quadratic form*. If, as in the present case, the q_i are measured from a position of minimum V_0 and this minimum is zero, then for all combinations of the

155

k_{ij}, q_i, and q_j, V is positive. It is then called a *positive definite quadratic form*.

In Section 2–6 we found that the kinetic energy T can be written as a homogeneous quadratic form in the velocities, namely,

$$T = \frac{1}{2} \sum_{i=1}^{n} \sum_{j=1}^{n} a_{ij}\dot{q}_i\dot{q}_j, \tag{5-3}$$

where the a_{ij} are in general functions of the generalized coordinates and contain the masses, or other inertial parameters, of the system. We may expand the quantities a_{ij} into a Taylor's series about the equilibrium values of the q_i in a manner similar to that shown in Eq. (5–1). Since the $\dot{q}_i$ are assumed to be small, we shall take the constant values of a_{ij} *at the equilibrium position* as an approximation and neglect all the higher order terms in the expansion. Call these constants m_{ij}. Then the quadratic form, Eq. (5–3), becomes

$$T = \frac{1}{2} \sum_{i=1}^{n} \sum_{j=1}^{n} m_{ij}\dot{q}_i\dot{q}_j, \tag{5-4}$$

where $m_{ij} = m_{ji}$. Since $T = \frac{1}{2}\sum_{j=1}^{n} m_j\dot{\mathbf{r}}_j^2$ is inherently positive and cannot vanish unless each velocity vanishes, it is a positive definite quadratic form.

Lagrange's equations follow from the Lagrangian function,

$$L = T - V = \frac{1}{2} \sum_{i,j=1}^{n} (m_{ij}\dot{q}_i\dot{q}_j - k_{ij}q_iq_j), \tag{5-5}$$

and we obtain as the equations of motion

$$\sum_{j=1}^{n} m_{ij}\ddot{q}_j = - \sum_{j=1}^{n} k_{ij}q_j \qquad (i = 1, 2, \ldots, n). \tag{5-6}$$

As an example, consider a system with two degrees of freedom. The analysis may be extended readily to more dimensions. In this case the equations of motion are

$$\begin{aligned} m_{11}\ddot{q}_1 + m_{12}\ddot{q}_2 &= -k_{11}q_1 - k_{12}q_2, \\ m_{21}\ddot{q}_1 + m_{22}\ddot{q}_2 &= -k_{21}q_1 - k_{22}q_2. \end{aligned} \tag{5-7}$$

We may interpret the quantity $k_{12} = k_{21}$ as a spring constant which couples the displacement in one coordinate with the restoring force due to displacement in the other coordinate. The terms $k_{12}q_2$ and $k_{21}q_1$ are called *static coupling* terms. The terms $m_{12}\ddot{q}_2$ and $m_{21}\ddot{q}_1$ are called *dynamic coupling* terms. They represent the influence of acceleration in one coordinate on the motion in the other. These differential equations, solved simultaneously, yield q_1 and q_2 as functions of the time.

Since we are interested in oscillatory motion in each of the coordinates, we shall assume solutions of Eq. (5–6) of the form

$$q_j = A_j e^{\lambda t},$$

where A_j and λ are complex constants to be determined. Substituting in Eq. (5–6) we have, in expanded form,

$$(m_{11}\lambda^2 + k_{11})A_1 + (m_{12}\lambda^2 + k_{12})A_2 + \cdots + (m_{1n}\lambda^2 + k_{1n})A_n = 0,$$

$$(m_{21}\lambda^2 + k_{21})A_1 + (m_{22}\lambda^2 + k_{22})A_2 + \cdots + (m_{2n}\lambda^2 + k_{2n})A_n = 0,$$

$$\cdot \qquad \qquad \cdot \qquad \qquad \cdot$$
$$\cdot \qquad \qquad \cdot \qquad \qquad \cdot$$
$$\cdot \qquad \qquad \cdot \qquad \qquad \cdot$$

$$(m_{n1}\lambda^2 + k_{n1})A_1 + (m_{n2}\lambda^2 + k_{n2})A_2 + \cdots + (m_{nn}\lambda^2 + k_{nn})A_n = 0.$$
$$\tag{5-8}$$

These will have a nontrivial solution for the A_j if the determinant

$$
\begin{vmatrix}
m_{11}\lambda^2 + k_{11} & m_{12}\lambda^2 + k_{12} \cdots m_{1n}\lambda^2 + k_{1n} \\
m_{21}\lambda^2 + k_{21} & m_{22}\lambda^2 + k_{22} \cdots m_{2n}\lambda^2 + k_{2n} \\
\cdot & \cdot \qquad\qquad \cdot \\
\cdot & \cdot \qquad\qquad \cdot \\
\cdot & \cdot \qquad\qquad \cdot \\
m_{n1}\lambda^2 + k_{n1} & m_{n2}\lambda^2 + k_{n2} \cdots m_{nn}\lambda^2 + k_{nn}
\end{vmatrix} = 0. \tag{5-9}
$$

The parameter λ, therefore, is given by this determinantal equation.

To show the character of the roots of Eqs. (5–9), we shall proceed in the following way. Any one of Eqs. (5–8) can be written in the form

$$\lambda^2 \sum_{j=1}^{n} m_{ij}A_j + \sum_{j=1}^{n} k_{ij}A_j = 0.$$

If we multiply through the ith equation by A_i and sum over i, we have

$$\lambda^2 \sum_{i=1}^{n}\sum_{j=1}^{n} m_{ij}A_iA_j + \sum_{i=1}^{n}\sum_{j=1}^{n} k_{ij}A_iA_j = 0. \tag{5-10}$$

But the double sum in the first term is the function $2T$ of Eq. (5–4) with A_i and A_j replacing $\dot{q}_i$ and $\dot{q}_j$. The double sum in the second term is the function $2V$ of Eq. (5–2) with the q_i and q_j replaced by A_i and A_j. Therefore Eq. (5–10) may be written

$$\lambda^2 T(A) + V(A) = 0,$$

where T and V are positive by definition for all sets of values of the variables. Hence

$$\lambda^2 = -\frac{V(A)}{T(A)} = i^2\omega^2 \qquad (i^2 = -1), \qquad (5\text{--}11)$$

and λ is a pure imaginary, $\pm i\omega$. The degree of the determinantal equation (5–9) is $2n$ in λ, and hence its roots will be $\pm i\omega_1,\ \pm i\omega_2,\ \ldots,\ \pm i\omega_n$. We shall assume that the roots are all distinct and nonzero. We have, then, the particular integrals for the q_j,

$$A_{j1}e^{\pm i\omega_1 t}, \qquad A_{j2}e^{\pm i\omega_2 t}, \ldots, A_{jn}e^{\pm i\omega_n t},$$

and, since the differential equations (5–6) are linear, we may write

$$q_j = \sum_{r=1}^{n} (A_{jr}e^{i\omega_r t} + \overline{A}_{jr}e^{-i\omega_r t}) \qquad (j = 1, 2, \ldots, n),$$

where $\overline{A}$ is the complex conjugate of A. This restriction on the complex coefficients is required in order to make q_j real. The constants A_{jr} and $\overline{A}_{jr}$ are determined from the initial conditions of the problem. By means of the well-known Euler relations, $e^{\pm i\theta} = \cos\theta \pm i\sin\theta$, we may combine the pairs of conjugate complex numbers to write

$$q_j = \sum_{r=1}^{n} C_{jr}\sin(\omega_r t + \psi_r) \qquad (j = 1, 2, \ldots, n), \qquad (5\text{--}12)$$

where the C_{jr} are now real amplitudes and ψ_r are the phase angles corresponding to the given ω_r.

The quantities ω_r are the *natural frequencies* of oscillation, one for each degree of freedom of the system. For each ω_r, there is a corresponding principal *mode of oscillation* in the coordinates q_j. Having determined the values of ω_r, we may rewrite Eq. (5–8) in the form

$$\sum_{j=1}^{n} (k_{ij} - m_{ij}\omega_r^2)A_{jr} = 0 \qquad (i = 1, 2, \ldots, n), \qquad (5\text{--}13)$$

for each value of r. These equations permit us to calculate the ratios of the coefficients corresponding to a given frequency. It is left for the reader to show that the constants C_{jr} may replace A_{jr} in Eq. (5–13).

5–2 An example: two statically coupled masses. An illustration of the foregoing theory is furnished by the simple mass and spring system shown in Fig. 5–1. Two equal masses are coupled by springs to each

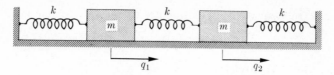

FIG. 5–1. Statically coupled masses.

other and to fixed walls. Let the coordinates q_1 and q_2, which describe the positions of the masses at time t, be measured from equilibrium. The masses are assumed to slide with negligible friction on a flat table. All springs have the same constant k.

The potential energy of the system is

$$V = \tfrac{1}{2}k[q_1^2 + q_2^2 + (q_1 - q_2)^2], \qquad (5\text{--}14)$$

and its kinetic energy is

$$T = \tfrac{1}{2}m[\dot{q}_1^2 + \dot{q}_2^2]. \qquad (5\text{--}15)$$

Hence the equations of motion (5–6) are

$$m\ddot{q}_1 = -2kq_1 + kq_2, \qquad m\ddot{q}_2 = kq_1 - 2kq_2. \qquad (5\text{--}16)$$

Since we have shown in Section 5–1 that periodic motion results from a system in which T and V are positive definite, we may go directly to principal modes of the form $q_j = C_j \sin(\omega t + \psi_j)$. Hence, substituting in Eqs. (5–16) the values

$$q_1 = C_1 \sin(\omega t + \psi_1) \qquad \text{and} \qquad q_2 = C_2 \sin(\omega t + \psi_2),$$

we find that C_1 and C_2 must satisfy the equations

$$(2k - m\omega^2)C_1 - kC_2 = 0, \qquad -kC_1 + (2k - m\omega^2)C_2 = 0. \qquad (5\text{--}17)$$

These correspond to Eq. (5–13) in our general analysis when the appropriate values of ω have been determined.

For Eqs. (5–17) to have a nontrivial solution,

$$\begin{vmatrix} (2k - m\omega^2) & -k \\ -k & (2k - m\omega^2) \end{vmatrix} = 0. \qquad (5\text{--}18)$$

Hence

$$\omega^2 = \frac{k}{m} \qquad \text{or} \qquad \frac{3k}{m}. \qquad (5\text{--}19)$$

The natural frequencies of oscillation are therefore

$$\omega_1 = \sqrt{k/m} \quad \text{and} \quad \omega_2 = \sqrt{3k/m}.$$

Equations (5–17) then yield

$$\frac{C_{21}}{C_{11}} = \frac{2k - m\omega_1^2}{k} = 1, \qquad \frac{C_{22}}{C_{12}} = \frac{2k - m\omega_2^2}{k} = -1. \qquad (5\text{–}20)$$

These equations imply that, at the lower of the natural frequencies, the masses oscillate in phase as a unit. At the higher frequency, ω_2, they oscillate toward or away from one another, that is, 180° out of phase.

The oscillations in the coordinates q_1 and q_2 are given by Eq. (5–12), namely,

$$q_1 = C_{11} \sin (\omega_1 t + \psi_1) + C_{12} \sin (\omega_2 t + \psi_2),$$
$$q_2 = C_{21} \sin (\omega_1 t + \psi_1) + C_{22} \sin (\omega_2 t + \psi_2), \qquad (5\text{–}21)$$

or, by use of Eqs. (5–20),

$$q_1 = C_{11} \sin (\omega_1 t + \psi_1) + C_{12} \sin (\omega_2 t + \psi_2),$$
$$q_2 = C_{11} \sin (\omega_1 t + \psi_1) - C_{12} \sin (\omega_2 t + \psi_2).$$

The evaluation of C_{11}, C_{12}, ψ_1, and ψ_2 from the initial conditions we shall defer for the moment.

5–3 Orthogonality and normalizing conditions. In this section we shall investigate certain fundamental properties of the C_{jr} that are important in determining their values from the initial conditions. For clarity, the discussion will be restricted to a system with two degrees of freedom. The results may be generalized to an n-dimensional system.

We first write Eqs. (5–21) in a different form by separating C_{jr} into a scale factor c_r appropriate to the particular mode of oscillation, and a second factor a_{jr}, whose properties will be defined. Thus,

$$q_1 = c_1 a_{11} \sin (\omega_1 t + \psi_1) + c_2 a_{12} \sin (\omega_2 t + \psi_2),$$
$$q_2 = c_1 a_{21} \sin (\omega_1 t + \psi_1) + c_2 a_{22} \sin (\omega_2 t + \psi_2), \qquad (5\text{–}22)$$

where c_1 and c_2 are the scale factors.

By writing $C_{jr} = c_r a_{jr}$ in Eq. (5–13) separately for each frequency, we are led to the equations

$$(k_{11} - m_{11}\omega_1^2)a_{11} + (k_{12} - m_{12}\omega_1^2)a_{21} = 0, \qquad (5\text{–}23)$$
$$(k_{21} - m_{21}\omega_1^2)a_{11} + (k_{22} - m_{22}\omega_1^2)a_{21} = 0, \qquad (5\text{–}24)$$

$$(k_{11} - m_{11}\omega_2^2)a_{12} + (k_{12} - m_{12}\omega_2^2)a_{22} = 0, \qquad (5\text{–}25)$$

$$(k_{21} - m_{21}\omega_2^2)a_{12} + (k_{22} - m_{22}\omega_2^2)a_{22} = 0. \qquad (5\text{–}26)$$

Multiplying Eq. (5–23) by a_{12} and Eq. (5–24) by a_{22}, and adding, we obtain

$$(k_{11}a_{11}a_{12} + k_{12}a_{21}a_{12} + k_{21}a_{11}a_{22} + k_{22}a_{21}a_{22})$$
$$- \omega_1^2(m_{11}a_{11}a_{12} + m_{12}a_{21}a_{12} + m_{21}a_{11}a_{22} + m_{22}a_{21}a_{22}) = 0.$$
$$(5\text{–}27)$$

Similarly, we multiply Eq. (5–25) by a_{11} and Eq. (5–26) by a_{21}, and add to obtain

$$(k_{11}a_{11}a_{12} + k_{12}a_{11}a_{22} + k_{21}a_{12}a_{21} + k_{22}a_{21}a_{22})$$
$$- \omega_2^2(m_{11}a_{11}a_{12} + m_{12}a_{21}a_{22} + m_{21}a_{12}a_{21} + m_{22}a_{21}a_{22}) = 0.$$
$$(5\text{–}28)$$

Remembering that $k_{ij} = k_{ji}$ and that $m_{ij} = m_{ji}$, we now subtract Eq. (5–27) from Eq. (5–28) and simplify the result to

$$(\omega_1^2 - \omega_2^2)[m_{11}a_{11}a_{12} + m_{12}a_{11}a_{22} + m_{21}a_{12}a_{21} + m_{22}a_{21}a_{22}] = 0.$$
$$(5\text{–}29)$$

By hypothesis, $\omega_1 \neq \omega_2$. Hence Eq. (5–29) will be true only if the sum in the bracket vanishes. We write it as

$$\sum_{i=1}^{2} \sum_{j=1}^{2} m_{ij}a_{ir}a_{js} = 0 \qquad (r \neq s), \qquad (5\text{–}30)$$

and $r, s = 1, 2$.

The relation expressed by Eq. (5–30) is called an *orthogonality relation*. If there are more than two degrees of freedom, say n, it may be generalized to

$$\sum_{i=1}^{n} \sum_{j=1}^{n} m_{ij}a_{ir}a_{js} = 0 \qquad (r \neq s), \qquad (5\text{–}31)$$

and $r, s = 1, 2, \ldots, n$. The factors a_{ir} which appear here are called the *amplitude ratio factors*. As we shall see, the orthogonality relation will prove useful in establishing the constants resulting from the initial conditions.

A second condition customarily imposed upon the amplitude ratio factors is a *normalizing condition*. Equations (5–23), (5–24), (5–25), and (5–26) establish the ratios of these factors but do not fix their absolute values. To accomplish this, we arbitrarily set

$$\sum_{i=1}^{n} \sum_{j=1}^{n} m_{ij}a_{ir}a_{jr} = 1 \qquad (r = 1, 2, \ldots, n). \qquad (5\text{–}32)$$

As an example, consider the two-dimensional system in Section 5–2 (Fig. 5–1). In that example, dynamic coupling terms are absent. Hence $m_{12} = m_{21} = 0$. Furthermore $m_{11} = m_{22} = m$, and the frequencies are $\omega_1 = \sqrt{k/m}$, $\omega_2 = \sqrt{3k/m}$. The equations corresponding to Eqs. (5–23), (5–24), (5–25), and (5–26) are

$$(2k - m\omega_1^2)a_{11} - ka_{21} = 0,$$

$$-ka_{11} + (2k - m\omega_1^2)a_{21} = 0,$$

$$(2k - m\omega_2^2)a_{12} - ka_{22} = 0,$$

$$-ka_{12} + (2k - m\omega_2^2)a_{22} = 0.$$

Hence

$$a_{21} = a_{11}, \qquad \text{and} \qquad a_{22} = -a_{12}. \tag{5-33}$$

That the orthogonality condition is satisfied is evident by substitution in Eq. (5–30). We find, by using Eqs. (5–33),

$$a_{11}a_{12} + a_{21}a_{22} = 0. \tag{5-34}$$

The normalizing conditions prescribed by Eq. (5–32) are

$$ma_{11}^2 + ma_{21}^2 = 1, \tag{5-35}$$

$$ma_{12}^2 + ma_{22}^2 = 1. \tag{5-36}$$

By use of Eqs. (5–33) we have, therefore,

$$a_{21} = a_{11} = \sqrt{1/2m}, \qquad a_{12} = -a_{22} = \sqrt{1/2m}. \tag{5-37}$$

Substituting for the C_{jr} in Eqs. (5–21) leads to the displacements

$$q_1 = c_1\sqrt{(1/2m)} \sin (\omega_1 t + \psi_1) + c_2\sqrt{(1/2m)} \sin (\omega_2 t + \psi_2),$$
$$q_2 = c_1\sqrt{(1/2m)} \sin (\omega_1 t + \psi_1) - c_2\sqrt{(1/2m)} \sin (\omega_2 t + \psi_2). \tag{5-38}$$

Under the normalizing conditions, Eqs. (5–35) and (5–36), the quantities $\sqrt{m}a_{11}$ and $\sqrt{m}a_{21}$ have the properties of the sine and cosine of an angle. Suppose we considered these the components of a unit vector. Similarly, $\sqrt{m}a_{12}$ and $\sqrt{m}a_{22}$ could be interpreted as the components of a second unit vector. Then the orthogonality condition expressed by Eq. (5–30) or Eq. (5–34) is precisely the condition for these unit vectors to be mutually perpendicular. It is this similarity between the behavior of the amplitude ratio factors a_{jr} and the geometrical concepts expressed vectorially which gives rise to the concept of orthogonality in the more general sense as applied to a multidimensional space.

The scale factors c_1 and c_2 as well as the phase angles ψ_1 and ψ_2 appearing in Eqs. (5–38) may be evaluated in terms of the initial conditions. Let us consider the general two-dimensional case with static coupling where the masses are different. If m_1 and m_2 are the masses, the orthogonality and normalizing conditions are

$$m_1 a_{11} a_{12} + m_2 a_{21} a_{22} = 0,$$

$$m_1 a_{11}^2 + m_2 a_{21}^2 = 1,$$

$$m_1 a_{12}^2 + m_2 a_{22}^2 = 1.$$

Suppose that initially, at $t = 0$,

$$q_1(0) = Q_1, \qquad q_2(0) = Q_2,$$

$$\dot{q}_1(0) = \dot{Q}_1, \qquad \dot{q}_2(0) = \dot{Q}_2,$$

where Q_1, Q_2, $\dot{Q}_1$, and $\dot{Q}_2$ are the known displacements and velocities of the two masses. Then from Eqs. (5–22) we have

$$c_1 a_{11} \sin \psi_1 + c_2 a_{12} \sin \psi_2 = Q_1, \qquad (5\text{–}39)$$

$$c_1 a_{11} \omega_1 \cos \psi_1 + c_2 a_{12} \omega_2 \cos \psi_2 = \dot{Q}_1, \qquad (5\text{–}40)$$

$$c_1 a_{21} \sin \psi_1 + c_2 a_{22} \sin \psi_2 = Q_2, \qquad (5\text{–}41)$$

$$c_1 a_{21} \omega_1 \cos \psi_1 + c_2 a_{22} \omega_2 \cos \psi_2 = \dot{Q}_2. \qquad (5\text{–}42)$$

Multiplying Eq. (5–39) by $m_1 a_{11}$ and Eq. (5–41) by $m_2 a_{21}$, and adding the resulting equations, we obtain

$$(m_1 a_{11}^2 + m_2 a_{21}^2) c_1 \sin \psi_1 + (m_1 a_{11} a_{12} + m_2 a_{21} a_{22}) c_2 \sin \psi_2$$
$$= m_1 a_{11} Q_1 + m_2 a_{21} Q_2. \qquad (5\text{–}43)$$

By the normalizing and orthogonality conditions, the coefficient of $c_1 \sin \psi_1$ is 1 and that of $c_2 \sin \psi_2$ is 0. Therefore,

$$c_1 \sin \psi_1 = m_1 a_{11} Q_1 + m_2 a_{21} Q_2. \qquad (5\text{–}44)$$

In a similar way, from Eqs. (5–40) and (5–42) we find

$$c_1 \omega_1 \cos \psi_1 = m_1 a_{11} \dot{Q}_1 + m_2 a_{21} \dot{Q}_2. \qquad (5\text{–}45)$$

Solving Eqs. (5–44) and (5–45) simultaneously, we have

$$c_1 = \left\{[m_1a_{11}Q_1 + m_2a_{21}Q_2]^2 + \frac{1}{\omega_1^2}[m_1a_{11}\dot{Q}_1 + m_2a_{21}\dot{Q}_2]^2\right\}^{1/2}, \quad (5\text{–}46)$$

$$\psi_1 = \tan^{-1}\left\{\frac{\omega_1[m_1a_{11}Q_1 + m_2a_{21}Q_2]}{[m_1a_{11}\dot{Q}_1 + m_2a_{21}\dot{Q}_2]}\right\}. \qquad (5\text{–}47)$$

Proceeding in an analogous fashion with multipliers m_1a_{12} and m_2a_{22}, we obtain

$$c_2 = \left\{[m_1a_{12}Q_1 + m_2a_{22}Q_2]^2 + \frac{1}{\omega_2^2}[m_1a_{12}\dot{Q}_1 + m_2a_{22}\dot{Q}_2]^2\right\}^{1/2}, \qquad (5\text{–}48)$$

$$\psi_2 = \tan^{-1}\left\{\frac{\omega_2[m_1a_{12}Q_1 + m_2a_{22}Q_2]}{[m_1a_{12}\dot{Q}_1 + m_2a_{22}\dot{Q}_2]}\right\}. \qquad (5\text{–}49)$$

The orthogonality and normalizing relations are seen to be very useful in solving for the scale factors and the phase angles.

In the two-mass system whose motion is described by Eqs. (5–38), let the initial conditions be

$$Q_1 = q_1(0) = 5 \text{ cm}, \qquad Q_2 = q_2(0) = 10 \text{ cm},$$

$$\dot{Q}_1 = \dot{q}_1(0) = 0, \qquad \dot{Q}_2 = \dot{q}_2(0) = 0.$$

Following the analysis terminating in Eqs. (5–46), (5–47), (5–48), and (5–49), we find

$$c_1 = 15\sqrt{\tfrac{1}{2}m}, \qquad \psi_1 = \tfrac{1}{2}\pi,$$

$$c_2 = -5\sqrt{\tfrac{1}{2}m}, \qquad \psi_2 = \tfrac{1}{2}\pi.$$

The displacements are, therefore,

$$q_1 = 7.5 \cos \omega_1 t - 2.5 \cos \omega_2 t,$$

$$q_2 = 7.5 \cos \omega_1 t + 2.5 \cos \omega_2 t.$$

5–4 Normal coordinates. A problem in small oscillations like that discussed in the foregoing sections is one of multiple periodicity. In general, a given coordinate, say q_j, will depend upon the a_{jr} and the frequencies of all modes of oscillation at the same time. Only in certain special circumstances will the system oscillate at *one* of the natural frequencies alone while all other principal modes are zero. When it does and when the c_r of such an oscillation is unity in each coordinate, we speak of a *normal* *mode* of oscillation. For example, in the two-dimensional system, which we shall discuss for simplicity, one normal mode is specified by

$$q_1 = a_{11} \sin (\omega_1 t + \psi_1), \qquad q_2 = a_{21} \sin (\omega_1 t + \psi_1). \qquad (5\text{–}50)$$

A similar set of equations denotes the normal mode for frequency ω_2, namely,

$$q_1 = a_{12} \sin (\omega_2 t + \psi_2), \qquad q_2 = a_{22} \sin (\omega_2 t + \psi_2). \qquad (5\text{–}51)$$

In general, the displacements q_1 and q_2 consist of a linear combination of normal modes, as shown in Eqs. (5–22).

We shall now consider a coordinate system in which the sine functions in Eqs. (5–50) and (5–51) serve as coordinates. Let $\xi_1 = \sin (\omega_1 t + \psi_1)$ and $\xi_2 = \sin (\omega_2 t + \psi_2)$ denote these new coordinates. Then Eqs. (5–22) with all $c_j = 1$ become

$$q_1 = a_{11}\xi_1 + a_{12}\xi_2, \qquad q_2 = a_{21}\xi_1 + a_{22}\xi_2, \qquad (5\text{–}52)$$

and

$$\dot{q}_1 = a_{11}\dot{\xi}_1 + a_{12}\dot{\xi}_2, \qquad \dot{q}_2 = a_{21}\dot{\xi}_1 + a_{22}\dot{\xi}_2. \qquad (5\text{–}53)$$

These define a linear transformation of the original space of the q's into a new space of ξ's. The coordinates ξ_1 and ξ_2 are called *normal coordinates*. In general, for a system with n degrees of freedom, the normal coordinates, ξ_j, are defined by the linear equations

$$
\begin{aligned}
q_1 &= a_{11}\xi_1 + a_{12}\xi_2 + \cdots + a_{1n}\xi_n, \\
q_2 &= a_{21}\xi_1 + a_{22}\xi_2 + \cdots + a_{2n}\xi_n, \\
&\quad\cdot \qquad\quad \cdot \qquad\quad \cdot \qquad\qquad \cdot \\
&\quad\cdot \qquad\quad \cdot \qquad\quad \cdot \qquad\qquad \cdot \\
&\quad\cdot \qquad\quad \cdot \qquad\quad \cdot \qquad\qquad \cdot \\
q_n &= a_{n1}\xi_1 + a_{n2}\xi_2 + \cdots + a_{nn}\xi_n,
\end{aligned}
\qquad (5\text{–}54)
$$

with corresponding equations for the velocities $\dot{q}_j$.

An important theorem in the theory of matrices* states that if two quadratic forms such as

$$2T = \sum_{i,j=1}^{n} m_{ij}\dot{q}_i\dot{q}_j \quad \text{and} \quad 2V = \sum_{i,j=1}^{n} k_{ij}q_i q_j$$

---

* For a further discussion, see E. T. Whittaker, *Analytical Dynamics*. Cambridge: Cambridge University Press, 1937, pp. 178 ff.

have real coefficients with $m_{ij} = m_{ji}$ and $k_{ij} = k_{ji}$, and the first of these forms is positive definite, a linear transformation

$$q_i = \sum_{r=1}^{n} a_{ir}\xi_r \qquad (i = 1, 2, \ldots, n)$$

can be found such that

$$2T = \sum_{r=1}^{n} \dot{\xi}_r^2 \qquad \text{and} \qquad 2V = \sum_{r=1}^{n} \alpha_r \xi_r^2, \qquad (5\text{--}55)$$

where the quantities $\alpha_1, \alpha_2, \ldots, \alpha_n$ are roots of the determinantal equation

$$\begin{vmatrix} \alpha m_{11} - k_{11} & \alpha m_{12} - k_{12} \cdots \alpha m_{1n} - k_{1n} \\ \alpha m_{21} - k_{21} & \alpha m_{22} - k_{22} \cdots \alpha m_{2n} - k_{2n} \\ \cdot & \cdot \qquad\qquad \cdot \\ \cdot & \cdot \qquad\qquad \cdot \\ \cdot & \cdot \qquad\qquad \cdot \\ \alpha m_{n1} - k_{n1} & \alpha m_{n2} - k_{n2} \cdots \alpha m_{nn} - k_{nn} \end{vmatrix} = 0. \qquad (5\text{--}56)$$

In terms of the normal coordinates, the Lagrangian function is

$$L = \frac{1}{2} \sum_{r=1}^{n} (\dot{\xi}_r^2 - \alpha_r \xi_r^2),$$

and hence the equations of motion become

$$\ddot{\xi}_r + \alpha_r \xi_r = 0 \qquad (r = 1, 2, \ldots, n). \qquad (5\text{--}57)$$

The solutions of these equations will be periodic if the values of α_r are positive. Putting $\alpha_r = \omega_r^2$ and assuming a unit amplitude, we have as solutions of Eqs. (5–57),

$$\xi_r = \sin(\omega_r t + \psi_r) \qquad (r = 1, 2, \ldots, n). \qquad (5\text{--}58)$$

The reader should note that when α is replaced by ω^2 the determinantal equation (5–56) is the same as Eq. (5–9) with $\lambda^2 = -\omega^2$.

We shall find the transformation from the q-coordinates to the ξ-coordinates useful in discussing the forced vibrations of a system.

In a two-dimensional system, the transformation from the (q_1, q_2) coordinates into the (ξ_1, ξ_2) space can be portrayed geometrically. Consider such a system with no dynamic coupling in which the kinetic and potential energies are, respectively,

$$T = \tfrac{1}{2}(m_1 \dot{q}_1^2 + m_2 \dot{q}_2^2), \qquad V = \tfrac{1}{2}(k_0 q_1^2 + k_1 q_1 q_2 + k_2 q_2^2).$$

A curve $2T = m_1\dot{q}_1^2 + m_2\dot{q}_2^2$, for constant T, in a $(\dot{q}_1,\dot{q}_2)$ coordinate system is an ellipse with principal axes along the coordinate axes. Likewise the curve $2V = k_0 q_1^2 + k_1 q_1 q_2 + k_2 q_2^2$, for constant V, is an ellipse in a (q_1,q_2) coordinate system. Here, however, the axes of the ellipse are askew to the coordinate axes, but the center of the ellipse is at the origin.

Now let $\eta_1 = \sqrt{m_1}\,q_1$ and $\eta_2 = \sqrt{m_2}\,q_2$; also $\dot{\eta}_1 = \sqrt{m_1}\,\dot{q}_1$ and $\dot{\eta}_2 = \sqrt{m_2}\,\dot{q}_2$. Then the ellipse of constant kinetic energy becomes

$$2T = \dot{\eta}_1^2 + \dot{\eta}_2^2$$

in the $(\dot{\eta}_1,\dot{\eta}_2)$ plane. This is a circle. Furthermore, the curve of constant potential energy in the (η_1,η_2) plane becomes

$$2V = \frac{k_0}{m_1}\,\eta_1^2 + \frac{k_1 \eta_1 \eta_2}{\sqrt{m_1 m_2}} + \frac{k_2}{m_2}\,\eta_2^2,$$

which is still an ellipse with center at the origin. The cross-product term $(k_1/\sqrt{m_1 m_2})\eta_1\eta_2$ can be removed by rotating the (η_1,η_2) axes according to the standard equations,

$$\eta_1 = \xi_1 \cos\theta - \xi_2 \sin\theta, \qquad \eta_2 = \xi_1 \sin\theta + \xi_2 \cos\theta, \qquad (5\text{–}59)$$

where θ is given by $\tan 2\theta = (k_1\sqrt{m_1 m_2})/(m_2 k_0 - m_1 k_2)$.

The corresponding transformation in the velocity space,

$$\dot{\eta}_1 = \dot{\xi}_1 \cos\theta - \dot{\xi}_2 \sin\theta, \qquad \dot{\eta}_2 = \dot{\xi}_1 \sin\theta + \dot{\xi}_2 \cos\theta,$$

leaves the circle of constant kinetic energy unchanged. That is,

$$2T = \dot{\eta}_1^2 + \dot{\eta}_2^2 = \dot{\xi}_1^2 + \dot{\xi}_2^2,$$

as the reader may easily verify.

Thus successive transformations from the (q_1,q_2) plane into the (ξ_1,ξ_2) plane of the form

$$q_1 = \frac{1}{\sqrt{m_1}}\,(\xi_1 \cos\theta - \xi_2 \sin\theta),$$

$$q_2 = \frac{1}{\sqrt{m_2}}\,(\xi_1 \sin\theta + \xi_2 \cos\theta),$$

lead to the forms

$$2T = \dot{\xi}_1^2 + \dot{\xi}_2^2, \qquad 2V = \omega_1^2 \xi_1^2 + \omega_2^2 \xi_2^2,$$

for curves of constant T and V respectively.

For illustration consider the double mass and spring problem of Section 5-2. Here $m_1 = m_2 = m$ and $k_0 = k_1 = k_2 = k$. Hence

$$2T = m[\dot{q}_1^2 + \dot{q}_2^2], \qquad 2V = 2k[q_1^2 - q_1q_2 + q_2^2].$$

Setting $\eta_1 = \sqrt{m}\,q_1$, $\eta_2 = \sqrt{m}\,q_2$, $\dot{\eta}_1 = \sqrt{m}\,\dot{q}_1$, $\dot{\eta}_2 = \sqrt{m}\,\dot{q}_2$, we have

$$2T = \dot{\eta}_1^2 + \dot{\eta}_2^2, \qquad 2V = \frac{2k}{m}\,[\eta_1^2 - \eta_1\eta_2 + \eta_2^2]. \qquad (5\text{-}60)$$

The curve $2T = $ constant is a circle of radius $\sqrt{2T}$. We have only effected a change of scale by the transformation here. The curve $2V = $ constant in the original (q_1,q_2) plane is the ellipse shown in Fig. 5-2. In the (η_1,η_2) plane, this ellipse has the same form and orientation.

Now we rotate the axes in the (η_1,η_2) plane so as to remove the cross-product term $(\eta_1\eta_2)$. The required angle is given by

$$\tan 2\theta = +\infty,$$

or $\theta = 45°$. Hence, by Eqs. (5-59), the transformation equations are

$$\eta_1 = 0.707[\xi_1 - \xi_2], \qquad \eta_2 = 0.707[\xi_1 + \xi_2].$$

Substitution of these in Eqs. (5-60) yields

$$2V = \frac{k}{m}\,[\xi_1^2 + 3\xi_2^2],$$

which may be put in the form

$$\frac{\xi_1^2}{(2mV/k)} + \frac{\xi_2^2}{(2mV/3k)} = 1.$$

This is the standard form for an ellipse with principal axes coincident with the coordinate axes.

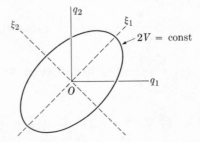

FIG. 5-2. Ellipse in displacement and normal coordinate systems.

We find that the curve of constant kinetic energy in the $(\dot{\xi}_1, \dot{\xi}_2)$ plane is

$$2T = \dot{\xi}_1^2 + \dot{\xi}_2^2.$$

Since, by the analysis in Section 5–2, $\omega^2 = k/m$ or $\omega^2 = 3k/m$, we see that the potential energy curve becomes

$$2V = \omega_1^2 \xi_1^2 + \omega_2^2 \xi_2^2,$$

in conformity with Eqs. (5–55) with $\alpha_r = \omega_r^2$.

With T and V as given, Lagrange's equations in normal coordinates are

$$\ddot{\xi}_1 + \omega_1^2 \xi_1 = 0, \qquad \ddot{\xi}_2 + \omega_2^2 \xi_2 = 0,$$

where $\omega_1^2 = k/m$ and $\omega_2^2 = 3k/m$. Hence the solutions of unit amplitude are

$$\xi_1 = \sin(\omega_1 t + \psi_1), \qquad \xi_2 = \sin(\omega_2 t + \psi_2).$$

5–5 An example of dynamic coupling. The double pendulum, discussed in general in Section 2–6, is a simple example of a dynamically coupled system. We shall restrict the motion to small amplitudes and for convenience take the masses of the bobs and the lengths of the supports to be the same for each pendulum, as shown in Fig. 5–3. To terms of the second order, we have

$$T = \tfrac{1}{2}ml^2[2\dot{q}_1^2 + \dot{q}_2^2 + 2\dot{q}_1\dot{q}_2],$$

$$V = \tfrac{1}{2}mgl[2q_1^2 + q_2^2].$$

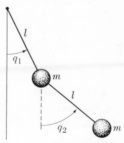

From $L = T - V$ we obtain the Lagrangian equations

$$2\ddot{q}_1 + 2\frac{g}{l}q_1 + \ddot{q}_2 = 0, \quad (5\text{–}61)$$

$$\ddot{q}_1 + \ddot{q}_2 + \frac{g}{l}q_2 = 0. \qquad (5\text{–}62)$$

FIG. 5–3. Dynamically coupled pendulums.

Therefore this is a system with no static coupling and with dynamic coupling represented by the term $\ddot{q}_2$ in Eq. (5–61) and the term $\ddot{q}_1$ in Eq. (5–62). These obviously result from the term $\dot{q}_1\dot{q}_2$ in the kinetic energy. We shall show that it is possible to reduce the system to one with static coupling only.

Let

$$q_1 = \lambda_1 x_1 + \mu_1 x_2, \qquad q_2 = \lambda_2 x_1 + \mu_2 x_2, \qquad (5\text{–}63)$$

where x_1 and x_2 are new generalized coordinates and $\lambda_1, \lambda_2, \mu_1, \mu_2$ are constants to be determined. Substituting for $\dot{q}_1$ and $\dot{q}_2$ in the expression for T, we have

$$T = \tfrac{1}{2}ml^2[(2\lambda_1^2 + \lambda_2^2 + 2\lambda_1\lambda_2)\dot{x}_1^2 + (2\mu_1^2 + \mu_2^2 + 2\mu_1\mu_2)\dot{x}_2^2$$
$$+ 2(2\lambda_1\mu_1 + \lambda_2\mu_2 + \lambda_1\mu_2 + \lambda_2\mu_1)\dot{x}_1\dot{x}_2].$$

If the term in $\dot{x}_1\dot{x}_2$ is to vanish, we must choose the constants so that its coefficient is zero. Hence we may take

$$\lambda_1 \text{ arbitrary}, \quad \lambda_2 = -\lambda_1, \quad \mu_1 = 0, \quad \mu_2 = 1$$

as one possible set. Furthermore, we may arbitrarily set $\lambda_1 = 1$. Then Eqs. (5–63) become

$$q_1 = x_1, \quad q_2 = -x_1 + x_2,$$

and we find

$$T = \tfrac{1}{2}ml^2(\dot{x}_1^2 + \dot{x}_2^2).$$

With this choice of coordinates, the potential energy reduces to

$$V = \tfrac{1}{2}mgl[3x_1^2 + x_2^2 - 2x_1x_2],$$

and we have the Lagrangian equations

$$\ddot{x}_1 = -\frac{3g}{l}x_1 + \frac{g}{l}x_2, \quad \ddot{x}_2 = -\frac{g}{l}x_2 + \frac{g}{l}x_1.$$

These exhibit static coupling between the coordinates x_1 and x_2. From this point on, the problem is identical with that of the coupled masses discussed in Section 5–2. We leave the solution as an exercise for the reader. The method exhibited here may be extended to systems with more than two degrees of freedom.

5–6 Forced oscillations. Consider a mass-spring system, as shown in Fig. 5–4, whose motion is one-dimensional. An impressed force Q is applied to the mass, and we seek the displacement $q(t)$ due to the action of Q. We assume that Q has the form $Q_0 \sin \omega t$, where ω is the driving frequency.

The equation of motion is

$$m\ddot{q} + kq = Q_0 \sin \omega t. \tag{5–64}$$

Its general solution consists of the free vibration, $q = C \sin(\omega_0 t + \psi)$, and the particular integral q_p, which we assume to be of the form $q_p =$

$A \sin \omega t + B \cos \omega t$. The quantities A and B are to be determined so that q_p satisfies Eq. (5–64). Substituting and collecting terms, we find

$$A = \frac{Q_0}{k - m\omega^2}, \qquad B = 0.$$

Since the frequency of free vibration is $\omega_0 = \sqrt{k/m}$, A becomes $Q_0/m(\omega_0^2 - \omega^2)$. Thus the amplitude of the forced oscillation is larger as the driving frequency approaches the natural frequency of the system. When $\omega = \omega_0$, the phenomenon of

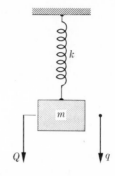

FIG. 5–4. Oscillating mass under an external force.

resonance occurs, and we would expect the value of q_p to become infinite. However, our restriction to small oscillations and the presence of frictional damping preclude this. For the moment, we assume no damping and restrict ω to values different from ω_0. The steady-state oscillation $q_p = \{Q_0/m(\omega_0^2 - \omega^2)\} \sin \omega t$ is called the *forced oscillation* of the system.

These basic ideas for a one-dimensional system may be employed in analyzing a multiply periodic system. Let generalized forces Q_1, $Q_2, \ldots, Q_n$ act on the component masses of the system. Then, by virtue of the linearity of the system, the work done by these in displacements $q_1, q_2, \ldots, q_n$ will be $\sum_{i=1}^{n} Q_i q_i$, and this must be the same as the work done by a corresponding set of forces $R_1, R_2, \ldots, R_n$ in the normal coordinate system during displacements $\xi_1, \xi_2, \ldots, \xi_n$. Hence

$$\sum_{i=1}^{n} Q_i q_i = \sum_{r=1}^{n} R_r \xi_r. \tag{5–65}$$

Substituting for each q_i its value in terms of the a_{ir} and ξ_r from Eqs. (5–54) and equating terms in ξ_r, we have

$$R_r = \sum_{i=1}^{n} a_{ir} Q_i \qquad (r = 1, 2, \ldots, n) \tag{5–66}$$

for the rth mode of oscillation.

In the normal coordinates, each mode of oscillation is independent of the others. Furthermore, Eq. (5–66) implies that if Q_i is periodic with frequency ω, the forces R_r will also be periodic and of the same frequency. Suppose that $Q_i = Q_{0i} \cos (\omega t + \psi)$. Then

$$R_r = \sum_{i=1}^{n} a_{ir} Q_{0i} \cos (\omega t + \psi) = R_{0r} \cos (\omega t + \psi).$$

If the equations

$$\ddot{\xi}_r + \omega_r^2 \xi_r = R_{0r} \cos(\omega t + \psi) \qquad (r = 1, 2, \ldots, n) \qquad (5\text{-}67)$$

are solved for the steady-state oscillations, we have by analogy with the solution of Eq. (5–64),

$$\xi_{rs} = \frac{R_{0r}}{\omega_r^2 - \omega^2} \cos(\omega t + \psi) \qquad (r = 1, 2, \ldots, n), \qquad (5\text{-}68)$$

where the subscript s denotes the solution due to the forced motion.

By the linear transformation, Eqs. (5–54), relating the ξ_r with the q_i, we obtain

$$q_{is} = \sum_{r=1}^{n} \frac{a_{ir} R_{0r}}{\omega_r^2 - \omega^2} \cos(\omega t + \psi) \qquad (i = 1, 2, \ldots, n). \qquad (5\text{-}69)$$

For the two-dimensional oscillator, as an example,

$$q_{1s} = \left[a_{11} \left\{ \frac{a_{11}Q_{01} + a_{21}Q_{02}}{\omega_1^2 - \omega^2} \right\} + a_{12} \left\{ \frac{a_{12}Q_{01} + a_{22}Q_{02}}{\omega_2^2 - \omega^2} \right\} \right] \cos(\omega t + \psi),$$

$$(5\text{-}70)$$

$$q_{2s} = \left[a_{21} \left\{ \frac{a_{11}Q_{01} + a_{21}Q_{02}}{\omega_1^2 - \omega^2} \right\} + a_{22} \left\{ \frac{a_{12}Q_{01} + a_{22}Q_{02}}{\omega_2^2 - \omega^2} \right\} \right] \cos(\omega t + \psi).$$

The introduction of normal coordinates simplifies the analysis of forced motion. We solve the simplified normal coordinate equations first, and then by making use of the a_{ir} transform the steady-state normal coordinate solution back to the displacement coordinates.

Suppose the mass-spring system shown in Fig. 5–1 is subjected to the forces $Q_1 = 0$, $Q_2 = 10 \cos \omega t$. The steady-state solution for normal coordinates is

$$\xi_{1s} = \left(\frac{7.07}{\omega_1^2 - \omega^2} \right) \frac{1}{\sqrt{m}} \cos \omega t,$$

$$\xi_{2s} = \left(\frac{7.07}{\omega_2^2 - \omega^2} \right) \frac{1}{\sqrt{m}} \cos \omega t,$$

and for the displacement coordinates

$$q_{1s} = \left[\frac{0.707}{m} \frac{(7.07)}{\omega_1^2 - \omega^2} - \frac{0.707}{m} \frac{(7.07)}{\omega_2^2 - \omega^2} \right] \cos \omega t,$$

$$q_{2s} = \left[\frac{0.707}{m} \frac{(7.07)}{\omega_1^2 - \omega^2} + \frac{0.707}{m} \frac{(7.07)}{\omega_2^2 - \omega^2} \right] \cos \omega t.$$

5–7 Nonconservative systems. In the preceding sections it was assumed that the generalized forces acting on the system were derivable from a potential function; that is,

$$Q_i = -\frac{\partial V}{\partial q_i} = -\sum_{j=1}^{n} k_{ij}q_j \qquad (i = 1, 2, \ldots, n). \qquad (5\text{–}71)$$

The total work W_i done by such a force in a complete cycle of the respective coordinate q_i is given by a line integral such as

$$W_i = \oint Q_i\, dq_i = \oint \left(-\sum_{j=1}^{n} k_{ij}q_j\right) dq_i \qquad (i = 1, 2, \ldots, n). \qquad (5\text{–}72)$$

To obtain the total work done by all the forces, we sum the integrals for the degrees of freedom $i = 1, 2, \ldots, n$. For example, in the case $n = 3$, we have

$$W = \oint [Q_1\, dq_1 + Q_2\, dq_2 + Q_3\, dq_3] \qquad (5\text{–}73)$$

or

$$W = \oint \{[k_{11}q_1 + k_{12}q_2 + k_{13}q_3]\, dq_1 + [k_{21}q_1 + k_{22}q_2 + k_{23}q_3]\, dq_2$$
$$+ [k_{31}q_1 + k_{32}q_2 + k_{33}q_3]\, dq_3\}. \qquad (5\text{–}74)$$

If the force field is conservative, the line integral in Eq. (5–73) is independent of the path of integration. A necessary and sufficient condition* for this is that

$$\frac{\partial Q_2}{\partial q_3} - \frac{\partial Q_3}{\partial q_2} = 0, \qquad \frac{\partial Q_3}{\partial q_1} - \frac{\partial Q_1}{\partial q_3} = 0, \qquad \frac{\partial Q_1}{\partial q_2} - \frac{\partial Q_2}{\partial q_1} = 0.$$

But from Eq. (5–74) this implies

$$k_{23} = k_{32}, \qquad k_{31} = k_{13}, \qquad k_{12} = k_{21}. \qquad (5\text{–}75)$$

These are precisely the restrictions placed upon the k_{ij} in the discussion in the preceding sections. If one of the conditions $k_{ij} = k_{ji}$ is not fulfilled, the system is *nonconservative*.

A common type of nonconservative system is one in which the forces are proportional to the first power of the velocities. Such systems are called *dissipative* systems. Frictional forces in viscous damping problems

---

* See, for example, W. Kaplan, *Advanced Calculus*. Reading, Massachusetts: Addison-Wesley Publishing Company, Inc., 1952, p. 280.

are examples of this type. Suppose the generalized forces acting on the system are linear combinations of the velocities; that is,

$$-Q_1 = f_{11}\dot{q}_1 + f_{12}\dot{q}_2 + f_{13}\dot{q}_3 + \cdots + f_{1n}\dot{q}_n,$$

$$-Q_2 = f_{21}\dot{q}_1 + f_{22}\dot{q}_2 + f_{23}\dot{q}_3 + \cdots + f_{2n}\dot{q}_n,$$

$$\cdot \quad \cdot \quad \cdot \quad \cdot \quad \cdot \quad (5\text{–}76)$$

$$-Q_n = f_{n1}\dot{q}_1 + f_{n2}\dot{q}_2 + f_{n3}\dot{q}_3 + \cdots + f_{nn}\dot{q}_n,$$

where the coefficients f_{ij} are, in general, constants.

The total work done by the forces Q_i per unit time may be written $Q_1\dot{q}_1 + Q_2\dot{q}_2 + \cdots + Q_n\dot{q}_n$ or, by Eqs. (5–76),

$$W = -\sum_{i=1}^{n}\sum_{j=1}^{n} f_{ij}\dot{q}_i\dot{q}_j. \qquad (5\text{–}77)$$

We distinguish two cases:

Case I. Suppose $f_{ij} = f_{ji}$. Then the corresponding cross-product terms $\dot{q}_i\dot{q}_j$ combine, and we find that

$$\frac{\partial W}{\partial \dot{q}_i} = -2\sum_{j=1}^{n} f_{ij}\dot{q}_j = 2Q_i \qquad (i = 1, 2, \ldots, n). \qquad (5\text{–}78)$$

Observe that $(\partial W/\partial \dot{q}_i)$ bears the same relationship to the nonconservative force Q_i that $(\partial W/\partial q_i)$ does in the conservative case. Hence we introduce a function

$$D = -\frac{1}{2}W = \frac{1}{2}\sum_{i=1}^{n}\sum_{j=1}^{n} f_{ij}\dot{q}_i\dot{q}_j, \qquad (5\text{–}79)$$

called the *dissipation function*, such that

$$\frac{\partial D}{\partial \dot{q}_i} = -Q_i \qquad (i = 1, 2, \ldots, n). \qquad (5\text{–}80)$$

D plays the same part with respect to the velocities in the dissipative system that V plays relative to the coordinates in the conservative system.

By the introduction of the augmented Lagrangian function, $L = T + D - V$, we obtain the equations of motion

$$\frac{d}{dt}\left(\frac{\partial T}{\partial \dot{q}_i}\right) + \frac{\partial D}{\partial \dot{q}_i} - \frac{\partial T}{\partial q_i} + \frac{\partial V}{\partial q_i} = 0 \qquad (i = 1, 2, \ldots, n). \quad (5\text{–}81)$$

(The velocity vector is v = ẋi + ẏj. Hence Q·v = 2ω (ẏi − ẋj) · (ẋi + ẏj) sin φ = 0, so that Q and v are perpendicular.

For the oscillatory system, these become

$$\sum_{j=1}^{n} m_{ij}\ddot{q}_i + \sum_{j=1}^{n} f_{ij}\dot{q}_i + \sum_{j=1}^{n} k_{ij}q_i = 0 \qquad (i = 1, 2, \ldots, n). \qquad (5\text{--}82)$$

Case II. Suppose $f_{ij} = -f_{ji}$ for every i and j in Eq. (5–77). This implies that $f_{11} = f_{22} = f_{33} = \cdots = f_{nn} = 0$. Hence $W = 0$, and the forces in this case do no work. Forces of this type are called *gyroscopic forces*. A force of this type is perpendicular to the velocity vector at the point upon which it acts. The Coriolis force, $-2m(\boldsymbol{\omega} \times \mathbf{v})$, discussed in Chapter 1, is perpendicular to $\mathbf{v}$ (that is, to the plane of $\boldsymbol{\omega}$ and $\mathbf{v}$). Hence this is an example of a gyroscopic force. The equations of motion, (1–126) and (1–127), for the Foucault pendulum show this. The forces are $2\omega\dot{y}\sin\phi$ and $-2\omega\dot{x}\sin\phi$, so that $\mathbf{Q} = Q_1\mathbf{i} + Q_2\mathbf{j} = 2\omega(\dot{y}\mathbf{i} - \dot{x}\mathbf{j})\sin\phi$. The velocity vector is $\mathbf{v} = \dot{x}\mathbf{i} + \dot{y}\mathbf{j}$. Hence $\mathbf{Q}\cdot\mathbf{v} = 2\omega(\dot{y}\mathbf{i} - \dot{x}\mathbf{j}) \cdot (\dot{x}\mathbf{i} + \dot{y}\mathbf{j})\sin\phi = 0$, so that $\mathbf{Q}$ and $\mathbf{v}$ are perpendicular.

The differential equations of motion are

$$\sum_{j=1}^{n} m_{ij}\ddot{q}_j + \sum_{\substack{(j=1) \\ (j \neq i)}}^{n} f_{ij}\dot{q}_j + \sum_{j=1}^{n} k_{ij}q_i = 0 \qquad (i = 1, 2, \ldots, n). \qquad (5\text{--}83)$$

Two examples will suffice to illustrate Cases I and II.

EXAMPLE 1. A damped oscillatory two-mass system is shown in Fig. 5–5. We have discussed the undamped system in Sections 5–2 and 5–4. There we found that the introduction of normal coordinates ξ_1 and ξ_2 by the equations

$$q_1 = \frac{0.707}{\sqrt{m}}(\xi_1 - \xi_2), \qquad (5\text{--}84)$$

$$q_2 = \frac{0.707}{\sqrt{m}}(\xi_1 + \xi_2), \qquad (5\text{--}85)$$

led to the following expressions for the kinetic and potential energies:

$$T = \tfrac{1}{2}[\dot{\xi}_1^2 + \dot{\xi}_2^2], \qquad (5\text{--}86)$$

$$V = \tfrac{1}{2}[\omega_1^2\xi_1^2 + \omega_2^2\xi_2^2], \qquad (5\text{--}87)$$

where ω_1 and ω_2 are the frequencies of oscillation.

The dissipation function in the system shown here is

$$D = \tfrac{1}{2}f[\dot{q}_1^2 + \dot{q}_2^2],$$

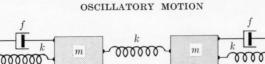

FIG. 5–5. Coupled damped oscillator.

or, in terms of the normal coordinates.

$$D = \tfrac{1}{2}\frac{f}{m}\,[\dot{\xi}_1^2 + \dot{\xi}_2^2].\tag{5-88}$$

Hence the modified Lagrangian function, $L = T + D - V$, becomes

$$L = \tfrac{1}{2}[\dot{\xi}_1^2 + \dot{\xi}_2^2] + \tfrac{1}{2}\frac{f}{m}\,[\dot{\xi}_1^2 + \dot{\xi}_2^2] - \tfrac{1}{2}[\omega_1^2\xi_1^2 + \omega_2^2\xi_2^2],$$

and Lagrange's equations are

$$\ddot{\xi}_1 + \frac{f}{m}\,\dot{\xi}_1 + \omega_1^2\xi_1 = R_1,\tag{5-89}$$

$$\ddot{\xi}_2 + \frac{f}{m}\,\dot{\xi}_2 + \omega_2^2\xi_2 = R_2,\tag{5-90}$$

where R_1 and R_2 are the generalized driving forces associated with the normal coordinates.

Suppose, first, that R_1 and R_2 are zero; then the substitutions $\xi_1 = c_1 e^{\lambda_1 t}$ and $\xi_2 = c_2 e^{\lambda_2 t}$ yield

$$\lambda_1^2 + \frac{f}{m}\,\lambda_1 + \omega_1^2 = 0, \qquad \lambda_2^2 + \frac{f}{m}\,\lambda_2 + \omega_2^2 = 0.$$

The values λ_1 and λ_2 are

$$\lambda_1 = -\frac{f}{2m} \pm \frac{1}{2}\,\sqrt{(f/m)^2 - 4\omega_1^2},$$

$$\lambda_2 = -\frac{f}{2m} \pm \frac{1}{2}\,\sqrt{(f/m)^2 - 4\omega_2^2}.$$

The values of λ_1 and λ_2 are complex and hence yield periodic values of ξ_1 and ξ_2 if $(f/m)^2 < 4\omega_1^2$ and $(f/m)^2 < 4\omega_2^2$. We assume this to be the case and write

$$\lambda_1 = -\frac{f}{2m} \pm i\sqrt{\omega_1^2 - (f/2m)^2}\,,$$

$$\lambda_2 = -\frac{f}{2m} \pm i\sqrt{\omega_2^2 - (f/2m)^2} \qquad (i^2 = -1).$$

Let

$$\alpha_1 = \sqrt{\omega_1^2 - (f/2m)^2}, \tag{5–91}$$

$$\alpha_2 = \sqrt{\omega_2^2 - (f/2m)^2}. \tag{5–92}$$

Then the values of ξ_1 and ξ_2 with unit initial amplitude become

$$\xi_1 = e^{-ft/2m} \sin(\alpha_1 t + \beta_1), \tag{5–93}$$

$$\xi_2 = e^{-ft/2m} \sin(\alpha_2 t + \beta_2), \tag{5–94}$$

where β_1 and β_2 are constants.

The values of ξ_1 and ξ_2 found here are similar to those found in Eq. (5–58) for the undamped case. They differ, however, in two important respects: (a) as $t \to \infty$, the exponential factors approach zero, and hence $\xi_1 \to 0$, $\xi_2 \to 0$; (b) the frequencies of oscillation α_1 and α_2 are less than the frequencies ω_1 and ω_2. These solutions for ξ_1 and ξ_2 are called the *transient* solutions of the problem.

Having found ξ_1 and ξ_2, we write the transient solutions for q_1 and q_2 as

$$q_1 = \frac{0.707}{\sqrt{m}} e^{-ft/2m}[c_1 \sin(\alpha_1 t + \psi_1) - c_2 \sin(\alpha_2 t + \psi_2)],$$

$$q_2 = \frac{0.707}{\sqrt{m}} e^{-ft/2m}[c_1 \sin(\alpha_1 t + \psi_1) + c_2 \sin(\alpha_2 t + \psi_2)],$$

where the scale factors c_1 and c_2 together with the phase angles ψ_1 and ψ_2 are to be obtained from the initial conditions.

Suppose the left-hand mass in Fig. 5–5 is driven by a force $Q_1 = q_0 \cos \omega t$, while no external force is applied to the right-hand mass. Then by Eqs. (5–65), (5–84), and (5–85) we find

$$R_1 = \frac{0.707}{\sqrt{m}} q_0 \cos \omega t, \qquad R_2 = -\frac{0.707}{\sqrt{m}} q_0 \cos \omega t.$$

Applying these values in Eqs. (5–89) and (5–90), we obtain the particular integrals

$$\xi_{1p} = \frac{0.707 q_0}{\sqrt{m}\, \Delta_1} \sin(\omega t + \phi_1), \tag{5–95}$$

$$\xi_{2p} = -\frac{0.707 q_0}{\sqrt{m}\, \Delta_2} \sin(\omega t + \phi_2), \tag{5–96}$$

where

$$\Delta_1 = \left[(\omega_1^2 - \omega^2)^2 + \left(\frac{f\omega}{m}\right)^2 \right]^{1/2},$$

$$\Delta_2 = \left[(\omega_2^2 - \omega^2)^2 + \left(\frac{f\omega}{m}\right)^2 \right]^{1/2},$$

$$\phi_1 = \tan^{-1}\left[\frac{m(\omega_1^2 - \omega^2)}{f\omega} \right],$$

$$\phi_2 = \tan^{-1}\left[\frac{m(\omega_2^2 - \omega^2)}{f\omega} \right].$$

Hence, by Eqs. (5–84) and (5–85),

$$q_{1p} = \frac{q_0}{2m\Delta_1} \sin(\omega t + \phi_1) + \frac{q_0}{2m\Delta_2} \sin(\omega t + \phi_2), \qquad (5\text{–}97)$$

$$q_{2p} = \frac{q_0}{2m\Delta_1} \sin(\omega t + \phi_1) - \frac{q_0}{2m\Delta_2} \sin(\omega t + \phi_2). \qquad (5\text{–}98)$$

These solutions represent the *steady-state* motion of the system, that is, the motion, due to the external driving force, which persists after the transient displacements die out. Note that the steady-state oscillations have the same frequency ω as the driving force but differ in phase angle. The quantities Δ_1 and Δ_2, which appear in the steady-state values for q_1 and q_2, are called the *force-displacement impedances*. They play a role similar to the impedance $Z = \sqrt{[\omega L - (1/\omega C)]^2 + R^2}$ in a series electrical circuit.

EXAMPLE 2. To illustrate Case II, we shall consider again the rotating top whose motion was discussed in Section 4–9. The kinetic and potential energies are

$$T = \tfrac{1}{2}\{ I(\dot\theta^2 + \dot\phi^2 \sin^2\theta) + I_3(\dot\psi + \dot\phi \cos\theta)^2 \}, \qquad (5\text{–}99)$$

$$V = mgl \cos\theta, \qquad (5\text{–}100)$$

where θ, ϕ, ψ are the Eulerian angles.

Equation (4–78) shows that

$$I_3(\dot\psi + \dot\phi \cos\theta) = L_\psi \qquad \text{(a constant)}.$$

Hence we may write

$$T = \tfrac{1}{2}\{ I(\dot\theta^2 + \dot\phi^2 \sin^2\theta) + L_\psi(\dot\psi + \dot\phi \cos\theta) \}. \qquad (5\text{–}101)$$

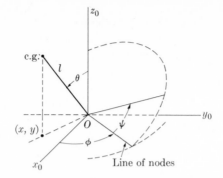

Fig. 5–6. Coordinate system for a top.

Let the projection of the center of gravity of the top on the (x_0, y_0) plane (Fig. 5–6) be the point (x, y). We shall now limit our discussion to motion in which x and y are so small that powers higher than two in x, y, $\dot{x}$, and $\dot{y}$ in the kinetic and potential energies may be neglected. That is, the motion of the top is such that its axis of spin is in the vicinity of the z_0-axis.

From the figure it is apparent that

$$x = l \sin \theta \sin \phi, \qquad y = -l \sin \theta \cos \phi. \qquad (5\text{–}102)$$

From these we find that

$$\dot{\theta} = \frac{\dot{x} \sin \phi - \dot{y} \cos \phi}{l \cos \theta},$$

$$\dot{\phi} = \frac{\dot{x} \cos \phi + \dot{y} \sin \phi}{l \sin \theta}, \qquad (5\text{–}103)$$

$$l^2 \sin^2 \theta = x^2 + y^2,$$

and hence

$$\dot{\phi} \cos \theta = (x\dot{y} - y\dot{x}) \left(\frac{1}{x^2 + y^2} - \frac{1}{2l^2} \right),$$

$$\dot{\theta}^2 + \dot{\phi}^2 \sin^2 \theta = \frac{1}{l^2} (\dot{x}^2 + \dot{y}^2).$$

Therefore we have for the kinetic energy

$$T = \frac{1}{2} \left\{ \frac{I}{l^2} (\dot{x}^2 + \dot{y}^2) + L_\psi (x\dot{y} - y\dot{x}) \left(\frac{1}{x^2 + y^2} - \frac{1}{2l^2} \right) + L_\psi \dot{\psi} \right\},$$

$$(5\text{–}104)$$

and similarly

$$V = mgl\{ 1 - \tfrac{1}{2l^2}(x^2 + y^2) \}. \qquad (5\text{–}105)$$

In terms of x and y, then, the Lagrangian equations are

$$I\ddot{x} - mglx + L_\psi \dot{y} = 0, \qquad I\ddot{y} - mgly - L_\psi \dot{x} = 0.$$

These may be written

$$\ddot{x} = \alpha^2 x - \beta \dot{y}, \tag{5-106}$$

$$\ddot{y} = \alpha^2 y + \beta \dot{x}, \tag{5-107}$$

where

$$\alpha^2 = \frac{mgl}{I}, \qquad \beta = \frac{L_\psi}{I}.$$

Equations (5–106) and (5–107) are equivalent to those of a unit mass moving in the xy-plane under a repelling force $\mathbf{F} = \alpha^2(x\mathbf{i} + y\mathbf{j})$ and a gyroscopic force $\mathbf{G} = \beta(-\dot{y}\mathbf{i} + \dot{x}\mathbf{j})$. These equations are the two-dimensional equivalents to Eq. (5–83). Since the velocity $\mathbf{v} = \dot{x}\mathbf{i} + \dot{y}\mathbf{j}$, we observe that

$$\mathbf{G}\cdot\mathbf{v} = \beta(-\dot{y}\mathbf{i} + \dot{x}\mathbf{j})\cdot(\dot{x}\mathbf{i} + \dot{y}\mathbf{j}) = 0.$$

The gyroscopic forces do no work.

Suppose the top is spinning with its axis vertical and is disturbed slightly. Equations (5–106) and (5–107) show that the departure of the center of gravity projection tends to increase, and at the same time it swings about the origin either clockwise or counterclockwise, depending on the sign of β. In other words, the top starts to precess.

We ask, then, whether the motion is stable, that is, whether the axis will remain in the neighborhood of the z_0-axis if the top is disturbed. Let $x = Ae^{\lambda t}$ and $y = Be^{\lambda t}$ and substitute in Eqs. (5–106) and (5–107) to obtain

$$A(\lambda^2 - \alpha^2) + B\lambda\beta = 0, \qquad -A\lambda\beta + B(\lambda^2 - \alpha^2) = 0.$$

These will have a nontrivial solution for A and B if

$$\begin{vmatrix} \lambda^2 - \alpha^2 & \beta\lambda \\ -\beta\lambda & \lambda^2 - \alpha^2 \end{vmatrix} = 0.$$

From this we find

$$\lambda = \pm\tfrac{1}{2}(i\beta \pm \sqrt{4\alpha^2 - \beta^2}). \tag{5-108}$$

If $\beta^2 > 4\alpha^2$, the values of λ will be pure imaginary and the values of x and y periodic with constant amplitude. In this case the motion of the top is said to be *stable*. Expressed in terms of the angular momentum

L_ψ and the other physical constants, the condition for stability is

$$L_\psi^2 > 4Imgl.$$

In the case under discussion, L_ψ is very nearly $I_3\dot\psi$, where $\dot\psi$ is the constant spin velocity. Hence for $\dot\psi$ large enough, the axis of the top remains permanently in the neighborhood of the z_0-axis.

If $\beta^2 < 4\alpha^2$ in Eq. (5–108), there are two pairs of conjugate complex roots. In one of these the real part is positive; in the other the real part is negative. The motion in this case is said to be *unstable*.

Suppose $\beta^2 > 4\alpha^2$ so that the motion is stable. Let the roots of Eq. (5–108) be

$$\lambda_1 = i\left(\frac{\beta}{2} + \frac{1}{2}\sqrt{\beta^2 - 4\alpha^2}\right) = i\mu,$$

$$\lambda_2 = i\left(-\frac{\beta}{2} - \frac{1}{2}\sqrt{\beta^2 - 4\alpha^2}\right) = -i\mu,$$

$$\lambda_3 = i\left(\frac{\beta}{2} - \frac{1}{2}\sqrt{\beta^2 - 4\alpha^2}\right) = i\nu,$$ (5–109)

$$\lambda_4 = i\left(-\frac{\beta}{2} + \frac{1}{2}\sqrt{\beta^2 - 4\alpha^2}\right) = -i\nu.$$

Then the solutions of Eqs. (5–106) and (5–107) for x and y are

$$x = A_1 e^{i\mu t} + A_2 e^{-i\mu t} + A_3 e^{i\nu t} + A_4 e^{-i\nu t},$$ (5–110)
$$y = B_1 e^{i\mu t} + B_2 e^{-i\mu t} + B_3 e^{i\nu t} + B_4 e^{-i\nu t},$$

where

$$B_k = \frac{A_k(\alpha^2 - \lambda_k^2)}{\beta\lambda_k} \qquad (k = 1, 2, 3, 4).$$ (5–111)

By using the values of λ from Eqs. (5–109) together with Eq. (5–111), the solutions for x and y can be put in the form

$$x = C_1 \sin(\mu t + \psi_1) + C_2 \sin(\nu t + \psi_2),$$ (5–112)

$$y = C_1\left(\frac{\alpha^2 + \mu^2}{-\beta\mu}\right)\cos(\mu t + \psi_1) + C_2\left(\frac{\alpha^2 + \nu^2}{-\beta\nu}\right)\cos(\nu t + \psi_2),$$
(5–113)

where the constants C_1, C_2, ψ_1, ψ_2 are to be determined from the initial conditions. The motion of the projection of the center of gravity of the top on the xy-plane consists, therefore, of the superposition of two elliptic harmonic motions. One has a frequency μ and the other a frequency ν.

5–8 Stability of oscillatory motion. Consider an oscillating mass m moving under a restoring force $-kq$ and a dissipative force $-b\dot{q}$, where q is the displacement at time t. The differential equation of motion is

$$m\ddot{q} + b\dot{q} + kq = 0. \tag{5–114}$$

Assuming $q = Ae^{\lambda t}$ as a solution, we find the characteristic equation

$$m\lambda^2 + b\lambda + k = 0, \tag{5–115}$$

from which we find

$$\lambda = \frac{-b \pm \sqrt{b^2 - 4km}}{2m}. \tag{5–116}$$

If m, b, and k are such that λ is nonpositive, the oscillatory motion is said to be *stable*. We observe that this will be the case if $b > 0$ and $k > 0$, since m is always positive. Stability of the motion implies that, following the initial disturbance or state of motion, the mass either oscillates indefinitely at constant amplitude or its amplitude diminishes with the time.

For systems with several degrees of freedom, the question of stability is answered by a study of the characteristic equation in λ resulting from the differential equations. We assume here that these are linear, that is, all forces are linear functions of the displacements or of the velocities. Examples 1 and 2 of the previous section illustrate such systems.

The linear system is *said to be stable, if and only if, the roots of the characteristic equation*

$$f(\lambda) = a_0\lambda^n + a_1\lambda^{n-1} + a_2\lambda^{n-2} + a_3\lambda^{n-3} + \cdots + a_n = 0 \tag{5–117}$$

have negative real parts. This is a strong criterion. If, for example, some of the roots of $f(\lambda) = 0$ are pure imaginary, periodic solutions with constant amplitude result, and these are stable in a sense. However, if the physical constants are altered only slightly, instability may set in. If $b = 0$ in the simple one-dimensional example at the beginning of this section, the solution is $q = A \sin (\sqrt{k/m}\, t + \psi)$, and this is stable in a weaker sense than is the solution $q = Ae^{-(b/2m)t} \sin (\omega t + \psi)$, which represents the transient.

Questions concerning the stability of dynamical systems led Routh[*] to study extensively the conditions on the coefficients of $f(\lambda) = 0$, Eq. (5–117), and to devise methods of determining the stability of a linear

---

[*] See E. J. Routh, *Advanced Dynamics of a System of Rigid Bodies* (6th edition, 1905). New York: Dover Publications, Inc., 1955. Chapter VI.

system. These investigations were preceded by another by A. Hurwitz[*] who, in 1895, published necessary and sufficient conditions that $f(\lambda) = 0$ have roots with negative real parts only. We shall consider the Routh-Hurwitz criterion briefly here, but will refer the reader to other sources for its proof.[†]

Routh-Hurwitz criterion. Let the characteristic equation for a linear system be

$$f(\lambda) = a_0\lambda^n + a_1\lambda^{n-1} + a_2\lambda^{n-2} + \cdots + a_{n-1}\lambda + a_n = 0, \qquad (5\text{–}118)$$

and assume $a_0 > 0$. This can be done without any loss of generality. Form the determinants

$$\Delta_1 = a_1 \qquad\qquad \Delta_2 = \begin{vmatrix} a_1 & a_0 \\ a_3 & a_2 \end{vmatrix}$$

$$\Delta_3 = \begin{vmatrix} a_1 & a_0 & 0 \\ a_3 & a_2 & a_1 \\ a_5 & a_4 & a_3 \end{vmatrix} \qquad\qquad \Delta_4 = \begin{vmatrix} a_1 & a_0 & 0 & 0 \\ a_3 & a_2 & a_1 & a_0 \\ a_5 & a_4 & a_3 & a_2 \\ a_7 & a_6 & a_5 & a_4 \end{vmatrix}$$

$$\Delta_n = \begin{vmatrix} a_1 & a_0 & \cdots & 0 \\ a_3 & a_2 & \cdots & 0 \\ a_5 & a_4 & \cdots & 0 \\ \cdot & & & \\ \cdot & & & \\ \cdot & & & \\ a_{2n-1} & a_{2n-2} & \cdots & a_n \end{vmatrix} \qquad (5\text{–}119)$$

where in Δ_n all letters with suffix greater than n and all letters with negative suffix are replaced by zero. Then all roots of Eq. (5–118) will have negative real parts if, and only if, all $\Delta_i > 0$ $(i = 1, 2, \ldots, n)$.

Consider the following four examples:

EXAMPLE 1. The relation $m\ddot{q} + b\dot{q} + kq = 0$ yields the characteristic equation $m\lambda^2 + b\lambda + k = 0$. Here

$$\Delta_1 = b \qquad \Delta_2 = \begin{vmatrix} b & m \\ 0 & k \end{vmatrix} = bk.$$

For stability, $k > 0$, $b > 0$, and $m > 0$, as we can deduce directly by solving the quadratic equation.

---

[*] A. Hurwitz, "Über die Bedingungen unter welchen eine Gleichung nur Wurzeln mit negativen reellen Theilen besitzt," *Math. Ann.*, Vol. 46, pp. 273–284 (1895).

[†] See, for example, J. V. Uspensky, *Theory of Equations.* New York: McGraw-Hill Book Company, Inc., 1948, pp. 304 ff.

EXAMPLE 2. Suppose the characteristic equation is the cubic $\lambda^3 + a\lambda^2 + b\lambda + c = 0$.

Then

$$\Delta_1 = a \qquad \Delta_2 = \begin{vmatrix} a & 1 \\ c & b \end{vmatrix} = ab - c$$

$$\Delta_3 = \begin{vmatrix} a & 1 & 0 \\ c & b & a \\ 0 & 0 & c \end{vmatrix} = (ab - c)c.$$

Hence by the Routh-Hurwitz criterion, the roots λ will have negative real parts if $a > 0$, $ab > c$, and $c > 0$. This implies also that $b > 0$. Hence all coefficients of the cubic should have like signs if the stability criterion is to be satisfied. This, however, is not a sufficient condition for stability.

Note that Δ_2 and Δ_3 in Example 2 are related. This will occur in general. That is,

$$\Delta_n = a_n \Delta_{n-1}, \tag{5–120}$$

and we may write the criterion as $a_0 > 0$, $\Delta_1 > 0, \ldots, \Delta_{n-1} > 0$, $a_n > 0$.

A consequence of the stability criterion, as stated above, is that the coefficients occurring in $f(\lambda)$ for a stable linear system all have the same sign and none of them are zero. For, suppose $-r_1, -r_2, -r_3, \ldots, -r_j$ and $-s_1 \pm it_1, -s_2 \pm it_2, \ldots, -s_k \pm it_k$ $(j + k = n)$ are the roots of $f(\lambda) = 0$, where multiple roots have been included individually and where $r_1, r_2, \ldots, r_j$ and $s_1, s_2, \ldots, s_k$ and $t_1, t_2, \ldots, t_k$ are all real. Then $f(\lambda) = 0$ can be represented by the product of factors $a_0(\lambda + r_1)$ $(\lambda + r_2) \ldots (\lambda + r_j)(\lambda^2 + 2s_1\lambda + s_1^2 + t_1^2) \ldots (\lambda^2 + 2s_k\lambda + s_k^2 + t_k^2) = 0$.

If the product is expanded, we obtain a polynomial equation,

$$a_0(\lambda^n + b_1\lambda^{n-1} + b_2\lambda^{n-2} + \cdots + b_n) = 0, \tag{5–121}$$

in which all the coefficients $b_1, b_2, \ldots, b_n$ are positive and nonzero because they are formed of the sums and products of positive quantities. Hence if $a_0 > 0$, all coefficients in Eq. (5–121) will be positive; if $a_0 < 0$, all coefficients will be negative.

This necessary criterion is sometimes useful in determining stability. For instance, if $f(\lambda) = \lambda^3 + \lambda^2 + 2 = 0$, we note that the coefficient $b_2 = 0$, so the system, of which $f(\lambda) = 0$ is the characteristic equation, is unstable.

On the other hand, the condition above is not sufficient. Suppose the characteristic equation is $\lambda^3 + \lambda^2 + \lambda + 2 = 0$.   Here all coefficients are positive but, by Example 2, $ab < c$. Hence the system is unstable.

An alternative to the Routh-Hurwitz criterion has been given by Wall.* We simply illustrate the method without proof.

Let the characteristic equation under consideration be

$$f(\lambda) = a_0\lambda^n + a_1\lambda^{n-1} + \cdots + a_n = 0, \tag{5–122}$$

and let

$$g(\lambda) = a_1\lambda^{n-1} + a_3\lambda^{n-3} + a_5\lambda^{n-5} + \cdots \tag{5–123}$$

be a polynomial which consists of the alternate terms of $f(\lambda)$.   The last term in $g(\lambda)$ will be a_n if n is odd, or $a_{n-1}\lambda$ if n is even.

Dividing f by g, we find

$$\frac{f}{g} = p_0\lambda + 1 + \frac{f_1}{g} = p_0\lambda + 1 + \frac{1}{(g/f_1)},$$

where f_1 is a polynomial of degree $n - 2$.

Again dividing f_1 into g, we have

$$\frac{g}{f_1} = p_1\lambda + \frac{f_2}{f_1} = p_1\lambda + \frac{1}{(f_1/f_2)},$$

where f_2 is a polynomial of degree $n - 3$.

Once more, dividing f_2 into f_1, we obtain

$$\frac{f_1}{f_2} = p_2\lambda + \frac{f_3}{f_2} = p_2\lambda + \frac{1}{(f_2/f_3)},$$

where f_3 is a polynomial of degree $n - 4$. We continue this process until the remainder is zero.   What we have done arithmetically is to develop g/f in a continued fraction expansion, namely

$$\frac{g}{f} = \cfrac{1}{p_0\lambda + 1 + \cfrac{1}{p_1\lambda + \cfrac{1}{p_2\lambda + \cfrac{1}{p_3\lambda + \ddots \atop \qquad + \cfrac{1}{p_{n-1}\lambda}}}}}. \tag{5–124}$$

---

* See H. S. Wall, "Polynomials whose zeros have negative real parts," *Amer. Math. Monthly*, Vol. 52, pp. 308–322 (1945).

Suppose this process is applied to $f(\lambda)$ and $g(\lambda)$ as given in Eqs. (5–122) and (5–123). We find that

$$p_0 = \frac{a_0}{a_1} = \frac{a_0}{\Delta_1}, \qquad p_3 = \frac{\Delta_3^2}{\Delta_2\,\Delta_4},$$

$$p_1 = \frac{\Delta_1^2}{\Delta_2}, \qquad\qquad \begin{array}{c} \cdot \\ \cdot \\ \cdot \end{array} \qquad\qquad (5\text{–}125)$$

$$p_2 = \frac{\Delta_2^2}{\Delta_1\,\Delta_3}, \qquad p_k = \frac{\Delta_k^2}{\Delta_{k-1}\,\Delta_{k+1}},$$

where the $\Delta_k(k = 1, 2, \ldots, n - 1)$ are the determinants in the Routh-Hurwitz criterion, Eq. (5–119). If all $\Delta_k > 0$, then all $p_k > 0$, and conversely. For we may set $a_0 > 0$ arbitrarily, and hence, if $p_0 > 0$, so is Δ_1. If $p_1 > 0$, since $\Delta_1^2 > 0$, $\Delta_2 > 0$, and so forth. The conditions that all $\Delta_k > 0$ in the Routh-Hurwitz criterion, or all $p_k > 0$ in the continued fraction expansion, are equivalent criteria for stability.

If any of the $\Delta_k = 0$, the coefficients p_k are undefined. This will occur in the algorithm if, in the division of one polynomial of degree m by another, the divisor is of degree less than $m - 1$. Or, if any of the $p_k = 0$, the continued fraction expansion does not exist.

EXAMPLE 3. Let the characteristic equation of a linear system be

$$\lambda^3 + a\lambda^2 + b\lambda + c = 0.$$

Applying the technique just described, we have

$$f(\lambda) = \lambda^3 + a\lambda^2 + b\lambda + c = 0,$$

$$g(\lambda) = a\lambda^2 + c,$$

$$\frac{f(\lambda)}{g(\lambda)} = \frac{1}{a}\lambda + 1 + \frac{(b - c/a)\lambda}{a\lambda^2 + c} \qquad \text{and} \qquad f_1(\lambda) = \left(b - \frac{c}{a}\right)\lambda,$$

$$\frac{g(\lambda)}{f_1(\lambda)} = \frac{a}{(b - c/a)}\lambda + \frac{c}{(b - c/a)\lambda} \qquad \text{and} \qquad f_2(\lambda) = c,$$

$$\frac{f_1(\lambda)}{f_2(\lambda)} = \frac{(b - c/a)\lambda}{c} + 0.$$

Hence

$$p_0 = \frac{1}{a}, \qquad p_1 = \frac{a}{b - c/a} = \frac{a^2}{ab - c}, \qquad p_2 = \frac{ab - c}{ac}.$$

Therefore we conclude that the system is stable if $a > 0$, $ab > c$, $c > 0$. The second of these implies $b > 0$. We find the same conditions for stability as in Example 2. By means of Eqs. (5–125) the reader may compare the relations between the p_k found here and the Δ_k found in Example 2.

EXAMPLE 4. As a final illustration, consider the coupled two-dimensional spring-mass system discussed in Section 5–7, Example 1. The differential equations of motion in terms of the displacement coordinates q_1 and q_2 are

$$m\ddot{q}_1 = -2kq_1 + kq_2 - f\dot{q}_1,$$
$$m\ddot{q}_2 = -2kq_2 + kq_1 - f\dot{q}_2.$$

Substituting $q_1 = Ae^{\lambda t}$ and $q_2 = Be^{\lambda t}$, we find the characteristic equation

$$\begin{vmatrix} m\lambda^2 + f\lambda + 2k & -k \\ -k & m\lambda^2 + f\lambda + 2k \end{vmatrix} = 0.$$

This may be written $f(\lambda) \equiv \lambda^4 + a\lambda^3 + b\lambda^2 + c\lambda + d = 0$, where $a = 2(f/m)$, $b = (f/m)^2 + 4(k/m)$, $c = 4(kf/m^2)$, $d = 3(k/m)^2$. Applying the continued fraction technique to determine the conditions of stability with $g(\lambda) = a\lambda^3 + c\lambda$, we find

$$\frac{g(\lambda)}{f(\lambda)} = \cfrac{1}{\cfrac{1}{a}\lambda + 1 + \cfrac{1}{\left(\cfrac{a^2}{ab-c}\right)\lambda + \cfrac{1}{\cfrac{(ab-c)^2\lambda}{a(abc - c^2 - a^2d)} + \cfrac{1}{\left(\cfrac{abc - c^2 - a^2d}{d}\right)\lambda}}}},$$

and hence the conditions for stability are $a > 0$, $ab - c > 0$, $abc - c^2 - a^2 d > 0$, and $d > 0$. These are fulfilled if (1) $f > 0$, $m > 0$, $k > 0$, or (2) $f < 0$, $m < 0$, $k > (-f^2/2m) > 0$. The second set of conditions obviously cannot be realized physically.

Let us check the conclusions directly. The characteristic equation $(m\lambda^2 + f\lambda + 2k)^2 - k^2 = 0$ yields

$$\lambda = -\frac{f}{2m} \pm \frac{\sqrt{f^2 - 4km}}{2m} \tag{5–126}$$

and

$$\lambda = -\frac{f}{2m} \pm \frac{\sqrt{f^2 - 12km}}{2m}. \tag{5–127}$$

Under conditions (1), the roots λ in Eqs. (5–126) and (5–127) are obviously either real and negative or complex with negative real parts. The latter case arises when $f^2 < 4km$. In this case the motion is oscillatory and damped.

5–9 The vibrating string. The theory of small oscillations for discrete mass particles may be extended to the study of a continuous mass distribution. For simplicity, we shall consider an approximately one-dimensional distribution, the vibrating string.

Consider N equal masses situated on a string of negligible mass, as shown in Fig. 5–7. Let the total length of the string be L. If we displace the masses and allow them to vibrate in a plane, say vertically, we have a set of coupled oscillators. The effect of gravity will be neglected. Suppose that T_1 is the tension in the string and that the displacements are small compared with the distance d between particles. Let the vertical displacements of the particles at any time be $y_1, y_2, \ldots, y_n$.

As in the two-dimensional oscillator discussed in Section 5–2, there will be as many natural frequencies as there are mass particles. These are given by

$$\omega_n^2 = \frac{2T_1}{md}\left[1 - \cos \frac{n\pi}{N}\right], \qquad (n = 1, 2, \ldots, N). \qquad (5\text{--}128)$$

Similarly, the displacement of any one mass will be a linear function of the displacements due to the N modes of oscillation. Hence we have

$$y_1 = \sum_{n=1}^{N} B_n \sin \frac{n\pi x_1}{L} \cos (\omega_n t + \psi_n),$$

$$y_2 = \sum_{n=1}^{N} B_n \sin \frac{n\pi x_2}{L} \cos (\omega_n t + \psi_n),$$

$$\cdot$$
$$\cdot$$
$$\cdot$$

$$y_n = \sum_{n=1}^{N} B_n \sin \frac{n\pi x_N}{L} \cos (\omega_n t + \psi_n),$$

(5–129)

where $x_1 = d/2$, $x_2 = 3d/2$, $x_3 = 5d/2, \ldots, x_n = (2N - 1)d/2$. These equations* show that the envelope of displacements for any given fre-

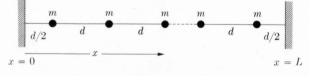

FIG. 5–7. Masses on a string.

---

* See Problem 5–19 for a derivation of Eqs. (5–128) and (5–129).

quency ω_n is a sine curve. The amplitude factors B_n are to be determined from the initial conditions. They may be separated into two parts; scale factors C_n similar to the c_r of Section 5–3, and amplitude ratio factors a_n, which are defined in the following paragraph.

In Section 5–4 we introduced normal coordinates ξ_1, ξ_2, ... such that the actual displacements were linear combinations of the ξ_j, and the resultant scale factors were all unity. In an analogous fashion, we introduce here ξ_1, ξ_2, ..., ξ_N by the equations

$$y_1 = \sum_{n=1}^{N} a_n \sin \frac{n\pi x_1}{L} \xi_n,$$

$$y_2 = \sum_{n=1}^{N} a_n \sin \frac{n\pi x_2}{L} \xi_n,$$

$$\vdots$$

(5–130)

$$y_N = \sum_{n=1}^{N} a_n \sin \frac{n\pi x_N}{L} \xi_n,$$

where $\xi_n = \cos(\omega_n t + \psi_n)$.

Since the ξ_n are *normal coordinates*, their coefficients are to satisfy orthogonality and normalizing conditions. This restricts the a_n. These conditions are

$$\sum_{i=1}^{N} a_n a_m \sin \frac{n\pi x_i}{L} \sin \frac{m\pi x_i}{L} = 0 \qquad (n \neq m),$$

(5–131)

$$\sum_{i=1}^{N} a_n^2 \sin^2 \frac{n\pi x_i}{L} = 1 \qquad (n = m),$$

for $n, m = 1, 2, \ldots, N$.

The first of these is the analog of Eq. (5–31) for N equal masses; the second is equivalent to Eq. (5–32). The normalizing condition serves to determine the a_n. The proof of the orthogonality condition is left as a problem for the reader.

Having found the values of a_n from the normalizing conditions, we obtain by Eqs. (5–130) the linear transformation from the normal coordinates into the actual displacements. Associated with each normal coordinate ξ_n is a frequency ω_n given by Eq. (5–128). If we calculate the potential energy of the system in terms of the normal coordinates, we find V expressed as the sum of squares of the ξ_n. This is in accord with the analysis in Section 5–4. The kinetic energy, too, will be expressed as the sum of squares of the velocities $\dot{\xi}_n$. Each normal coordinate satisfies the equation $\ddot{\xi}_n + \omega_n^2 \xi_n = 0$. The analysis is directly analogous to that of the simple two-dimensional oscillator already discussed.

Let us use as an example two equal masses on the string. For $N = 2$ we have frequencies given by

$$\omega_1^2 = \frac{2T_1}{m}\left(1 - \cos\frac{\pi}{N}\right) = \frac{2T_1}{m}, \tag{5-132}$$

$$\omega_2^2 = \frac{2T_1}{m}\left(1 - \cos\frac{2\pi}{N}\right) = \frac{4T_1}{m}. \tag{5-133}$$

The displacements are, by Eqs. (5–129) with $B_n = C_n a_n$,

$$y_1 = C_1 a_1 \sin\frac{\pi}{4}\cos(\omega_1 t + \psi_1) + C_2 a_2 \sin\frac{2\pi}{4}\cos(\omega_2 t + \psi_2), \tag{5-134}$$

$$y_2 = C_1 a_1 \sin\frac{3\pi}{4}\cos(\omega_1 t + \psi_1) + C_2 a_2 \sin\frac{6\pi}{4}\cos(\omega_2 t + \psi_2), \tag{5-135}$$

and the velocities are

$$\dot{y}_1 = -C_1 a_1 \omega_1 \sin\frac{\pi}{4}\sin(\omega_1 t + \psi_1) - C_2 a_2 \omega_2 \sin\frac{2\pi}{4}\sin(\omega_2 t + \psi_2), \tag{5-136}$$

$$\dot{y}_2 = -C_1 a_1 \omega_1 \sin\frac{3\pi}{4}\sin(\omega_1 t + \psi_1) - C_2 a_2 \omega_2 \sin\frac{6\pi}{4}\sin(\omega_2 t + \psi_2). \tag{5-137}$$

By Eqs. (5–131) we have for orthogonality and normalizing conditions,

$$a_1 a_2 \sin\frac{\pi}{4}\sin\frac{2\pi}{4} + a_1 a_2 \sin\frac{3\pi}{4}\sin\frac{6\pi}{4} = 0,$$

$$a_1^2 \sin^2\left(\frac{\pi}{4}\right) + a_1^2 \sin^2\left(\frac{3\pi}{4}\right) = 1,$$

$$a_2^2 \sin^2\left(\frac{2\pi}{4}\right) + a_2^2 \sin^2\left(\frac{6\pi}{4}\right) = 1.$$

From the last two equations, $a_1 = 1$, $a_2 = (1/\sqrt{2})$. Hence, by Eqs. (5–130), the transformation from normal coordinates to displacement coordinates is given by

$$y_1 = 0.707(\xi_1 + \xi_2), \qquad y_2 = 0.707(\xi_1 - \xi_2). \tag{5-138}$$

We observe from Eqs. (5–138), or Eqs. (5–134) and (5–135), that if the masses are vibrating with frequency ω_1 only, the displacements are equal, that is, the string and masses move up and down as a unit. If the string is vibrating with the frequency ω_2 only, the displacements y_1 and y_2 are always numerically equal but opposite in direction.

To find the scale factors C_n in Eqs. (5–134) and (5–135), we apply the technique used in Section 5–3 when the initial displacements and velocities are known. Suppose, for instance, that at $t = 0$, $y_1 = 2$ cm, $y_2 = 1$ cm, $\dot{y}_1 = \dot{y}_2 = 0$. Then we have initially

$$2 = \frac{C_1}{\sqrt{2}} \cos \psi_1 + \frac{C_2}{\sqrt{2}} \cos \psi_2,$$

$$1 = \frac{C_1}{\sqrt{2}} \cos \psi_1 - \frac{C_2}{\sqrt{2}} \cos \psi_2,$$

$$0 = -\frac{C_1\omega_1}{\sqrt{2}} \sin \psi_1 - \frac{C_2\omega_2}{\sqrt{2}} \sin \psi_2,$$

$$0 = -\frac{C_1\omega_1}{\sqrt{2}} \sin \psi_1 + \frac{C_2\omega_2}{\sqrt{2}} \sin \psi_2.$$

(5–139)

From the first two of Eqs. (5–139), upon multiplying each by $a_1 = 1$ or by $a_2 = (1/\sqrt{2})$ and adding, we find

$$C_1 \cos \psi_1 = \frac{3\sqrt{2}}{2} \quad \text{and} \quad C_2 \cos \psi_2 = \frac{\sqrt{2}}{2}.$$

Likewise, from the second pair of Eqs. (5–139), we have

$$C_1 \sin \psi_1 = 0 \quad \text{and} \quad C_2 \sin \psi_2 = 0.$$

Solving these, we find

$$\psi_1 = 0, \quad \psi_2 = 0, \quad C_1 = \frac{3\sqrt{2}}{2}, \quad C_2 = \frac{\sqrt{2}}{2},$$

so that the displacements are

$$y_1 = \tfrac{3}{2} \cos \omega_1 t + \tfrac{1}{2} \cos \omega_2 t,$$

$$y_2 = \tfrac{3}{2} \cos \omega_1 t - \tfrac{1}{2} \cos \omega_2 t.$$

If a periodic driving force were applied to one or both of the masses, the resulting analysis would follow exactly that discussed in Section 5–6 for the two-dimensional oscillator.

The transition from the weighted string to a continuous mass distribution may be considered as a limiting process in which we allow N to become indefinitely large, d to approach zero, and the mass particle m to decrease in such a way that m/d approaches μ, the mass per unit length of string. Equation (5–128) yields for the frequencies, as $N \to \infty$,

$$\omega_n^2 \to \frac{2T_1}{\mu d^2} \left\{ 1 - \left(1 - \frac{n^2 \pi^2 d^2}{2L^2} + \text{higher order terms} \right) \right\} = \frac{T_1}{\mu} \frac{n^2 \pi^2}{L^2}$$

or

$$\omega_n = \frac{n\pi}{L} \sqrt{T_1/\mu}. \tag{5–140}$$

The energy of the continuous mass distribution may be found in the following way. Consider the string to be deformed as shown, exaggerated, in Fig. 5–8. The net force on the mass particle at 1, for instance, is $T_1(\sin \theta_2 - \sin \theta_1)$, where T_1 is the tension in the cord. If the angles are small, this will be $T_1(\tan \theta_2 - \tan \theta_1)$ or

$$- \frac{T_1}{d} [2y_1 - (y_2 - y_1)].$$

Forces on the other particles may be found in a similar way. Since they are proportional to the relative displacements, the potential energy of each mass will be proportional to the square of the displacement. Hence

$$V = \frac{T_1}{2} \left\{ \frac{2y_1^2}{d} + \frac{(y_2 - y_1)^2}{d} + \frac{(y_3 - y_2)^2}{d} + \cdots + \frac{2y_N^2}{d} \right\}. \tag{5–141}$$

As $N \to \infty$ and $d \to 0$, each fraction $(y_{i+1} - y_i)/d$ approaches $\partial y/\partial x$ at the point concerned. The sum then becomes an integral

$$V = \frac{T_1}{2} \int_0^L \left(\frac{\partial y}{\partial x} \right)^2 dx. \tag{5–142}$$

In a similar way, the kinetic energy for the N particles,

$$T = \frac{1}{2} \sum_{i=1}^N m \dot{y}_i^2, \tag{5–143}$$

becomes

$$T = \frac{\mu}{2} \int_0^L \dot{y}^2 \, dx. \tag{5–144}$$

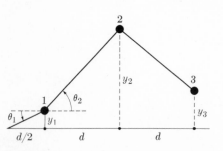

FIG. 5–8. Detail of string deformation.

Then the expressions for the displacements, Eqs. (5–129), are

$$y(x,t) = \sum_{n=1}^{\infty} B_n \sin \frac{n\pi x}{L} \cos \omega_n t, \qquad (5\text{–}145)$$

where we have arbitrarily set $\psi_n = 0$. Now suppose we separate B_n into a part C_n to be found from the initial conditions and a part a_n, as in Eqs. (5–130), and introduce normal coordinates ξ_n by writing

$$y(x,\xi) = \sum_{n=1}^{\infty} a_n \sin \frac{n\pi x}{L} \xi_n.$$

The normalizing condition, Eqs. (5–131), is

$$\int_0^L a_n^2 \sin^2 \frac{n\pi x}{L} dx = 1,$$

so that

$$a_n = \sqrt{2/L}$$

and

$$y(x,\xi) = \sum_{n=1}^{\infty} \sqrt{2/L} \sin \frac{n\pi x}{L} \xi_n. \qquad (5\text{–}146)$$

With this expression for $y(x,\xi)$, we are in a position to carry Eqs. (5–142) and (5–144) further. We have

$$\frac{\partial y}{\partial x} = \sum_{n=1}^{\infty} \sqrt{2/L} \cdot \frac{n\pi}{L} \cdot \cos \frac{n\pi x}{L} \xi_n,$$

and hence

$$V = \frac{T_1}{2} \int_0^L \left\{ \sum_{n=1}^{\infty} \sqrt{2/L} \frac{n\pi}{L} \xi_n \cos \frac{n\pi x}{L} \right\}^2 dx.$$

We assume that the order of the operations of integration and summation may be reversed. Then, when the integration is performed, all integrals involving $\cos (n\pi x/L) \cos (m\pi x/L)$ $(n \neq m)$ will vanish by virtue of orthogonality conditions analogous to Eqs. (5–131). There remains

$$V = \frac{T_1}{L} \sum_{n=1}^{\infty} \left\{ \frac{n^2\pi^2}{L^2} \xi_n^2 \int_0^L \cos^2 \frac{n\pi x}{L} dx \right\} = \frac{T_1}{2} \sum_{n=1}^{\infty} \frac{n^2\pi^2}{L^2} \xi_n^2 \qquad (5\text{–}147)$$

because

$$\int_0^L \cos^2 \frac{n\pi x}{L}\, dx = \frac{L}{2}.$$

Substituting in Eq. (5–144) for $\dot{y}$, we have

$$T = \frac{\mu}{2} \int_0^L \left\{ \sum_{n=1}^{\infty} \sqrt{2/L} \sin \frac{n\pi x}{L} \, \xi_n \right\}^2 dx,$$

which, upon simplification, becomes

$$T = \frac{\mu}{2} \sum_{n=1}^{\infty} \dot{\xi}_n^2. \tag{5–148}$$

Both V and T are sums of squares in the normal coordinates and velocities respectively. Lagrange's equations are easily formed from Eqs. (5–147) and (5–148). We find

$$\ddot{\xi}_n + \frac{n^2 \pi^2 T_1}{\mu L^2} \, \xi_n = 0, \qquad (n = 1, 2, \ldots), \tag{5–149}$$

so that the angular frequency of the nth normal mode is $\omega_n = (n\pi/L)\sqrt{T_1/\mu}$ in accord with Eq. (5–140).

We shall not discuss in detail the forced motion of the continuous string. The theory is analogous to the theory of motion for several particles. If Φ_n is the generalized force corresponding to the nth normal coordinate, we append it to the appropriate Eq. (5-149) and obtain a particular solution for ξ_n. The various Φ_n must be so chosen that the work done by them equals the work done by the actual applied forces in the actual displacements.

To illustrate, let $f(x,t)$ be an external force per unit length of string at any time. Then the work done in a vertical displacement dy at point x will be $f(x,t)\, dx\, dy$ for an element of the string. But $dy = \sqrt{2/L} \sin (n\pi x/L)\, d\xi_n$ for the nth normal coordinate. Hence for the whole string we will have

$$\Phi_n \, d\xi_n = d\xi_n \int_0^L \sqrt{2/L}\, f(x,t) \sin \frac{n\pi x}{L} \, dx,$$

from which the value of

$$\Phi_n = \sqrt{2/L} \int_0^L f(x,t) \sin \frac{n\pi x}{L} \, dx. \tag{5–150}$$

As an illustration, suppose $f(x,t) = F \sin \omega t$. Then

$$\Phi_n(t) = F\sqrt{2/L} \sin \omega t \int_0^L \sin \frac{n\pi x}{L} \, dx$$

$$= \frac{LF}{n\pi} \sqrt{2/L} \, (1 - \cos n\pi) \sin \omega t$$

$$= \frac{2LF}{n\pi} \sqrt{2/L} \sin \omega t \qquad (n \text{ odd})$$

$$= 0 \qquad\qquad (n \text{ even}).$$

Hence for n odd, we seek a particular solution of the equation

$$\ddot{\xi}_n + \omega_n^2 \xi_n = \frac{2LF}{\mu n\pi} \sqrt{2/L} \sin \omega t.$$

We find

$$\xi_{np} = \frac{2LF\sqrt{2/L}}{\mu n\pi(\omega_n^2 - \omega^2)} \sin \omega t \qquad (n \text{ odd}).$$

Hence, by Eq. (5–146), the particular solution is

$$y_p(x,t) = \sum_{n=1}^{\infty} \frac{4F \sin \omega t \sin [(n\pi x)/L]}{\mu(\omega_n^2 - \omega^2)n\pi} \qquad (n \text{ odd}).$$

In conclusion, we consider the motion of the continuous string subject to certain initial conditions. By combining Eqs. (5–145), (5–146), and the solution of the fundamental Eq. (5–149), we may write

$$y(x,t) = \sum_{n=1}^{\infty} C_n\sqrt{2/L} \sin \frac{n\pi x}{L} \cos (\omega_n t + \psi_n). \qquad (5\text{–}151)$$

Here C_n are the scale factors and ψ_n are the phase angles that must be determined by applying the initial conditions.

Suppose at $t = 0$ that $y(x,0) = \phi(x)$ and $\dot{y}(x,0) = 0$, that is, the string is released from rest. Then from Eq. (5–151),

$$y(x,0) = \sum_{n=1}^{\infty} C_n\sqrt{2/L} \sin \frac{n\pi x}{L} \cos \psi_n = \phi(x), \qquad (5\text{–}152)$$

and, by differentiation with respect to the time,

$$\dot{y}(x,0) = -\sum_{n=1}^{\infty} C_n\sqrt{2/L} \, \omega_n \sin \frac{n\pi x}{L} \sin \psi_n \equiv 0. \qquad (5\text{–}153)$$

Equation (5–153) is satisfied only if $\psi_n = 0$ or some integral multiple of π. We choose the former.

With $\psi_n = 0$, we multiply through Eq. (5–152) by $\sin (m\pi x/L)\, dx$ and integrate the resulting series term by term from 0 to L. We have

$$\int_0^L \phi(x) \sin \frac{m\pi x}{L}\, dx = \sum_{n=1}^\infty C_n \sqrt{2/L} \int_0^L \sin \frac{n\pi x}{L} \sin \frac{m\pi x}{L}\, dx.$$

But

$$\int_0^L \sin \frac{n\pi x}{L} \sin \frac{m\pi x}{L}\, dx = 0 \qquad \text{if } m \neq n$$

$$= \frac{L}{2} \qquad \text{if } m = n.$$

Hence all terms in the summation vanish except that for which $m = n$. We are left with

$$C_n = \sqrt{2/L} \int_0^L \phi(x) \sin \frac{n\pi x}{L}\, dx.$$

We have employed here the standard method for obtaining the coefficients of a Fourier series representation of the function $\phi(x)$.*

Having found the C_n appropriate to a specific function $\phi(x)$, the displacement is given by Eq. (5–151). It should be emphasized once more that we have carried over to the continuous string the same analysis as that used in earlier sections for a discrete system of masses. The continuous string problem may be solved equally well by establishing the partial differential equation representing the motion together with the boundary conditions, and separating the variables in a well-known way. We have attempted here to emphasize the extension of the analysis of coupled lumped mass systems and normal coordinates to the continuously distributed mass system.

---

* The reader will find details in any book on advanced calculus, such as W. Kaplan, *Advanced Calculus*. Reading, Massachusetts: Addison-Wesley Publishing Company, Inc., 1952, pp. 388 ff.

PROBLEMS

5–1. A mass m hangs on the end of a spring whose spring constant is k and whose mass per unit length is μ. The natural length of the spring is l. Each point of the spring oscillates vertically by an amount proportional to the distance of the point below the fixed support. (a) Find the kinetic energy of the system, including the mass of the spring. (b) Write the Lagrangian equation of motion, solve it, and show that the period of oscillation is $P = 2\pi\sqrt{(3m + \mu l)/3k}$. (Section 5–1)

5–2. A bar of weight W rests on top of two wheels whose centers are a distance $2l$ apart and which are driven with constant angular velocities, α, equal but in opposite directions, as shown in Fig. 5–9. The coefficient of friction between wheel and plank is μ. The bar is set in motion from equilibrium by a slight push with initial velocity v_0. Write the differential equation for its subsequent motion and solve it. (Section 5–1)

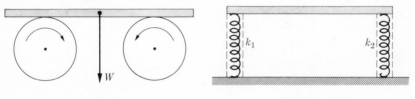

FIGURE 5–9   FIGURE 5–10

5–3. A uniform bar 8 ft long rests on confined vertical springs, as shown in Fig. 5–10. The bar weighs 4 lb/ft, and the moment of inertia with respect to a perpendicular axis through its center is $(16/3)m$, where m is its mass. The spring constants are $k_1 = 16$ lb/ft and $k_2 = 4$ lb/ft. If the left end of the bar is depressed slightly and released from rest, (a) write the differential equations of motion, and (b) find the frequencies of the resulting oscillations. (Sections 5–1 and 5–2)

5–4. Three disks are mounted on an elastic horizontal shaft at equal intervals, as shown in Fig. 5–11. The torsional stiffness (equivalent to spring constants) between disks is k. Two disks have moments of inertia I and the other $2I$. The left end of the shaft is held rigid. (a) Write the Lagrangian equations of motion for the system, and (b) find the approximate frequencies of oscillation. (c) Solve the equations of motion with the initial conditions that the

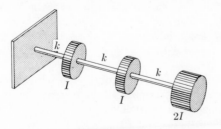

FIGURE 5–11

right-hand disk is turned θ_0, the others are fixed, and the system is released from rest. (d) Discuss the principal modes of oscillation. (e) Find the amplitude ratio factors, a_{jr}, and verify the orthogonality relation between them. (Section 5–3)

5–5. A double oscillator, shown in Fig. 5–12, is driven by a force $F = F_0 \sin \omega t$ applied at the upper mass. The constants of the system are: $m_1 = 9/g$, $m_2 = 10/g$, $k_1 = 216 \text{ lb/ft}$, $k_2 = 180 \text{ lb/ft}$. Measure the coordinates q_1 and q_2 from equilibrium and downward.

(a) Obtain by Lagrange's method the equations of motion for m_1 and m_2.

(b) Find the natural frequencies of free vibration of the system.

(c) Write the amplitude ratios for the modes of free vibration and find the numerical values of a_{ij} by use of equations similar to Eqs. (5–31) and (5–32).

(d) Express the values of q_1 and q_2 in terms of normal coordinates.

(e) Verify that T and V become sums of squares of normal velocities and coordinates respectively.

(f) Solve for the steady-state forced oscillation of the system under the driving force $F = F_0 \sin \omega t$. (Sections 5–1 through 5–6)

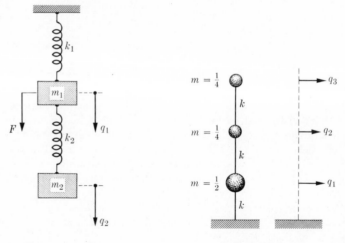

FIGURE 5–12   FIGURE 5–13

5–6. Three masses, $\frac{1}{4}$, $\frac{1}{4}$, $\frac{1}{2}$, are mounted on a vertical stiff rod, as shown in Fig. 5–13. The stiffness coefficient between masses is k. Choose lateral displacements q_1, q_2, q_3, which are positive as indicated in the figure.

(a) Show that the potential energy of the system is $V = \frac{1}{2}k\{2q_1^2 + 2q_2^2 + q_3^2 - 2q_1q_2 - 2q_2q_3\}$, and with $T = \frac{1}{2}\{\frac{1}{2}\dot{q}_1^2 + \frac{1}{4}\dot{q}_2^2 + \frac{1}{4}\dot{q}_3^2\}$, write the equations of motion for the system.

(b) Find the natural frequencies of vibration in terms of k.

(c) Compute the ratio of amplitudes and show the relative positions of the masses for each mode of vibration.

(d) Find the coefficients a_{ij} and write the equations for q_1, q_2, q_3 in terms of normal coordinates.

(e) If initially $q_1 = 2$, $q_2 = 2$, $q_3 = 0$, and $\dot{q}_1 = \dot{q}_2 = \dot{q}_3 = 0$, express subsequent values for q_1, q_2, q_3 in terms of the time.

(f) If, instead of conditions (e), the masses are initially on a vertical line and at rest, and the base of the rod is given the lateral displacement $Q_0 \sin \omega t$, express the subsequent q_1, q_2, and q_3 as functions of the time. (Sections 5–1 through 5–6)

5–7. Show that the total energy of a system of 3 degrees of freedom, oscillating about its equilibrium configuration, is equal to the sum of the energies of its principal modes of oscillation. (Section 5–1)

5–8. Show that the time average of the kinetic energy of a principal mode of oscillation is equal to the average potential energy when the averages are taken over a long interval of time. (Section 5–1)

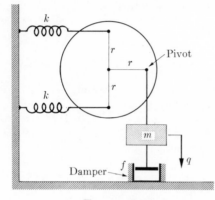

FIGURE 5–14

5–9. A mass m is suspended from a pivot on a disk as shown in Fig. 5–14. The disk, in a vertical plane, is free to rotate about its axis but is restrained by two springs. Attached to the mass is a damper which resists the motion with a force $-f\dot{q}$, where q is the displacement of the mass from equilibrium. The moment of inertia of the disk is I. (a) Write the expressions for the kinetic and potential energies and the dissipation function on the assumption that the displacements and velocities are small. (b) Set up the Lagrangian equation of motion for m and solve it under the initial conditions: $q = q_0$, $\dot{q} = 0$ at $t = 0$. (c) Distinguish among the three cases that may arise depending on the value of f. (Section 5–7)

5–10. The masses used as an illustration in Section 5–2 (Fig. 5–1) are coupled together through a damper as shown in Fig. 5–15. The left-hand mass is driven with a force $q = q_0 \cos \omega t$. Displacements from equilibrium are q_1 and q_2.

(a) Write the kinetic energy, the potential energy, and the dissipation function for the system under the assumption that the frictional force is proportional to the difference in velocity between the two masses.

(b) Set up the equations of motion for q_1 and q_2, write the characteristic equation, and solve it for the frequencies of free vibration. How do these compare with those of the undamped motion in Section 5–2?

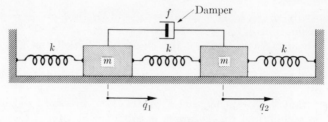

FIGURE 5–15

(c) Find the steady-state motion of the system under the driving force $q_0 \cos \omega t$. (Section 5–7)

5–11. Three masses are connected by springs, as shown in Fig. 5–16, with dampers of coefficient f between them.

(a) Set up the values of T, V, and D for this system, and write the equations of motion.

(b) Using solutions of the form $q_1 = Ae^{\lambda t}$, $q_2 = Be^{\lambda t}$, $q_3 = Ce^{\lambda t}$, write the characteristic equation of the system.

(c) Show that the characteristic equation can be written in the form $m\lambda^2(m\lambda^2 + f\lambda + k)(m\lambda^2 + 3f\lambda + 3k) = 0$. If this system is to have non-oscillatory motion, the discriminant of each of the last two quadratic factors must be ≥ 0. Show that $f \geq 2\sqrt{mk}$ will satisfy the condition for critical damping, that is, nonoscillatory motion. (Section 5–7)

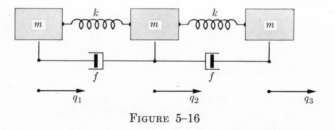

FIGURE 5–16

5–12. An automobile on shock absorbers and rubber tires can be represented schematically as in Fig. 5–17. The mass m_1 represents the body; the mass m_2 represents the axles, transmission, and so forth. The shock absorbers have a damping coefficient f_1 and the tires a coefficient f_2. Assuming coordinates q_1 and q_2, measured from equilibrium, write the Lagrangian function and Lagrange's equations for the system. (Section 5–7)

5–13. Four equal masses are mounted at the ends of a perpendicular cross of rods as shown in Fig. 5–18. The masses of the rods are negligible compared with the masses on their ends. The cross rests on a frictionless pivot at O and is rotating about OP with constant angular velocity ω. The axis OP is perpendicular to the plane of the cross. As the cross rotates, its axis is displaced slightly through an angle θ from the vertical. Discuss the motion of the system and particularly its stability. (Section 5–8)

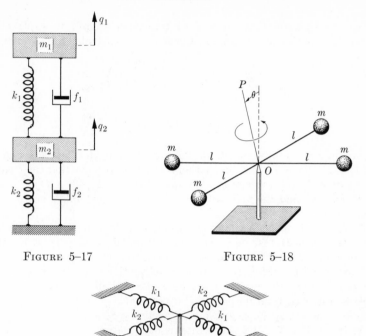

FIGURE 5–17

FIGURE 5–18

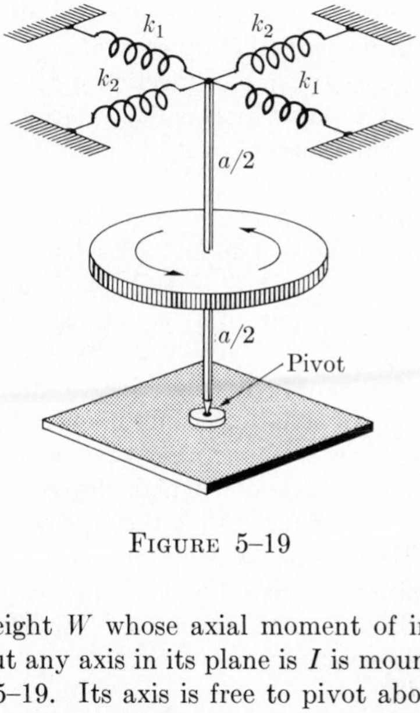

FIGURE 5–19

5–14. A wheel of weight W whose axial moment of inertia is I_3 and whose moment of inertia about any axis in its plane is I is mounted in a spring suspension as shown in Fig. 5–19. Its axis is free to pivot about the lower end. The wheel is rotating with constant angular velocity ω about its axis. If the upper support is displaced slightly from its equilibrium position, write the differential equations, by the Lagrangian method, for the ensuing motion. Discuss the stability of the system. (Section 5–8)

5–15. Discuss the stability or instability of the systems whose characteristic equations are: (a) $\lambda^5 + 3\lambda^4 + 8\lambda^3 + 14\lambda^2 + 3\lambda + 2 = 0$; (b) $\lambda^4 - 2\lambda^2 + 5 = 0$; (c) $7\lambda^4 + 4\lambda^3 + 8\lambda^2 + 3\lambda + 2 = 0$; (d) $3\lambda^3 + 5\lambda^2 + 11\lambda + 12 = 0$. (Section 5–8)

5-16. The equations that define the rotational motion of an airplane about a horizontal axis through its center of gravity perpendicular to its longitudinal axis are

$$\frac{d^2\theta}{dt^2} = -2\theta - \alpha\left(\frac{d\theta}{dt} + \frac{d\phi}{dt}\right),$$

$$\frac{d^2\phi}{dt^2} = -\beta(\theta + \phi) - \gamma\frac{d\phi}{dt},$$

where α and γ are positive constants, t is a time parameter, and β is a constant which is to be chosen so that the motion is stable. (a) Show that the characteristic equation of the system is $\lambda^4 + (\alpha + \gamma)\lambda^3 + (2 + \beta + \alpha\gamma)\lambda^2 + 2\gamma\lambda + 2\beta = 0$, and (b) find the value of β which will insure stability of the system. (Section 5-8)

5-17. A particle of mass m and charge e moves in a uniform electric field $\mathbf{E}$ and magnetic field $\mathbf{H}$. Its equation of motion is $m\ddot{\mathbf{r}} = e\mathbf{E} + e\mathbf{v} \times \mathbf{H}$, where $\mathbf{r}$ is the position vector of the particle. Taking the z-axis to be parallel to $\mathbf{H}$, (a) show that the cartesian equations of motion are: $m\ddot{x} = eE_x + eH\dot{y}$; $m\ddot{y} = eE_y - eH\dot{x}$; $m\ddot{z} = eE_z$. (b) Discuss the stability of its motion if the particle is disturbed from its path slightly so that $x = x_0 + q_1$, $y = y_0 + q_2$, $z = z_0 + q_3$, where q_1, q_2, q_3 are small. (Section 5-8)

5-18. Prove Eq. (5-131), the orthogonality relation, by using the trigonometrical identities of the form $\cos A - \cos B = -2\sin 1/2(A + B)\sin 1/2(A - B)$. (Section 5-9)

5-19. Consider N masses on a string of length L, as shown in Fig. 5-7. Neglect the action of gravity on the system and consider only the tension T_1 in the string to act upon each mass. (a) If $T = \frac{1}{2}m\sum_{j=1}^{N}\dot{y}_j^2$ and $V = (T_1/2d)\{2y_1^2 + (y_2 - y_1)^2 + . . . + 2y_N^2\}$, write the equations of motion for the mass particles. (b) Choose $y_j = C_je^{i\omega t}$ ($j = 1, 2, \ldots, N$) as a solution for each mass, and substitute in the equations of motion to obtain the equations to be satisfied by the C_j. This set of equations could be solved only if the determinant of the coefficients vanishes, as we have already seen, but this involves finding the roots of a characteristic equation of high degree. Another way is to let $C_j = e^{ijk}$ or e^{-ijk} and so determine k that the equations will be satisfied and the string displacement at the ends will be zero. (c) Perform this substitution and show that all equations except the first and last become $(T_1/d)(e^{ik} + e^{-ik}) + [m\omega^2 - (2T_1/d)] = 0$, and hence $m\omega^2 = (2T_1/d)(1 - \cos k)$. For the first equation we may write

$$-\frac{T_1}{d}C_1 + \left(m\omega^2 - \frac{2T_1}{d}\right)C_1 + \frac{T_1}{d}C_2 = 0.$$

This equation falls into the pattern of the others if we set $-C_1 = C_0$ in the first term, where C_0 is the hypothetical amplitude of a mass at $x = -\frac{1}{2}d$. In a similar way,

$$\frac{T_1}{d}C_{N-1} + \left(m\omega^2 - \frac{2T_1}{d}\right)C_N - \frac{T_1}{d}C_N = 0$$

falls into line if we postulate $-C_N = C_{N+1}$ in the last term, where C_{N+1} is a fictitious displacement at $x = \frac{1}{2}(2N + 1)\,d$. This is similar to the condition for an indefinitely long string where we hold stationary the midpoint of the string between two masses. This restriction, that at $x = 0$ and $x = L$ the value of y must be zero, implies that our quantities C_j must take the form $\sin k(j - 1/2)$, which obviously vanishes at $j = 1/2$ and will vanish at $j = N + 1/2$ if $kN = n\pi$, where n is an integer. Thus $k = (n\pi/N)$, and for each integer n we have a frequency ω_n. The number n can vary from 1 to N. (d) Show that this leads to a solution for the y_j as given in Eq. (5–129) and to the frequency relation, Eq. (5–128). (Section 5–9)

5–20. Four unit masses are placed on a string at distances 12.5 cm, 37.5 cm, 62.5 cm, 87.5 cm from the left end. The string is of negligible mass and is 100 cm long. It is pulled with a tension $T_1 = 10^5$ dynes. (a) Find the frequencies of oscillation of the system. (b) Find the numerical coefficients a_n that are necessary to express the displacements in terms of normal coordinates. (c) Prove the orthogonality of the a_n. (d) Write the potential energy in terms of the normal coordinates, and from it check the frequencies already found. (Section 5–9)

5–21. A string 100 cm long has a mass of 0.04 gm/cm and is pulled with a tension of 10^5 dynes. At $t = 0$ the center of the string is displaced 5 cm and released from rest. (a) Solve for the displacement $y(x,t)$. (b) State the frequencies of vibration for the string and show their harmonic relationship. (c) Compare the first four frequencies with the four frequencies of the weighted string in Problem 5–20. (Section 5–9)

CHAPTER 6

HAMILTON'S EQUATIONS AND PHASE SPACE

The formulation of dynamical problems in terms of Lagrange's equations has been shown to be elegant and straightforward. There is, however, another mathematical description that sometimes yields more insight into the behavior of complex systems. This is the Hamiltonian formulation in which momenta as well as coordinates, in the generalized sense, are emphasized. In this chapter we shall treat briefly the Hamiltonian equations of motion which are particularly useful in statistical mechanics and in the study of nonlinear oscillations. These lead naturally to a consideration of phase space which is helpful in the analysis of nonlinear problems in dynamics.

6–1 Hamilton's equations. Let the mechanical system be represented at any instant by the m generalized coordinates $q_k(k = 1, 2, \ldots, m)$, and let its Lagrangian function contain the time explicitly. Then

$$L = L(q_k, \dot{q}_k, t) \qquad (k = 1, 2, \ldots, m), \tag{6–1}$$

and we define the *generalized, or conjugate, momentum* p_k associated with the coordinate q_k to be

$$p_k = \frac{\partial L}{\partial \dot{q}_k} \qquad (k = 1, 2, \ldots, m). \tag{6–2}$$

It is apparent that, since the coordinates q_k may be lengths, angles, or of other dimensions, the p_k need not have dimensions MLT^{-1}. On the assumption that the potential energy does not contain terms in the velocities, we also note that $(\partial L/\partial \dot{q}_k) = (\partial T/\partial \dot{q}_k)$.

By Eq. (2–45) the kinetic energy is a quadratic form in the generalized velocities, namely

$$T = \frac{1}{2} \sum_{j=1}^{m} \sum_{k=1}^{m} a_{jk} \dot{q}_j \dot{q}_k,$$

where the a_{jk} depend upon the coordinates and possibly on the time. Therefore,

$$p_k = \sum_{j=1}^{m} a_{jk} \dot{q}_j \qquad (k = 1, 2, \ldots, m), \tag{6–3}$$

a *linear form* in the velocities. These m equations may be solved for the $\dot{q}_k$ in terms of the momenta, p_k.

For example, in the double pendulum problem discussed in Section 2–6, the momenta are

$$p_1 = (m_1 + m_2)l_1^2\dot{\theta}_1 + m_2 l_1 l_2 \cos(\theta_1 - \theta_2)\dot{\theta}_2,$$

$$p_2 = m_2 l_1 l_2 \cos(\theta_1 - \theta_2)\dot{\theta}_1 + m_2 l_2^2\dot{\theta}_2,$$

and these yield

$$\dot{\theta}_1 = \frac{l_2 p_1 - l_1 \cos(\theta_1 - \theta_2)p_2}{l_1^2 l_2[m_1 + m_2 \sin^2(\theta_1 - \theta_2)]},$$

$$\dot{\theta}_2 = \frac{-m_2 l_2 \cos(\theta_1 - \theta_2)p_1 + (m_1 + m_2)l_1 p_2}{m_2 l_1 l_2^2[m_1 + m_2 \sin^2(\theta_1 - \theta_2)]}.$$

In further discussion of the Hamiltonian formulation of dynamical problems, we shall assume that the velocities can be so found explicitly in terms of the momenta. It is shown in more advanced treatises that the transformation from the $\dot{q}_k$ to the p_k is always possible.*

In the place of the Lagrangian function, Hamilton introduced a related quantity, now called the Hamiltonian, by the definition

$$H = \sum_{k=1}^{m} p_k \dot{q}_k - L. \tag{6–4}$$

Since L is a function of q_k, $\dot{q}_k$, and t, and since the m equations defining the p_k can be solved explicitly for the $\dot{q}_k$ in terms of the p_k, q_k, and t, H can be expressed as a function of the p_k, q_k, and t.

Assume for the moment that L is a function only of the q_k and the $\dot{q}_k$; that is, L is independent of the time, and the potential energy V is not velocity dependent. Then from Eq. (6–4)

$$dH = \sum_{k=1}^{m} p_k \, d\dot{q}_k + \sum_{k=1}^{m} \dot{q}_k \, dp_k - \sum_{k=1}^{m} \frac{\partial L}{\partial q_k} \, dq_k - \sum_{k=1}^{m} \frac{\partial L}{\partial \dot{q}_k} \, d\dot{q}_k. \tag{6–5}$$

But, by the definition of p_k, the first and last terms of Eq. (6–5) disappear, and we observe that, since H is a function of the p_k and q_k,

$$\frac{\partial H}{\partial p_k} = \dot{q}_k, \qquad \frac{\partial H}{\partial q_k} = -\frac{\partial L}{\partial q_k} = -\dot{p}_k \qquad (k = 1, 2, \ldots, m). \tag{6–6}$$

The last of Eqs. (6–6) follows from Lagrange's equation for q_k.

---

* See, for example, W. D. MacMillan, *Theoretical Mechanics—Dynamics of Rigid Bodies*. New York: McGraw-Hill Book Company, 1936, pp. 358 ff.

Equations (6–6) are the *canonical Hamiltonian equations* of motion. Note that there are two equations for each degree of freedom. They are first order differential equations, whereas the Lagrangian ones were second order equations. Note, also, the symmetry in this formulation.

If H does contain the time explicitly, that is,

$$H(p_k, q_k, t) = \sum_{k=1}^{m} p_k \dot{q}_k - L(q_k, \dot{q}_k, t), \qquad (6\text{–}7)$$

Eq. (6–5) becomes

$$dH = \sum_{k=1}^{m} p_k \, d\dot{q}_k + \sum_{k=1}^{m} \dot{q}_k \, dp_k - \sum_{k=1}^{m} \frac{\partial L}{\partial q_k} \, dq_k - \sum_{k=1}^{m} \frac{\partial L}{\partial \dot{q}_k} \, d\dot{q}_k - \frac{\partial L}{\partial t} \, dt$$

$$= \sum_{k=1}^{m} \frac{\partial H}{\partial q_k} \, dq_k + \sum_{k=1}^{m} \frac{\partial H}{\partial p_k} \, dp_k + \frac{\partial H}{\partial t} \, dt,$$

and we see that

$$\frac{\partial H}{\partial p_k} = \dot{q}_k, \qquad \frac{\partial H}{\partial q_k} = -\frac{\partial L}{\partial q_k} = -\dot{p}_k, \qquad \frac{\partial H}{\partial t} = -\frac{\partial L}{\partial t}. \qquad (6\text{–}8)$$

The inclusion of t as an explicit independent variable simply adds the last of Eqs. (6–8) to the Hamiltonian equations, (6–6).

The nature of the function H, and in particular its physical significance when the time is not an explicit variable, is readily demonstrated. Since $H = H(p_k, q_k, t)$, we have

$$\frac{dH}{dt} = \sum_{k=1}^{m} \frac{\partial H}{\partial p_k} \, \dot{p}_k + \sum_{k=1}^{m} \frac{\partial H}{\partial q_k} \, \dot{q}_k + \frac{\partial H}{\partial t},$$

and, by Eqs. (6–8), the first and second terms in this expression vanish. We are left with

$$\frac{dH}{dt} = \frac{\partial H}{\partial t} = -\frac{\partial L}{\partial t}, \qquad (6\text{–}9)$$

so that, if H is independent of t explicitly, $H = $ constant.

Now T is a homogeneous quadratic function of the velocities $\dot{q}_k$, and no velocity dependent potentials are present. Hence, by Euler's theorem on homogeneous functions, we have

$$\sum_{k=1}^{m} \dot{q}_k \, \frac{\partial T}{\partial \dot{q}_k} = 2T.$$

But, under the conditions stated, $(\partial T/\partial \dot{q}_k) = (\partial L/\partial \dot{q}_k) = p_k$. Hence

$$2T = \sum_{k=1}^{m} p_k \dot{q}_k,$$

and

$$H = \sum_{k=1}^{m} p_k \dot{q}_k - L = 2T - (T - V) = T + V = E, \qquad (6\text{–}10)$$

the total energy of the system expressed in terms of coordinates and momenta.

6–2 An example: electron in motion. As an illustration of the Hamiltonian formulation, consider an electron of charge $-e$ moving in the field of a nucleus of charge Ze, where Z is the atomic number. We choose for generalized coordinates the usual spherical coordinates r, θ, ϕ, as shown in Fig. 6–1. Let the mass of the electron be m. Then

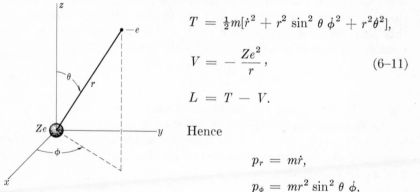

$$T = \tfrac{1}{2}m[\dot{r}^2 + r^2 \sin^2 \theta\, \dot{\phi}^2 + r^2 \dot{\theta}^2],$$

$$V = -\frac{Ze^2}{r},\qquad\qquad (6\text{–}11)$$

$$L = T - V.$$

Hence

$$p_r = m\dot{r},$$

$$p_\phi = mr^2 \sin^2 \theta\, \dot{\phi},$$

Fig. 6–1. Coordinate system for the electron.

$$p_\theta = mr^2 \dot{\theta}.$$

The Hamiltonian function by definition is

$$H = \frac{1}{2m} \left\{ p_r^2 + \frac{p_\phi^2}{r^2 \sin^2 \theta} + \frac{p_\theta^2}{r^2} \right\} - \frac{Ze^2}{r}. \qquad (6\text{–}12)$$

Applying Eqs. (6–6), we have

$$\dot{p}_r = \frac{p_\phi^2}{mr^3 \sin^2 \theta} + \frac{p_\theta^2}{mr^3} - \frac{Ze^2}{r^2}, \qquad \dot{r} = \frac{p_r}{m},$$

$$\dot{p}_\phi = 0, \qquad\qquad\qquad\qquad \dot{\phi} = \frac{p_\phi}{mr^2 \sin^2\theta}, \qquad (6\text{–}13)$$

$$\dot{p}_\theta = \frac{p_\phi^2 \cos \theta}{mr^2 \sin^3 \theta}, \qquad\qquad \dot{\theta} = \frac{p_\theta}{mr^2}.$$

These are the Hamiltonian equations of motion of the system. We might readily have written the expressions for $\dot{r}$, $\dot{\theta}$, $\dot{\phi}$ directly from the definitions of p_r, p_θ, p_ϕ since the coordinate system is orthogonal and hence H contains no cross-product terms in the momenta.

That these equations reduce to the Lagrangian equations of motion may be shown readily. We observe that $\dot{p}_\phi = 0$, and hence p_ϕ is constant in time. Call it c. Then $\dot{\phi} = c/(mr^2 \sin^2 \theta)$, and from the first pair of Eqs. (6–13) we have

$$m\ddot{r} - c^2/mr^3 \sin^2 \theta - mr\dot{\theta}^2 + \frac{Ze^2}{r^2} = 0. \tag{6–14}$$

From the last pair we have

$$\frac{d}{dt}(mr^2\dot{\theta}) = c^2 \cos \theta / mr^2 \sin^3 \theta. \tag{6–15}$$

Equations (6–14) and (6–15) do not involve ϕ in any way. Hence we conclude that the motion takes place in a plane. This we would expect since we are dealing with central force motion. If we arbitrarily choose this plane to be $\phi = 0$, then $\dot{\phi} = 0$, $c = 0$, and we have the familiar equations for plane motion,

$$m\ddot{r} - mr\dot{\theta}^2 + \frac{Ze^2}{r^2} = 0, \qquad \frac{d}{dt}(mr^2\dot{\theta}) = 0. \tag{6–16}$$

The results of this analysis are identical with those of Section 3–1.

The Hamiltonian description of a system is of no particular advantage in actually solving for the q_k as functions of the time. Its value lies in exhibiting clearly and simultaneously the behavior of the momenta as well as the coordinates.

6–3 Ignorable or cyclic coordinates. Consider a dynamical system representable by the coordinates $q_1, q_2, \ldots, q_m$, and assume that the Lagrangian is independent of the time. If one or more of the coordinates q_k does not appear in the Lagrangian, the coordinate is called *cyclic* or *ignorable*. The velocity corresponding to the cyclic coordinate, however, remains in L.

Reference to Eqs. (6–6) shows that in this case $(\partial L/\partial q_k) = \dot{p}_k = 0$, and hence the corresponding momentum is a constant. Furthermore, by the same equations $(\partial H/\partial q_k) = 0$, and q_k does not appear in the Hamiltonian.

Suppose $q_1, q_2, \ldots, q_r$ $(r < m)$ are cyclic coordinates and are, therefore, absent from the Hamiltonian. Let the corresponding constant momenta be $\alpha_1, \alpha_2, \ldots, \alpha_r$. Then the Hamiltonian is

$$H(p_{r+1}, p_{r+2}, \ldots, p_m; q_{r+1}, q_{r+2}, \ldots, q_m; \alpha_1, \alpha_2, \ldots, \alpha_r).$$

There thus remain $m - r$ coordinates and momenta, and the problem is essentially one with $m - r$ degrees of freedom. Hamiltonian equations corresponding to each of the $m - r$ degrees of freedom may be obtained while ignoring the r cyclic coordinates. Then $q_1, q_2, \ldots, q_r$ can be found from the equations

$$\dot{q}_k = \frac{\partial H}{\partial \alpha_k} \qquad (k = 1, 2, \ldots, r), \qquad (6\text{–}17)$$

which are the Hamiltonian equations corresponding to the constant momenta.

In the electron problem described in Section 6–2, the coordinate ϕ does not appear in the Hamiltonian, Eq. (6–12). Consequently we observe that $\dot{p}_\phi = 0$ in Eqs. (6–13). The coordinate ϕ is therefore cyclic. We note further that

$$\dot{\phi} = \frac{\partial H}{\partial p_\phi} = \frac{p_\phi}{mr^2 \sin^2 \theta},$$

which corresponds to Eq. (6–17) with p_ϕ as the constant momentum.

Routh has devised a procedure that combines the Lagrangian and the Hamiltonian formulations and which is useful particularly in treating problems in oscillatory motion. Suppose $q_1, q_2, \ldots, q_r$ are cyclic coordinates and, hence, are absent from the Lagrangian. Let $p_1 = \alpha_1$, $p_2 = \alpha_2, \ldots, p_r = \alpha_r$ be the corresponding conjugate momenta. Then we define a new function, called the Routhian, by

$$R = L - \sum_{k=1}^{r} \alpha_k \dot{q}_k. \qquad (6\text{–}18)$$

By means of the relations

$$\frac{\partial L}{\partial \dot{q}_k} = p_k = \alpha_k \qquad (k = 1, 2, \ldots, r),$$

we can find the $\dot{q}_k$ for the ignorable coordinates in terms of the α_k and the remaining coordinates and velocities. Hence we may write

$$R(q_{r+1}, q_{r+2}, \ldots, q_m; \dot{q}_{r+1}, \dot{q}_{r+2}, \ldots, \dot{q}_m; \alpha_1, \alpha_2, \ldots, \alpha_r). \quad (6\text{–}19)$$

Now, from Eq. (6–18),

$$dR = \sum_{k=r+1}^{m} \frac{\partial L}{\partial q_k} dq_k + \sum_{k=r+1}^{m} \frac{\partial L}{\partial \dot{q}_k} d\dot{q}_k$$

$$+ \sum_{k=1}^{r} \frac{\partial L}{\partial \dot{q}_k} d\dot{q}_k - \sum_{k=1}^{r} \alpha_k d\dot{q}_k - \sum_{k=1}^{r} \dot{q}_k d\alpha_k, \qquad (6\text{–}20)$$

and, from Eq. (6–19),

$$dR = \sum_{k=r+1}^{m} \frac{\partial R}{\partial q_k} \, dq_k + \sum_{k=r+1}^{m} \frac{\partial R}{\partial \dot{q}_k} \, d\dot{q}_k + \sum_{k=1}^{r} \frac{\partial R}{\partial \alpha_k} \, d\alpha_k. \qquad (6\text{–}21)$$

Comparison of corresponding terms in Eqs. (6–20) and (6–21) yields

$$\frac{\partial R}{\partial q_k} = \frac{\partial L}{\partial q_k} \qquad (k = r + 1, r + 2, \ldots, m), \qquad (6\text{–}22)$$

$$\frac{\partial R}{\partial \dot{q}_k} = \frac{\partial L}{\partial \dot{q}_k} \qquad (k = r + 1, r + 2, \ldots, m), \qquad (6\text{–}23)$$

$$\dot{q}_k = - \frac{\partial R}{\partial \alpha_k} \qquad (k = 1, 2, \ldots, r). \qquad (6\text{–}24)$$

Hence the Lagrangian equations of motion become

$$\frac{d}{dt}\left(\frac{\partial R}{\partial \dot{q}_k}\right) - \frac{\partial R}{\partial q_k} = 0 \qquad (k = r + 1, r + 2, \ldots, m). \qquad (6\text{–}25)$$

Using the Routhian in place of the Lagrangian, we have essentially a problem in $m - r$ degrees of freedom. Having solved this problem in the usual way, we may then find the coordinates which have been ignored by solving Eq. (6–24). That is,

$$q_k = - \int \frac{\partial R}{\partial \alpha_k} \, dt \qquad (k = 1, 2, \ldots, r). \qquad (6\text{–}26)$$

The process described here is sometimes called the *ignoration of coordinates*. Two examples will serve to illustrate Routh's procedure.

EXAMPLE 1. In the electron problem discussed in Section 6–2, ϕ is an ignorable coordinate, and hence

$$R = \frac{1}{2} \, m[\dot{r}^2 + r^2\dot{\theta}^2 + r^2 \sin^2 \theta \, \dot{\phi}^2] + \frac{Ze^2}{r} - \alpha\dot{\phi}, \qquad (6\text{–}27)$$

where

$$\alpha = \frac{\partial L}{\partial \dot{\phi}} = mr^2 \sin^2 \theta \, \dot{\phi}. \qquad (6\text{–}28)$$

Eliminating $\dot{\phi}$ from Eq. (6–27) by means of Eq. (6–28), we have

$$R = \frac{1}{2} \, m \left[\dot{r}^2 + r^2\dot{\theta}^2 - \frac{\alpha^2}{m^2 r^2 \sin^2 \theta} \right] + \frac{Ze^2}{r},$$

which we observe is a function of r, θ, $\dot{r}$, $\dot{\theta}$ and α. The problem has been reduced to one of two degrees of freedom.

Applying Eq. (6–25), we find

$$m\ddot{r} - mr\dot{\theta}^2 - \frac{\alpha^2}{mr^3 \sin^2 \theta} + \frac{Ze^2}{r^2} = 0,$$

$$\frac{d}{dt}(mr^2\dot{\theta}) - \frac{\alpha^2 \cos \theta}{mr^2 \sin^3 \theta} = 0. \tag{6–29}$$

Since α is a constant, fixed by the initial conditions, let us set it arbitrarily equal to zero. Then Eqs. (6–29) are identical with Eq. (6–16). The third coordinate, ϕ, may be obtained from

$$\phi = \frac{\alpha}{m}\int_{t_0}^{t}\frac{dt}{r^2 \sin^2 \theta}, \tag{6–30}$$

when r and θ have been found as functions of t from Eqs. (6–29). Of course, when α has been arbitrarily set at zero, ϕ vanishes also.

EXAMPLE 2. In Section 5–7, Example 2, we considered the gyroscopic forces acting on a rapidly spinning top whose axis was nearly vertical. Let us use the Routhian procedure to obtain similar results. There we found the equations of motion

$$\ddot{x} = \alpha^2 x - \beta\dot{y}, \qquad \ddot{y} = \alpha^2 y + \beta\dot{x}, \tag{6–31}$$

where

$$\alpha^2 = \frac{mgl}{I}, \qquad \beta = \frac{L_\psi}{I},$$

and x and y are small displacements of the center of gravity of the top in a plane perpendicular to the vertical.

Here,

$$L = \tfrac{1}{2}[I(\dot{\theta}^2 + \dot{\phi}^2 \sin^2 \theta) + I_3(\dot{\psi} + \dot{\phi}\cos\theta)^2] - mgl\cos\theta, \tag{6–32}$$

and we note that there are two ignorable coordinates, ψ and ϕ. Since we are interested in the two-dimensional motion of the center of gravity, we shall ignore only the ψ. The Routhian, therefore, is

$$R = L - L_\psi \dot{\psi},$$

where the constant

$$L_\psi = \frac{\partial L}{\partial \dot{\psi}} = I_3(\dot{\psi} + \dot{\phi}\cos\theta).$$

This plays the part of the α_k in Eq. (6–18). We find

$$R = \frac{1}{2} I\dot{\theta}^2 + \frac{1}{2} I\dot{\phi}^2 \sin^2 \theta + L_\psi \dot{\phi} \cos \theta - mgl \cos \theta - \frac{1}{2} \frac{L_\psi^2}{I_3}. \quad (6\text{–}33)$$

As in the previous discussion of this problem, let the projection of the center of gravity on the xy-plane be given by

$$x = l \sin \theta \sin \phi, \qquad y = -l \sin \theta \cos \phi.$$

Then, retaining only terms to the second order in x, y, $\dot{x}$, and $\dot{y}$, we find

$$\dot{\theta}^2 + \dot{\phi}^2 \sin^2 \theta = \frac{\dot{x}^2 + \dot{y}^2}{l^2},$$

$$\dot{\phi} \cos \theta = + \frac{1}{2l^2} (x\dot{y} - y\dot{x}) \left\{ \frac{1}{x^2 + y^2} - \frac{1}{2l^2} \right\}$$

$$\cos \theta = 1 - \frac{1}{2l^2} (x^2 + y^2),$$

so that

$$R = \frac{I}{2l^2} (\dot{x}^2 + \dot{y}^2) - \frac{L_\psi}{2l^2} (x\dot{y} - y\dot{x}) + \frac{mgl}{2l^2} (x^2 + y^2) + \text{constant}. \quad (6\text{–}34)$$

Hence

$$\frac{\partial R}{\partial \dot{x}} = \frac{I}{l^2} \dot{x} + \frac{L_\psi}{2l^2} y, \qquad \frac{\partial R}{\partial x} = -\frac{L_\psi}{2l^2} \dot{y} + \frac{mg}{l} x,$$

$$\frac{\partial R}{\partial \dot{y}} = \frac{I}{l^2} \dot{y} - \frac{L_\psi}{2l^2} x, \qquad \frac{\partial R}{\partial y} = \frac{L_\psi}{2l^2} \dot{x} + \frac{mg}{l} y. \qquad (6\text{–}35)$$

The equations of motion are

$$\frac{d}{dt} \left(\frac{\partial R}{\partial \dot{x}} \right) - \frac{\partial R}{\partial x} = 0, \qquad \frac{d}{dt} \left(\frac{\partial R}{\partial \dot{y}} \right) - \frac{\partial R}{\partial y} = 0,$$

or

$$\ddot{x} + \frac{L_\psi}{I} \dot{y} - \frac{mgl}{I} x = 0, \qquad \ddot{y} - \frac{L_\psi}{I} \dot{x} - \frac{mgl}{I} y = 0. \quad (6\text{–}36)$$

These are identical with Eqs. (6–31). By comparing the Routhian, Eq. (6–34), with the Lagrangian formed from Eqs. (5–104) and (5–105), the reader will note the simplification in form that results when the former is used.

6–4 Phase space. For each degree of freedom of the mechanical system there are now two quantities that assume independent roles, the q_k and the p_k. Imagine a space of $2m$ dimensions in which $p_1, p_2, \ldots, p_m,$ $q_1, q_2, \ldots, q_m$ are the "coordinates" associated with a point called the *representative point*. As the q_k and the p_k change in physical space with the time, the representative point moves in this $2m$ dimensional *phase space*.

The simple pendulum will serve to illustrate the concept of phase space. We may write, for small angular deflections, $L = \frac{1}{2}ml^2\dot{\theta}^2 - \frac{1}{2}mgl\theta^2$ and $p_\theta = ml^2\dot{\theta}$. Hence

$$H = \frac{p_\theta^2}{2ml^2} + \frac{\theta^2}{2/mgl} = E,$$

since the system is conservative. Here p_θ and θ are the coordinates in phase space. Figure 6–2 illustrates the simple two-dimensional space in this instance. For a given E, fixed by the initial circumstances of the motion, the representative point P is restricted to move on an ellipse, as shown in the figure. At any instant the velocity of the representative point in phase space is given by the canonical equations

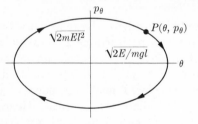

$$\dot{p}_\theta = -\frac{\partial H}{\partial \theta} = -mgl\theta,$$

$$(6\text{–}37)$$

$$\dot{\theta} = \frac{\partial H}{\partial p_\theta} = \frac{p_\theta}{ml^2}.$$

FIG. 6–2. Phase space for the simple pendulum.

The differential equation of the representative curve in the two-dimensional phase space is given by the ratio $\dot{p}_\theta/\dot{\theta}$ obtained from Eqs. (6–37). In general,

$$\frac{dp}{dq} = -\frac{(\partial H/\partial q)}{(\partial H/\partial p)},$$

$$(6\text{–}38)$$

where we make the assumption that the partial derivatives do not vanish simultaneously. In the case of the problem just discussed,

$$\frac{dp_\theta}{d\theta} = -\frac{mgl\theta}{(p_\theta/ml^2)},$$

$$(6\text{–}39)$$

so that, by integration,

$$\frac{p_\theta^2}{2ml^2} = -\frac{mgl\theta^2}{2} + E,$$

$$(6\text{–}40)$$

which is the equation of an ellipse. This idea may be extended to the general case where $\dot{p}$ and $\dot{q}$ are functions of both p and q. The two-dimensional phase space is commonly referred to as the *phase plane*.

As a second example, consider the phase space for the electron motion discussed in Section 6–2. We would expect a six-dimensional space, but due to the fact that the motion takes place in a plane and that in this plane the angular momentum p_θ is constant, we need use only three dimensions, p_r, r, θ. For this system

$$H = \frac{p_r^2}{2m} + \frac{p_\theta^2}{2mr^2} - \frac{Ze^2}{r} = E. \qquad (6\text{–}41)$$

Suppose E is fixed by the initial conditions of motion. Then Eq. (6–41) represents a cylindrical surface in the phase space illustrated in Fig. 6–3. Solving for p_r, we have

$$p_r = \pm\sqrt{2m\{E + (Ze^2/r) - (p_\theta^2/2mr^2)\}}, \qquad (6\text{–}42)$$

which implies that the surface $H = $ constant is symmetrical with respect to the (r, θ) plane.

As the electron moves in its orbit about the nucleus, the representative point in phase space moves on the surface. Its path will be a spiral since θ increases by 2π radians for each complete cycle in r. Its velocity in the θ direction varies with r, however, since $\dot{\theta} = (p_\theta/mr^2)$ and p_θ is constant.

For the purely inverse square force considered here, the successive portions of the spiral in which θ varies by 2π radians are identical. Hence each successive segment may be superposed on the portion having $\theta = 0$ to 2π, and only one curve results. In this instance the representative point moves in a one-dimensional region in the three-dimensional phase space.

On the other hand, if there is a precessional drift in the physical orbit due to some perturbing force, successive portions of the spiral will not coincide if superposed. In this case the sections of spiral, when collapsed onto the region $\theta = 0$ to 2π, fill the surface uniformly densely, and the

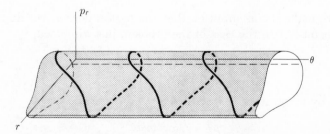

Fig. 6–3. Phase space for electron motion.

representative point moves in a two-dimensional region in the three-dimensional phase space.

In case the phase space is multidimensional, it is convenient to use partial phase space diagrams. For example, we might plot p_r against r and p_θ against θ in the preceding example. Diagrams of this kind assist in understanding the behavior of a complex system. In many applications where linear momenta are involved and the moving mass remains constant, the phase space (or phase plane in two dimensions) is described by the coordinates $\dot{q}$ (velocity) and q (displacement).

6–5 Liouville's theorem. An important property of the $2m$-dimensional phase space for statistical physical applications is described by Liouville's theorem. In the previous section we have shown that the motion of a pendulum, a system with one degree of freedom, may be described by the trajectory of a representative point in a two-dimensional (p, q) space. In that space, the equations representing the motion of the point are

$$\dot{p} = -\frac{\partial H}{\partial q}, \quad \text{and} \quad \dot{q} = \frac{\partial H}{\partial p}. \qquad (6\text{--}43)$$

Suppose, now, that a large number of identical one-dimensional systems are present. Each has a representative point in the (p, q) plane, tracing out a curve such as the ellipse shown in Fig. 6–2. Obviously the energies of the different mass particles may be different, and hence the shapes and positions of the ellipses will differ. But the trajectory corresponding to each energy can be found from Eqs. (6–43), since $H = E$.

At a given point in the (p, q) plane and within an area element $dp\, dq$, there will be many representative points at any instant. Suppose the density of such points is $\rho(p, q, t)$. By the density we mean the number of points divided by the elemental area as the latter approaches zero. We consider the totality of points as moving in much the same way that an element of a fluid would flow over the plane. Consider a fixed element of area as shown in Fig. 6–4. The number of representative points moving into $dp\, dq$ on its left edge will be

$$\rho \dot{q}\, dp \qquad (6\text{--}44)$$

per unit time. The number moving out of $dp\, dq$ through its right edge will be

$$\left\{\rho \dot{q} + \frac{\partial}{\partial q}(\rho \dot{q})\, dq\right\} dp. \qquad (6\text{--}45)$$

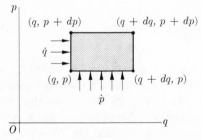

FIG. 6–4. Element of area in phase space.

Hence the net increase in ρ in the element is

$$- \frac{\partial}{\partial q}(\rho \dot{q}) \, dp \, dq. \qquad (6\text{-}46)$$

In a similar way we find the net gain due to flow in the vertical direction to be

$$- \frac{\partial}{\partial p}(\rho \dot{p}) \, dp \, dq. \qquad (6\text{-}47)$$

The total increase in density in the element is, therefore,

$$- \left\{ \frac{\partial}{\partial p}(\rho \dot{p}) + \frac{\partial}{\partial q}(\rho \dot{q}) \right\} dp \, dq \qquad (6\text{-}48)$$

per unit time. But this equals $(\partial \rho / \partial t) \, dp \, dq$. Hence we find

$$\frac{\partial \rho}{\partial t} + \left\{ \frac{\partial}{\partial p}(\rho \dot{p}) + \frac{\partial}{\partial q}(\rho \dot{q}) \right\} = 0. \qquad (6\text{-}49)$$

Expanding the derivatives in the brace, we have

$$\frac{\partial \rho}{\partial t} + \left\{ \dot{p} \, \frac{\partial \rho}{\partial p} + \dot{q} \, \frac{\partial \rho}{\partial q} \right\} + \rho \left\{ \frac{\partial \dot{p}}{\partial p} + \frac{\partial \dot{q}}{\partial q} \right\} = 0. \qquad (6\text{-}50)$$

However, $\dot{p}$ and $\dot{q}$ satisfy Eqs. (6-43). Therefore the last brace vanishes, and there remains

$$\frac{\partial \rho}{\partial t} + \dot{p} \, \frac{\partial \rho}{\partial p} + \dot{q} \, \frac{\partial \rho}{\partial q} = 0. \qquad (6\text{-}51)$$

This is Liouville's theorem for the system with one degree of freedom. It has a simple physical intepretation. Written in the form

$$\frac{\partial \rho}{\partial t} \, dt + \frac{\partial \rho}{\partial p} \, \dot{p} \, dt + \frac{\partial \rho}{\partial q} \, \dot{q} \, dt = 0, \qquad (6\text{-}52)$$

the first term is an increment in ρ in time dt at a fixed point in the (p,q) plane. The second and third terms are increments in ρ due to changes in p and q respectively with the time. Thus Eq. (6-52) states that the total increment in ρ, as the state of the system (the *phase*) varies, is zero. Expressed in other terms, Liouville's theorem states that *the density of an element of phase space corresponding to the motion of a system of particles remains constant during the motion.*

The result deduced above for a system with one degree of freedom may be generalized readily for a system with m degrees of freedom. If the representative point in phase space is defined by the coordinates $q_1, q_2, \ldots, q_m, p_1, p_2, \ldots, p_m$, Liouville's theorem becomes

$$\frac{\partial \rho}{\partial t} + \sum_{k=1}^{m} \left\{ \frac{\partial \rho}{\partial p_k} \dot{p}_k + \frac{\partial \rho}{\partial q_k} \dot{q}_k \right\} = 0, \tag{6–53}$$

or, by Eqs. (6–43),

$$\frac{\partial \rho}{\partial t} + \sum_{k=1}^{m} \left(\frac{\partial \rho}{\partial q_k} \frac{\partial H}{\partial p_k} - \frac{\partial \rho}{\partial p_k} \frac{\partial H}{\partial q_k} \right) = 0. \tag{6–54}$$

Liouville's theorem is a conservation theorem that attains considerable importance in statistical mechanics, where the physical particles concerned may be the molecules of a gas.[*] It is also useful in studying the distribution of stars in the field of the galaxy,[†] where the problem may be inverted; that is, given the observed distribution function ρ, we may find the potential field V (in $H = T + V$) which will yield the observed ρ.

As an illustration of the application of Liouville's theorem, consider a large number of simple pendulums each of length l and mass m, which possess energies lying between E_1 and E_2. The Hamiltonian for each is

$$H = \frac{p^2}{2ml^2} + \frac{q^2}{(2/mgl)} = E \qquad (E_1 < E < E_2).$$

The representative points in phase space occupy the area between the two ellipses shown in Fig. 6–5. At a given time, say t_0, the area A will contain a number of the points. As time advances, these points will move to an adjoining area. Liouville's theorem states that the area occupied by the points is a time invariant. This may be shown in an elementary way. We have

$$A = \int_{p_1(t)}^{p_2(t)} f(p) \, dp, \tag{6–55}$$

where

$$f(p) = \left(\frac{2E_2}{mgl} \right)^{1/2} \left(1 - \frac{p^2}{2ml^2 E_2} \right)^{1/2} - \left(\frac{2E_1}{mgl} \right)^{1/2} \left(1 - \frac{p^2}{2ml^2 E_1} \right)^{1/2}, \tag{6–56}$$

---

[*] See, for example, R. B. Lindsay, *Physical Statistics*. New York: John Wiley and Sons, Inc., 1941, Chapter VI.

[†] S. Chandrasekhar, *Principles of Stellar Dynamics*. Chicago: University of Chicago Press, 1942, Chapter III.

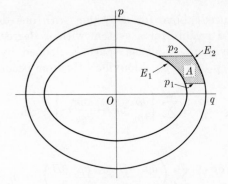

FIG. 6–5. Area in phase space of simple pendulum.

and, since $f(p)$ does not depend upon the time explicitly,

$$\frac{dA}{dt} = \int_{p_1(t)}^{p_2(t)} \frac{d[f(p)\dot{p}]}{dp} \, dp. \qquad (6\text{--}57)$$

But the integrand is a simplified form of Liouville's theorem in which $f(p)$ replaces the density ρ. Hence the integrand vanishes and $(dA/dt) = 0$, which shows the constancy of the area in phase space occupied by the cluster of representative points. The same result may be achieved by writing Eq. (6–57) in the form

$$\frac{dA}{dt} = f(p)\dot{p} \Big]_{p_1(t)}^{p_2(t)},$$

and using the Hamiltonian equation $\dot{p} = -mglq$, together with $f(p)$ expressed in terms of q, to show formally that $(dA/dt) = 0$.

The result obtained here may be generalized for a multidimensional phase space to show that an arbitrary volume

$$V = \int dq_1, dq_2, \ldots, dq_n; dp_1, dp_2, \ldots, dp_n$$

remains invariant with respect to the time.

6–6 Phase plane analysis. Complex motion in one dimension, and particularly periodic motion under nonlinear restoring forces, is most efficiently studied by use of the phase plane. We shall indicate in this section the elements of such an analysis.

Consider first a damped linear oscillator whose equation of motion is

$$m\ddot{q} + a\dot{q} + bq = 0, \qquad (6\text{--}58)$$

where q is the displacement from equilibrium. By writing $p = m\dot{q}$, we obtain the two Hamiltonian equations

$$\dot{q} = \frac{p}{m}\,, \qquad \dot{p} = -bq - \frac{ap}{m}\,. \tag{6–59}$$

Hence, by Eq. (6–38), the curve traced by the representative point in the phase plane is given by the solution of

$$\frac{dp}{dq} = -a - \frac{mbq}{p}\,. \tag{6–60}$$

We need not solve Eq. (6–60) in order to visualize the character of the curve. We shall use the method of *isoclines* and also a construction due to Liénard.

Let us set the right side of Eq. (6–60) equal to a parameter k. The parameter k then represents the slope of an integral curve of Eq. (6–60). If we plot the curves

$$-a - \frac{mbq}{p} = k,$$

we have for each value of k a locus which is crossed by all integral curves of Eq. (6–60) at the same slope. Such a locus is called an *isocline*. The isoclines for Eq. (6–60) are shown in Fig. 6–6. They are straight lines through the origin. The arrows indicate the direction at which the integral curves cross the isoclines. These curves are spirals toward the origin.

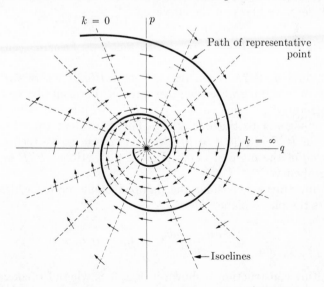

FIG. 6–6. Phase plane curve for damped oscillator.

Wherever a spiral crosses the q-axis, the velocity of the moving particle is zero.   The excursions in q obviously diminish with each successive oscillation.   Similarly, when the particle moves through the position $q = 0$, its velocity, or momentum, at each succeeding pass is diminished because the spiral intersects the p-axis closer and closer to the origin. The nature of the damped motion may, therefore, be deduced by a study of the path of the representative point in the phase plane.

In some instances, the construction due to Liénard is useful in sketching the integral curves in the phase plane. This is particularly true when the restoring force is a linear function of the displacement but the dissipative forces are nonlinear functions of the velocity, hence of the momentum. Suppose the motion of a particle of unit mass is described by $\dot{p} + \phi(p) + q = 0$.   Then the Hamiltonian equations of motion are

$$\dot{p} = -\phi(p) - q, \qquad \dot{q} = p,$$

so that the differential equation of the curve in the phase plane traced by the representative point is

$$\frac{dp}{dq} = \frac{-\phi(p) - q}{p}. \qquad (6\text{-}61)$$

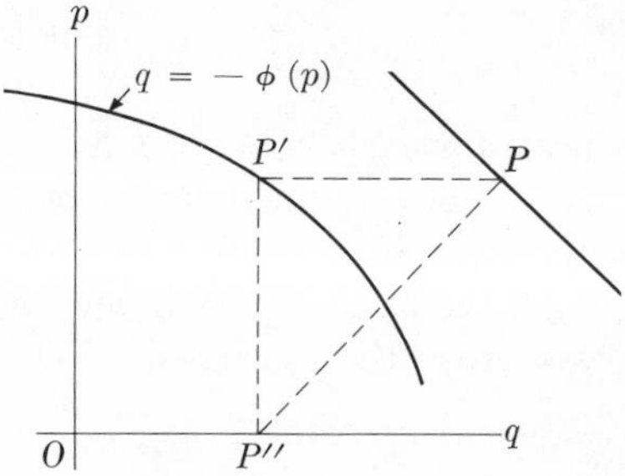

By Liénard's construction, we seek the direction of the integral curves of Eq. (6-61) at any point of the phase plane.   We first plot the curve

$$q = -\phi(p),$$

Fig. 6-7. Liénard's construction.

as shown in Fig. 6-7. Then at any point $P(q,p)$ where we desire the direction of an integral curve, we project horizontally to the curve $q = -\phi(p)$ at P'; thence vertically to P''. An integral curve through P will be orthogonal to the line $P''P$. This is evident from the fact that the slope of $P''P$ is $p/[q + \phi(p)]$, which is the negative reciprocal of the slope dp/dq of the integral curve [Eq. (6-61)]. Hence $P''P$ is normal to the integral curve.

As an illustration, consider the damped oscillator for which Fig. 6-6 represents the phase plane. Here

$$\frac{dp}{dq} = \frac{-ap - mbq}{p} \qquad (a > 0, b > 0).$$

The resulting construction is shown in Fig. 6-8, where for convenience we have taken $mb = 1$. The integral curve has been approximated by a

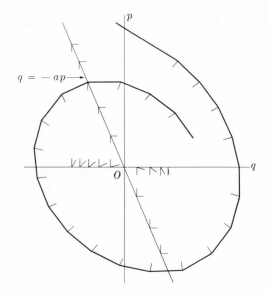

$q = -ap \longrightarrow$

Fig. 6–8. Liénard's construction for the damped oscillator.

sequence of chords. Its spiral nature is evident, and the result of the previous analysis (Fig. 6–6) is duplicated.

6–7 Nonlinear oscillatory motion.   As a final example of the phase plane analysis of motion, we shall discuss an undamped spring-mass oscillator in which the restoring force is nonlinear, that is, *not* proportional to the displacement.   The potential energy function in this case contains terms of degree higher than two in the displacement.   Let the displacement be $q(t)$ and the velocity $\dot{q}(t)$.   Then let us assume the potential energy to be $V(q) = \alpha q^2 + \beta q^4$, where $\alpha > 0$.   The restoring force, therefore, is $-2\alpha q - 4\beta q^3$.   If $\beta = 0$, the restoring force is linear; if $\beta > 0$, we have what is called a "hard" spring; if $\beta < 0$, we have a "soft" spring.   If the spring is hard, the restoring force increases more rapidly with large displacements than it would in the linear spring.   If the spring is soft, the restoring force at large displacements is less than that of a linear spring.

The Hamiltonian for the system is

$$H = \frac{p^2}{2m} + \alpha q^2 + \beta q^4 = E \qquad (\alpha > 0), \qquad (6\text{–}62)$$

where E is the total energy. Hence the Hamiltonian equations of motion are

$$\dot{q} = \frac{p}{m} \qquad \text{and} \qquad \dot{p} = -2\alpha q - 4\beta q^3. \qquad (6\text{–}63)$$

The energy curves in the (p,q) phase plane are given by Eq. (6–62) with E held constant.

When the oscillations are limited to small values of q, the term αq^2 dominates βq^4, and to a first approximation the energy curves are elliptical in shape and symmetric about both the p- and q-axes. For small oscillations $E > 0$ by Eq. (6–62). These energy curves are closed with

$$q_{\text{max}}^2 = a^2 = \frac{-\alpha + \sqrt{\alpha^2 + 4E\beta}}{2\beta}, \qquad (6\text{–}64)$$

which we obtain by setting $p = 0$ and taking the sign for the radical which makes a^2 small and positive. If $\beta > 0$ in Eq. (6–64), the radical dominates $-\alpha$ and $a^2 > 0$; if $\beta < 0$, $-\alpha$ dominates the radical but the denominator provides the change in sign to make $a^2 > 0$. Figure 6–9 indicates the phase paths for two values of E.

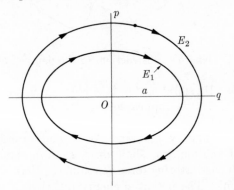

FIG. 6–9. Phase plane diagram for small oscillations of hard spring.

For the hard spring, $\beta > 0$, all the energy curves are closed, and the motion is periodic regardless of the assumption of small amplitude. We may compute the period of the oscillation by the expression

$$P = 4 \int_0^a \frac{dq}{\dot{q}} = 4\sqrt{\frac{m}{2}} \int_0^a \frac{dq}{\sqrt{E - (\alpha q^2 + \beta q^4)}}, \qquad (6\text{–}65)$$

where a is given by Eq. (6–64).

Since a^2 is a root of $E - \alpha q^2 - \beta q^4 = 0$, we may write the radicand in Eq. (6–65) as $\beta(a^2 - q^2)(b^2 + q^2)$, where

$$b^2 = a^2 + \frac{\alpha}{\beta} \qquad \text{and} \qquad E = a^2 b^2 \beta.$$

Therefore

$$P = 4\sqrt{(m/2\beta)} \int_0^a \frac{dq}{\sqrt{(a^2 - q^2)(b^2 + q^2)}},$$

which may be rewritten in trigonometric form by use of the substitution $q = a \sin \phi$. We obtain

$$P = 4\sqrt{(m/2\beta)} \int_0^{\pi/2} \frac{d\phi}{\sqrt{b^2 + a^2 \sin^2 \phi}},$$

and, upon writing $\phi = (\pi/2) - \theta$, $\cos \phi = \sin \theta$,

$$P = 4\sqrt{(m/2\beta)} \int_0^{\pi/2} \frac{d\theta}{\sqrt{a^2 + b^2}\,\sqrt{1 - (a^2 \sin^2 \theta)/(a^2 + b^2)}}$$

$$= 4\sqrt{m/(4\beta a^2 + 2\alpha)} \int_0^{\pi/2} \frac{d\theta}{\sqrt{1 - k^2 \sin^2 \theta}}, \qquad (6\text{–}66)$$

where $k^2 = [a^2/(a^2 + b^2)] = [\beta a^2/(2\beta a^2 + \alpha)]$. The last integral is a complete elliptic integral of the first kind whose value may be found in any standard mathematical table. In the case $\beta > 0$, P is always given by Eq. (6–66), and as the amplitude of oscillation increases, P decreases or the frequency increases.

Referring to the phase plane diagram (Fig. 6–9) and to Eq. (6–63), we see that when p and q are positive, $\dot{p} < 0$ and $\dot{q} > 0$, so that the representative point in phase space moves in the direction indicated by the arrows in Fig. 6–9.

For the soft spring, $\beta < 0$, the energy curves in the (p,q) plane may or may not be closed about the origin. If they are, Eq. (6–66) gives the period of the motion. This obviously occurs only when $2\alpha + 4\beta a^2 > 0$. If $2\alpha + 4\beta a^2 \leq 0$, the period is meaningless. In contrast to the hard spring, the period of oscillation for the soft spring increases as a^2 increases. We shall examine more fully the situation for $\beta < 0$ when the oscillations are not small.

In the expression for H, Eq. (6–62), let us write $\beta = -\delta^2$ and solve for p to obtain

$$p = \pm\{2m(E - \alpha q^2 + \delta^2 q^4)\}^{1/2}. \qquad (6\text{–}67)$$

Obviously the curves of constant energy in the (p,q) plane will cross the q-axis at points for which

$$q^2 = \frac{\alpha \pm \sqrt{\alpha^2 - 4E\delta^2}}{2\delta^2}. \qquad (6\text{–}68)$$

There are then three cases to consider.

Case I. $E = (\alpha^2/4\delta^2)$. Here $q^2 = (\alpha/2\delta^2)$, and upon using this value of E in Eq. (6–67), we find that the energy curves are parabolas as shown in Fig. 6–10 at I. They intersect the q-axis at the values $q = \pm (1/\delta)\sqrt{\alpha/2}$

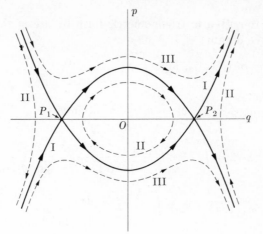

FIG. 6–10. Phase plane diagram for nonlinear spring.

and the p-axis at $p = \pm(\alpha/\delta)\sqrt{m/2}$. An analysis of the derivatives $\dot{p}$ and $\dot{q}$ indicates that the representative point in phase space moves along the curves in the directions indicated by the arrows. The points P_1 and P_2 are points of unstable equilibrium. We note, also, that the origin is a point of stable equilibrium since the force vanishes there. When the representative point reaches P_1 or P_2, its velocity is zero and it may take off on either branch of the parabolic paths.

Case II. $E < (\alpha^2/4\delta^2)$. By Eq. (6–68), q^2 is real. The energy curves intersect the q-axis at values

$$q = \pm \left\{ \frac{\alpha \pm \sqrt{\alpha^2 - 4E\delta^2}}{2\delta^2} \right\}^{1/2}.$$

If the negative sign is chosen for the interior radical, the energy curves are closed about the origin. If the positive sign is chosen, the curves are open. Typical curves of these two types are shown at II in Fig. 6–10. In one instance, stable oscillatory motion results; in the other, the representative point moves continuously along an open-branched curve.

Case III. $E > (\alpha^2/4\delta^2)$. In this case, by Eq. (6–68), q^2 is complex and the energy curves do not intersect the q-axis. They are shown at III in Fig. 6–10.

To summarize the results of the analysis, we conclude that oscillatory motion of the nonlinear spring and mass system will result when (a) $\beta > 0$, that is, for the hard spring, and (b) $\beta < 0$, that is, for the soft spring, and $E < -(\alpha^2/4\beta)$ where β is the factor introducing the nonlinearity into the system. The phase plane analysis aids materially in studying the motion.

6–8 Stability of periodic motion.   In Section 5–8 we discussed the stability of oscillatory motion by an examination of the roots of the characteristic equation of a system of linear differential equations. A phase plane analysis lends itself to the establishment of stability criteria for more general types of periodic motions. We shall discuss here briefly the Poincaré stability criterion as applied to a system having one degree of freedom. The general theory for multidimensional systems may be found elsewhere.*

Consider a particle of mass m whose displacement and momentum are, respectively, $q(t)$ and $p(t)$. Then, in general, the Hamiltonian equations will be

$$\dot{q} = f(q,p), \qquad \dot{p} = g(q,p). \tag{6–69}$$

We shall assume that $f(q,p)$ and $g(q,p)$ have continuous second derivatives with respect to q and p. Equations (6–69) define the velocity of a representative point in the phase plane.

Suppose that the system has a periodic motion of period P. Its representative point then moves in the phase plane on a closed curve C. We shall assume that this is a curve at all points of which $\dot{p}$ and $\dot{q}$ do not vanish simultaneously. A typical curve is shown in Fig. 6–11, where for convenience the origin of time has been chosen as the point where the curve crosses the positive q-axis. We shall assume also that this curve is normal to the q-axis at q_0. If this were not the case, a rotation of axes would make it so. The coordinates $q(t)$, $p(t)$ of any point on C satisfy the differential Eqs. (6–69). Suppose an alternative set of initial conditions used in conjunction with Eqs. (6–69) results in another path $C(\lambda)$

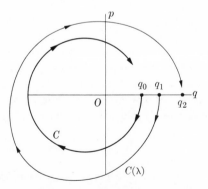

FIG. 6–11. Representative and varied phase plane curves for periodic motion.

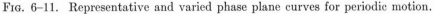

* See E. T. Whittaker, *Analytical Dynamics*. Cambridge: Cambridge University Press, 1937, pp. 397 ff.

lying very close to the original but starting at $(q_1,0)$. This path will be assumed sufficiently close to C that at some later time it again returns to the q-axis at a point $(q_2,0)$. The quantity λ is a parameter defining any one of a family of paths close to C.

Then orbital stability in the given periodic motion represented by C may be defined as follows: *the motion is stable if any solution curve $C(\lambda)$ originating in a sufficiently small neighborhood of $(q_0,0)$ is either a closed curve or a spiral that approaches asymptotically the curve C as $t \to \infty$.*

This may be expressed in a more quantitative way. Let $q(t)$, $p(t)$ be a point on C, and $q(t,\lambda)$, $p(t,\lambda)$ be a point on $C(\lambda)$. We assume that the curves $C(\lambda)$ arise by a continuous variation of λ such that the curve C corresponds to $\lambda = 0$. It is convenient to take as initial conditions

$$q(0) = q_0, \qquad q(0,\lambda) = q_0 + \lambda,$$
$$p(0) = 0, \qquad p(0,\lambda) = 0, \tag{6-70}$$

so that the curve $C(\lambda)$ begins $(t = 0)$ on the q-axis, and λ is the distance $q_1 - q_0$ (Fig. 6-11). The coordinates $q(t,\lambda)$ and $p(t,\lambda)$ are assumed to have continuous second partial derivatives with respect to λ. Let the first return of the solution curve $C(\lambda)$ to the positive q-axis be $(q_2,0)$, as indicated in Fig. 6-11. Then *the solution curve C represents a stable orbital motion if the first returns of all curves $C(\lambda)$ to the positive q-axis for $t > 0$ are such that $|q_2 - q_0| \leq |\lambda|$. If $|q_2 - q_0| > |\lambda|$, C represents an unstable periodic motion.* This criterion will now be expressed in terms of a single *stability index*.

Refer to the curve C and an adjacent varied path $C(\lambda)$, as shown in Fig. 6-12. We introduce variations

$$\delta q(t) = q(\alpha t,\lambda) - q(t), \qquad \delta p(t) = p(\alpha t,\lambda) - p(t), \tag{6-71}$$

where the parameter α has been introduced into the time scale so as to make the curve $C(\lambda)$ return to the positive q-axis at the end of the period P. Obviously this need not occur in general since the time required for the representative point to traverse $C(\lambda)$ might be different from the time required for the cycle C. By this restriction (Fig. 6-12),

$$\delta p(P) = 0, \qquad \delta q(P) = q_2 - q_0, \qquad \delta q(0) = \lambda. \tag{6-72}$$

The scale factor α will be small, in general, and will depend upon λ.

From Fig. 6-12 and the definitions above, it is apparent that $\delta q(P)$ is some multiple of λ. Thus we may write

$$\delta q(P) = \beta\lambda, \tag{6-73}$$

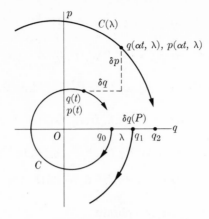

FIG. 6–12. Variations in the phase plane.

where β is a function of λ. Then the stability criterion may be expressed as follows for sufficiently small λ: (a) if $|\beta| \leq 1$, the cycle C represents stable motion; (b) if $|\beta| > 1$, the cycle C represents unstable motion.

When $\lambda = 0$ the cycle C and the solution curve $C(\lambda)$ coincide and $\alpha = 1$. For small λ, therefore, we assume that

$$\alpha(\lambda) = 1 + \alpha_0'\lambda + \text{higher order terms in } \lambda. \qquad (6\text{--}74)$$

Similarly we assume that

$$\beta(\lambda) = \beta_0 + \beta_0'\lambda + \text{higher order terms in } \lambda. \qquad (6\text{--}75)$$

In these expansions, β_0 is the value approached by $\beta(\lambda)$ as $\lambda \to 0$; β_0' and α_0' are the derivatives of β and α with respect to λ evaluated at $\lambda = 0$. We shall call β_0 the *stability index* and will show that as $\lambda \to 0$ there is a $\beta_0 > 0$. If $\beta_0 \leq 1$, the motion will be stable; if $\beta_0 > 1$, it will be unstable.

For small λ and α, we have

$$q(\alpha t, \lambda) = q(t, 0) + \left(\frac{\partial q}{\partial(\alpha t)}\right)_{\alpha=1}(\alpha - 1)t + \left(\frac{\partial q}{\partial \lambda}\right)_{\lambda=0}\lambda + \cdots. \qquad (6\text{--}76)$$

But at $\alpha = 1$, $[\partial q/\partial(\alpha t)] = q_t$, where the subscript denotes a partial derivative. Hence, if we neglect terms of the second order and higher in λ, by Eqs. (6–71), (6–74), and (6–76) we have

$$\delta q(t) = \alpha_0' t \lambda q_t(t, 0) + \lambda q_\lambda(t, 0). \qquad (6\text{--}77)$$

Similarly,

$$\delta p(t) = \alpha_0' t \lambda p_t(t, 0) + \lambda p_\lambda(t, 0). \qquad (6\text{--}78)$$

But when $t = P$, by Eqs. (6-72) and (6-73),

$$\delta q(P) = \beta\lambda = \alpha_0'P\lambda q_t(P, 0) + \lambda q_\lambda(P, 0), \qquad (6\text{-}79)$$

$$\delta p(P) = 0 = \alpha_0'P\lambda p_t(P, 0) + \lambda p_\lambda(P, 0), \qquad (6\text{-}80)$$

and, to terms of the first order in λ, from Eq. (6-75),

$$\beta_0 = \alpha_0'P q_t(P, 0) + q_\lambda(P, 0), \qquad (6\text{-}81)$$

$$0 = \alpha_0'P p_t(P, 0) + p_\lambda(P, 0). \qquad (6\text{-}82)$$

Eliminating α_0' from these, we obtain

$$\beta_0 = \frac{1}{p_t(P, 0)} \begin{vmatrix} q_\lambda(P, 0) & q_t(P, 0) \\ p_\lambda(P, 0) & p_t(P, 0) \end{vmatrix}. \qquad (6\text{-}83)$$

Now we define in general a function $W(t,\lambda)$ by the relation

$$W(t, \lambda) = \begin{vmatrix} q_\lambda(t, \lambda) & q_t(t, \lambda) \\ p_\lambda(t, \lambda) & p_t(t, \lambda) \end{vmatrix}, \qquad (6\text{-}84)$$

where we are assured of the continuity of W by virtue of the continuity conditions imposed on the partial derivatives. At $t = 0$, we have

$$W(0, \lambda) = \begin{vmatrix} q_\lambda(0, \lambda) & q_t(0, \lambda) \\ p_\lambda(0, \lambda) & p_t(0, \lambda) \end{vmatrix}. \qquad (6\text{-}85)$$

By virtue of the initial conditions, Eqs. (6-70),

$$q_\lambda(0,\lambda) = 1, \qquad p_\lambda(0,\lambda) = 0. \qquad (6\text{-}86)$$

Furthermore, since the curve C has been taken normal to the q-axis and since $p_t(t,\lambda)$ is a continuous function of λ, we have $p_t(0,0) \neq 0$ and, therefore, $p_t(0,\lambda) \neq 0$ if λ is sufficiently small. Substitution in Eq. (6-85) yields

$$W(0, \lambda) = p_t(0, \lambda) \neq 0. \qquad (6\text{-}87)$$

Now the cycle $C = C(0)$ is closed and, therefore, by Eq. (6-87),

$$p_t(P, 0) = p_t(0, 0) = W(0, 0) \neq 0, \qquad (6\text{-}88)$$

so that

$$\beta_0 = \frac{W(P, 0)}{W(0, 0)}. \tag{6–89}$$

The coordinate axes have been so chosen that these functions $W(P,0)$ and $W(0,0)$ have the same sign when evaluated along C. Therefore $\beta_0 > 0$.

To evaluate the functions defining β_0, we note from Eq. (6–84) that

$$W_t(t, \lambda) = q_\lambda p_{tt} + p_t q_{\lambda t} - p_\lambda q_{tt} - q_t p_{\lambda t}. \tag{6–90}$$

But from Eqs. (6–69),

$$q_{tt} = f_q q_t + f_p p_t, \qquad p_{tt} = g_q q_t + g_p p_t,$$

$$q_{\lambda t} = f_q q_\lambda + f_p p_\lambda, \qquad p_{\lambda t} = g_q q_\lambda + g_p p_\lambda,$$

and, substituting in Eq. (6–90), we obtain

$$W_t(t, \lambda) = (f_q + g_p)W(t, \lambda). \tag{6–91}$$

Integration with respect to t then yields

$$\log \frac{W(t, \lambda)}{W(0, \lambda)} = \int_0^t (f_q + g_p)\, dt. \tag{6–92}$$

Hence, from Eq. (6–89),

$$\log \beta_0 = \int_0^P (f_q + g_p)\, dt. \tag{6–93}$$

This line integral, *evaluated along the cycle C in the sense of advancing t*, indicates the stability or instability of the motion. If $\log \beta_0 < 0$, the motion is stable; if $\log \beta_0 > 0$, the motion is unstable. The case $\log \beta_0 = 0$ will not be discussed. For the cases discussed here, the cycle C is isolated in the sense that within a sufficiently small neighborhood of it there are no other closed solution curves. Equation (6–93) and the deductions above constitute the Poincaré stability criterion.

As an illustration, consider a unit mass moving under the action of a spring in a resisting medium in which the coefficient of resistance depends upon the displacement. To be specific, let the equation of motion be

$$\ddot{q} + \epsilon(q^2 - 1)\dot{q} + q = 0, \tag{6–94}$$

where ϵ is a parameter and q is the displacement from equilibrium.

If $\epsilon = 0$, Eq. (6–94) is simply that of an undamped simple harmonic oscillator. The solution is $q = A \sin(t + \psi)$. In the phase plane the representative point would move on the circle $q = A \sin(t + \psi)$, $p = A \cos(t + \psi)$. The constants A and ψ depend upon the initial conditions.

If $\epsilon \neq 0$ but is very small, it can be shown that there exist periodic solutions of the nonlinear equation whose representative points move in the phase plane in the neighborhood of the circle $q = 2 \sin t$, $p = 2 \cos t$.* The actual phase plane trajectory for one of these is *very nearly* a circle of radius 2. This curve was called by Poincaré a *limit cycle*. If the parameter ϵ is large, the curve becomes more nearly a parallelogram. We shall assume here that ϵ is small and investigate the stability of the limit cycle.

Here Eqs. (6–69) become

$$\dot{q} = f(q,p) = p, \qquad \dot{p} = g(q,p) = -q - \epsilon(q^2 - 1)p. \qquad (6\text{–}95)$$

Hence

$$f_q = 0, \qquad g_p = -\epsilon(q^2 - 1),$$

and inserting these in Eq. (6–93), we have

$$\log \beta_0 = -\epsilon \int_0^P (q^2 - 1)\, dt.$$

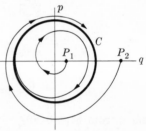

The integral is to be evaluated over the limit cycle, which in this case we shall approximate by the circle

$$q = 2 \sin t, \qquad p = 2 \cos t.$$

Fig. 6–13. Limit cycle and asymptotic spirals.

We find

$$\log \beta_0 \cong -\epsilon \int_0^{2\pi} [4 \sin^2 t - 1]\, dt = -4\pi\epsilon. \qquad (6\text{–}96)$$

Hence if $\epsilon > 0$, $\log \beta_0 < 0$, and the motion is stable. If $\epsilon < 0$, $\log \beta_0 > 0$, and the motion is unstable. Figure 6–13 illustrates the stable situation. The curve C, nearly circular, is the limit cycle. Motion under initial conditions such that the trajectory in phase space starts at P_1 is represented by a spiral which, as time goes on, approaches C asymptotically. Similarly, if the representative point starts at P_2, its path spirals toward C. The cycle C represents stable periodic motion.

---

* See, for example, A. A. Andronow and C. E. Chaikin, *Theory of Oscillations*. Princeton, New Jersey: Princeton University Press, 1949, pp. 315 ff.

Problems

6–1. Derive the Hamiltonian equations of motion [Eqs. (6–6)] directly from Hamilton's principle. (Section 6–1)

6–2. (a) Deduce the Hamiltonian function and Hamilton's equations for the spinning top discussed in Section 4–9. (b) Show that these equations reduce to those found in Section 4–9. (Section 6–1)

6–3. An electron moves in a central force field $-(Ze^2/r^2)$. Its relativistic mass is $m_0[1 - (v/c)^2]^{-1/2}$. (a) Set up the Hamiltonian function and write the Hamiltonian equations of motion in rectangular cartesian coordinates. (b) Does the Hamiltonian equal the total energy $T + V$? (c) Compute the quantity $\frac{1}{2}m_0[p_x^2 + p_y^2 + p_z^2]$, where p_x, p_y, p_z are the momenta, and (d) compare it with the nonrelativistic expression. (Sections 6–1 and 6–2)

6–4. In Problem 2–21 the Lagrangian function for relativistic motion of a particle was given. (a) Write the expressions for the momenta and for the Hamiltonian function. (b) Is the kinetic energy a homogeneous function of the velocities in this case? (c) If $H = T + V$ in this problem, is $L = T - V$? (Sections 6–1 and 6–2)

6–5. Use Routh's procedure to eliminate both ψ and ϕ from the Lagrangian for the spinning top. Show that the resulting equations of motion are the same as those obtained in Section 4–9. (Section 6–3)

6–6. A mass m slides under gravity on the inside of the surface $z = x^2 + y^2$. (a) Use Routh's procedure to reduce the problem in cylindrical coordinates to one degree of freedom. (b) Find the equations of motion. (Section 6–3)

6–7. A dynamical system has kinetic energy

$$T = \frac{1}{2}\left\{\dot{q}_1^2 + \frac{\dot{q}_2^2}{a + bq_1^2}\right\}$$

and potential energy $V = \frac{1}{2}(k_1 q_1^2 + k_2)$, where a, b, k_1, k_2 are constants. (a) Use Routh's procedure to reduce the problem to one degree of freedom. (b) Write the equations of motion and find q_1 and q_2 as functions of the time. (Section 6–3)

6–8. A particle of mass m moves in a conservative force field which is symmetrical about the Z-axis of a fixed inertial system, $OXYZ$. A second system of axes, $OX'Y'Z'$, rotates about OZ with constant angular velocity Ω. (a) What is the Hamiltonian function in terms of the rotating coordinates? (b) Does this H remain constant during the motion? (Sections 6–1 and 6–2)

6–9. A mass m is acted upon by a force whose x- and y-components are $-kx$ and $-ly$. It moves accordingly in the xy-plane. The constants k and l are elastic constants. (a) Derive the Hamiltonian for the system and write Hamilton's equations. (b) Draw phase space diagrams and determine the character of the motion. (Section 6–4)

6–10. A spherical pendulum, consisting of a large mass m suspended on a long light rod of length R, is free to move under gravity in any direction subject to the constraints. (a) Write the Hamiltonian function and Hamilton's equations for the motion. (b) Construct phase space diagrams to obtain a qualitative insight into the motion. (c) Is H the total energy of the system? (d) What are the differential equations for the curves of constant energy in the phase space diagrams? (Section 6–4)

6–11. Suppose that the bob of the pendulum of Problem 6–10 moves in a medium which resists the motion with a force proportional to the velocity. (a) Write the Hamiltonian equations in this case. (b) Can the variables in the equations of motion now be separated? (c) Show that p_θ decreases exponentially with the time if θ is the angle which the plane of the pendulum makes with the xy-plane. (Section 6–4)

6–12. The simple pendulum used in Section 6–4 to illustrate the concept of phase space was restricted to small amplitudes so that $\sin\theta \doteq \theta$. (a) Remove this restriction and write the Hamiltonian equations for its motion in general. (b) Sketch the phase space diagram and distinguish between the types of motion that may arise. (Section 6–4)

6–13. (a) Analyze by means of Hamilton's equations the motion of a projectile of mass m fired at an angle α with the horizontal at speed v_0. (b) Sketch the phase space diagrams for the motion. (c) What is the differential equation of the curve traced by the representative point in phase space? (Section 6–4)

6–14. An electron of mass m and charge $-e$ moves in a uniform electric field $\mathbf{F}$ parallel to the q-axis. (a) Write the Hamiltonian equations of motion on the assumption that the mass of the electron remains constant. (b) Display the phase space diagram for a total energy E. (c) Show that an area of the phase plane bounded by horizontal lines $p_1 =$ constant and $p_2 =$ constant and by curves E_1 and E_2 remains invariant when, as the phase changes with time, p_1 becomes p_1' and p_2 becomes p_2'. (Section 6–5)

6–15. A mass m moves on a straight line subject to the restoring force $-kq$ and to a resisting force $-a\dot{q}^2$, where q is the displacement from equilibrium. (a) Write the Hamiltonian equations of motion. (b) Display the differential equation for a representative curve in phase space. Sketch such a curve by using Liénard's construction. Assume that a is positive and small and that $k > 0$. Discuss the character of the motion. (Sections 6–6 and 6–7)

6–16. A unit mass moves on a straight line under the action of a force $-kq$ in a medium which resists the motion with a force $a\dot{q} + b\dot{q}^3$, where q is the displacement and $a > 0$, $b < 0$ are constants. (a) Write the Hamiltonian equations of motion and the differential equation for the trajectory of the representative point in phase space. (b) Plot the curves in phase space for $a = 1$, $b = -\frac{1}{4}$ starting from several initial points on the q-axis. (Sections 6–6 and 6–7)

CHAPTER 7

THE HAMILTON-JACOBI EQUATION

In Section 6–2 we found that when a coordinate was missing from the Hamiltonian, the corresponding momentum was a constant. The Hamiltonian equations were simplified thereby, and the number of degrees of freedom was reduced by one. Similarly in studying the spinning top by Routh's procedure in Section 6–3, we observed that there were two ignorable coordinates and that the integrals of the Hamiltonian equations were directly obtained.

Whether a system possesses ignorable coordinates obviously depends upon the generalized coordinates chosen for its representation. In this chapter we shall see how the Hamiltonian approach to dynamics may be extended by so transforming the coordinate system that ignorable coordinates are the only ones appearing in $H(p_k, q_k, t)$.

7–1 Canonical transformations. We recall first the familiar point transformation in the change from cartesian to polar coordinates in the plane. If, for example, a pendulum bob has, at any instant, coordinates (x, y) referred to an origin at the point of support, its kinetic energy will be $T = \frac{1}{2}m(\dot{x}^2 + \dot{y}^2)$ and its potential energy will be $V = -mgy$. If these are transformed by the relations $x = l \sin \theta$, $y = l \cos \theta$, we have $T = \frac{1}{2}ml^2\dot{\theta}^2$ and $V = -mgl \cos \theta$, where θ is the angle between the bob and the vertical. Thus the Lagrangian function, and hence the Hamiltonian, is simplified to depend upon a single coordinate. The number of Hamiltonian equations for the system is reduced from four to two by the transformation to polar coordinates.

In the Hamiltonian formulation of mechanics, however, the momenta as well as the coordinates are to be transformed since they play equal roles. The transformation is to be such that the new momenta and coordinates satisfy the same form of canonical equations that are satisfied by the original coordinates (p, q). The transformation is one in phase space. Such a transformation is called a *contact* or *canonical* transformation because surfaces in contact in the original (p, q) space will remain so after being transformed.

Let p_k and q_k denote one set of variables and P_k, Q_k denote another set where $k = 1, 2, \ldots, m$. Then if the two sets satisfy a differential form,

$$dS = \sum_{k=1}^{m} q_k \, dp_k - \sum_{k=1}^{m} Q_k \, dP_k, \tag{7-1}$$

where dS is an exact differential, the transformation from the set (p_k, q_k) to (P_k, Q_k) is a *contact* or *canonical* transformation.

For example, suppose the motion is one-dimensional and is represented in phase space by a point with the coordinates (p,q). Then if $Q = p$ and $P = -q$, we have $dQ = dp$, $dP = -dq$, so that Eq. (7–1) becomes

$$q\, dp - Q\, dP = -P\, dQ - Q\, dP = -d(PQ),$$

which is an exact differential. Hence the transformation $Q = p$, $P = -q$ is a contact transformation.

The equations of transformation, in general, are

$$P_k = P_k(q_k, p_k, t), \qquad Q_k = Q_k(q_k, p_k, t) \qquad (k = 1, 2, \ldots, m), \quad (7\text{–}2)$$

where P_k and Q_k are the new canonical coordinates. If the form of Hamilton's equations is to be preserved, there must exist a new function $K(P_k, Q_k, t)$ such that

$$\dot{Q}_k = \frac{\partial K}{\partial P_k}, \qquad \dot{P}_k = -\frac{\partial K}{\partial Q_k}. \tag{7–3}$$

The function K plays the part of the Hamiltonian in the new coordinate system.

According to Hamilton's principle, Eq. (2–32), the Lagrangian function L satisfies the variational equation

$$\delta \int_{t_0}^{t_1} L\, dt = 0. \tag{7–4}$$

But since $L = \sum_{k=1}^{m} p_k \dot{q}_k - H$,

$$\delta \int_{t_0}^{t_1} \left\{ \sum_{k=1}^{m} p_k \dot{q}_k - H \right\} dt = 0, \tag{7–5}$$

with H a function of p_k, q_k, and t.

In a similar manner the new Hamiltonian, $K(P_k, Q_k, t)$, is to satisfy the equation

$$\delta \int_{t_0}^{t_1} \left\{ \sum_{k=1}^{m} P_k \dot{Q}_k - K \right\} dt = 0. \tag{7–6}$$

For a given dynamical system, Eqs. (7–5) and (7–6) must be satisfied simultaneously. This does not mean, however, that the two integrands are equal. They may differ by the total time derivative of an arbitrary function S, which is called the *generating function* of the transformation.

In the particular context in which we shall use S, it has been called by Jacobi the *substitution function*. It links, in general, the old coordinate system with the new. The introduction of S leads, then, to the equation

$$L = \sum_{k=1}^{m} P_k \dot{Q}_k - K + \frac{dS}{dt} = \sum_{k=1}^{m} p_k \dot{q}_k - H. \qquad (7\text{--}7)$$

Multiplying Eq. (7–7) by dt and rewriting it, we have

$$dS = \sum_{k=1}^{m} p_k \, dq_k - \sum_{k=1}^{m} P_k \, dQ_k + (K - H) \, dt. \qquad (7\text{--}8)$$

The similarity between this and Eq. (7–1), defining the general contact transformation, is apparent.

To a certain extent the choice of the independent variables in S is arbitrary. If we take S to be a function of the original coordinates q_k, the new coordinates Q_k, and the time, we have $S = S(q_k, Q_k, t)$ and

$$dS = \sum_{k=1}^{m} \frac{\partial S}{\partial q_k} \, dq_k + \sum_{k=1}^{m} \frac{\partial S}{\partial Q_k} \, dQ_k + \frac{\partial S}{\partial t} \, dt. \qquad (7\text{--}9)$$

Comparing Eq. (7–9) with Eq. (7–8), we see that

$$p_k = \frac{\partial S}{\partial q_k}, \qquad -P_k = \frac{\partial S}{\partial Q_k}, \qquad K - H = \frac{\partial S}{\partial t}. \qquad (7\text{--}10)$$

These equations link the new coordinates (P_k, Q_k) with the original coordinates (p_k, q_k) through the function S in such a way that

$$\dot{Q}_k = \frac{\partial K}{\partial P_k}, \qquad \dot{P}_k = - \frac{\partial K}{\partial Q_k}. \qquad (7\text{--}11)$$

The proof of this we leave as an exercise for the reader. If S does not depend upon the time explicitly, we note from Eqs. (7–10) that $K = H$; the Hamiltonian functions in the two systems are the same.

Had we chosen $S = S(q_k, P_k, t)$ instead of $S = S(q_k, Q_k, t)$, an equally valid transformation would result. The theory of contact transformations* indicates that if $S_1 = S_1(q_k, P_k, t)$ is the new generating function, the relation between $S(q_k, Q_k, t)$ and S_1 will be

$$S_1 - S = \sum_{k=1}^{m} P_k Q_k. \qquad (7\text{--}12)$$

---

* See, for example, H. Goldstein, *Classical Mechanics*. Reading, Massachusetts: Addison-Wesley Publishing Company, Inc., 1950, Chapters 8 and 9.

From Eq. (7–12),

$$dS_1 = \sum_{k=1}^{m} \left[\left(P_k + \frac{\partial S}{\partial Q_k} \right) dQ_k + Q_k\, dP_k + \frac{\partial S}{\partial q_k}\, dq_k \right] + \frac{\partial S}{\partial t}\, dt \cdot \qquad (7\text{–}13)$$

But,

$$dS_1 = \sum_{k=1}^{m} \left[\frac{\partial S_1}{\partial q_k}\, dq_k + \frac{\partial S_1}{\partial P_k}\, dP_k \right] + \frac{\partial S_1}{\partial t}\, dt \cdot \qquad (7\text{–}14)$$

Hence, comparing Eq. (7–14) with Eq. (7–13) and using Eqs. (7–10), we find

$$\frac{\partial S_1}{\partial q_k} = \frac{\partial S}{\partial q_k} = p_k, \qquad \frac{\partial S_1}{\partial P_k} = Q_k, \qquad \frac{\partial S_1}{\partial t} = \frac{\partial S}{\partial t} = K - H. \qquad (7\text{–}15)$$

Similarly, by a substitution for S in Eq. (7–7),

$$L = \sum_{k=1}^{m} p_k \dot{q}_k - H = - \sum_{k=1}^{m} Q_k \dot{P}_k - K + \frac{\partial S_1}{\partial t} \cdot \qquad (7\text{–}16)$$

Use of the right side of Eq. (7–16) in Hamilton's principle will indicate that the canonical Hamiltonian equations (7–3) are preserved in the transformation generated by the function $S_1(q_k, P_k, t)$.

The transformations generated by S and S_1 are the two most important for our purposes. By their use it is possible to transform the canonical variables in a dynamical problem so that either the *new momenta or the new coordinates or both are constant in time*. This is the objective of the transformation theory.

7–2 The Hamilton-Jacobi equation. Obviously the applicability of the transformation theory hinges on the possibility of finding an appropriate generating function. This is done by solving a first order partial differential equation, known as the Hamilton-Jacobi equation.

Consider first a simple example. Let the displacement of a mass m moving in simple harmonic motion be q and let its momentum be p. Its energy, and consequently the Hamiltonian function, will be

$$H = \frac{p^2}{2m} + \frac{kq^2}{2} = E, \qquad (7\text{–}17)$$

where k is the restoring force constant.

By either Eqs. (7–10) or Eqs. (7–15), $p = (\partial S/\partial q)$, so that substitution in Eq. (7–17) yields

$$\frac{1}{2m} \left(\frac{\partial S}{\partial q} \right)^2 + \frac{kq^2}{2} = E. \qquad (7\text{–}18)$$

This is a first order partial differential equation for S. By integration,

$$S = \int \sqrt{2m(E - \tfrac{1}{2}kq^2)} \, dq + C. \qquad (7\text{–}19)$$

If S is chosen to be $S(q, P)$, by analogy with S_1 of the preceding section, then by Eqs. (7–15) we can compute Q and, since H is independent of time, $K = H$. In future discussion, we shall drop the subscript for S_1 and call the generating function S regardless of whether the independent variables are q_k, Q_k, and t or q_k, P_k, and t.

Let us *arbitrarily select E to be the new momentum*. Since the force field is conservative, E will be constant. Then we have, by Eqs. (7–15),

$$Q = \frac{\partial S}{\partial P} \equiv \frac{\partial S}{\partial E} = \sqrt{\tfrac{1}{2}m} \int \frac{dq}{\sqrt{E - \tfrac{1}{2}kq^2}}. \qquad (7\text{–}20)$$

Integrating and solving for q, we find

$$q = \sqrt{(2E/k)} \, \sin \sqrt{(k/m)} \, Q, \qquad (7\text{–}21)$$

where the constant of integration has been set equal to zero.

Substitution of this value of q in Eq. (7–17) yields

$$p = \sqrt{2mE} \, \cos \sqrt{(k/m)} \, Q. \qquad (7\text{–}22)$$

Equations (7–21) and (7–22) express the original coordinate q and momentum p in terms of the new coordinate Q and new momentum E, which now is constant. Attention again is directed to the fact that we have *forced* the latter condition.

The transformation from the (p, q) phase plane to the (P, Q) plane, defined by Eqs. (7–21) and (7–22), is shown in Fig. 7–1. For a given E,

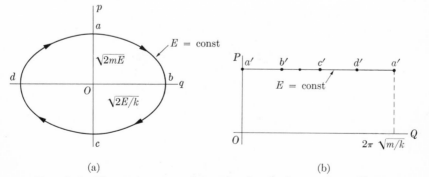

(a)   (b)

FIG. 7–1. Phase plane transformation for the harmonic oscillator.

fixed by the initial conditions, the representative point in the (p, q) plane moves on an ellipse. The corresponding point in the (P, Q) plane moves on the line $P \equiv E =$ constant. Successive passages of the point around the ellipse are imaged into successive sections of the line of length $2\pi\sqrt{m/k}$ in the (P, Q) plane. Figure 7–1(a) shows one cycle of the motion of the representative point denoted by the letters a, b, c, d, a, and Fig. 7–1 (b) shows their images a', b', c', d', a'.

Suppose we carry the example one step further. It is clear by Eqs. (7–3) or (7–11) that if the transformation is such that $K(P, Q, t) \equiv 0$, we shall have $\dot{Q} = 0$, $\dot{P} = 0$, and hence the representative point in the new (P, Q) phase plane will be fixed at one point. Referring to Eqs. (7–15), we see that if $K \equiv 0$, $H + (\partial S/\partial t) = 0$, where $H = H(p, q, t)$, the original Hamiltonian. Furthermore, since $(\partial S/\partial q) = p$, we may write, by Eq. (7–17),

$$\frac{1}{2m}\left(\frac{\partial S}{\partial q}\right)^2 + \frac{kq^2}{2} + \frac{\partial S}{\partial t} = 0. \tag{7–23}$$

This is a first order partial differential equation to be solved for the function S. We assume a trial solution, $S(q, t) = S_1(q) + S_2(t)$, and substitute in Eq. (7–23). There results

$$\frac{1}{2m}\left(\frac{dS_1}{dq}\right)^2 + \frac{kq^2}{2} + \frac{dS_2}{dt} = 0,$$

which may be written

$$\frac{1}{2m}\left(\frac{dS_1}{dq}\right)^2 + \frac{kq^2}{2} = -\frac{dS_2}{dt}. \tag{7–24}$$

The left side is a function of q alone, and the right side is a function of t alone. Hence for the equation to be true, both sides must equal a constant, say α_1. Then upon integration there results

$$S_1 = \int \sqrt{2m(\alpha_1 - \tfrac{1}{2}kq^2)}\, dq,$$

$$S_2 = -\alpha_1 t,$$

where the constants of integration have been omitted. The substitution function is, therefore,

$$S(q, \alpha_1, t) = \int \sqrt{2m(\alpha_1 - \tfrac{1}{2}kq^2)}\, dq - \alpha_1 t. \tag{7–25}$$

Now we choose, arbitrarily, $\alpha_1 \equiv P$, the new momentum which is constant. Then by Eqs. (7–15),

$$Q = \frac{\partial S}{\partial \alpha_1} = \sqrt{\tfrac{1}{2}m} \int \frac{dq}{\sqrt{\alpha_1 - \tfrac{1}{2}kq^2}} - t. \qquad (7\text{–}26)$$

But by choosing $K(P, Q, t) = 0$ we have *forced Q to be a constant, say* β_1. Hence

$$\sqrt{\tfrac{1}{2}m} \int \frac{dq}{\sqrt{\alpha_1 - \tfrac{1}{2}kq^2}} - t = \beta_1. \qquad (7\text{–}27)$$

Solving for q as a function of t, we have

$$q = \sqrt{(2\alpha_1/k)} \sin \sqrt{(k/m)} \, (t + \beta_1). \qquad (7\text{–}28)$$

This is the solution to the dynamical problem with α_1 and β_1 to be determined by the initial conditions. In the phase plane, the representative point, now at (α_1, β_1), does not vary with the time. This simple example illustrates the transformation theory of dynamics as applied through the method developed by Hamilton and Jacobi. We now generalize the ideas to a multidimensional dynamical system.

Let the original dynamical system be described by the Hamiltonian $H(p_k, q_k, t)$, where $k = 1, 2, \ldots, m$. And let the transformed Hamiltonian be $K(P_k, Q_k, t)$. Then by arbitrarily setting $K \equiv 0$, we are assured by the transformation theory that $\dot{Q}_k = 0$ and $\dot{P}_k = 0$ for all k. Hence Q_k and P_k are constants in time. If we know their values at $t = 0$ and have a transformation linking them with the q_k and p_k, the problem is solved.

By Eqs. (7–10) or (7–15) with $K = 0$, we have

$$H(q_k, p_k, t) + \frac{\partial S}{\partial t} = 0 \qquad (k = 1, 2, \ldots, m), \qquad (7\text{–}29)$$

and substituting $(\partial S/\partial q_k)$ for p_k in H,

$$H \left\{ q_k, \frac{\partial S}{\partial q_k}, t \right\} + \frac{\partial S}{\partial t} = 0 \qquad (k = 1, 2, \ldots, m). \qquad (7\text{–}30)$$

This first order partial differential equation for the function S is called the *Hamilton-Jacobi equation.*

Since there are m independent variables q_k plus the time in the

Hamilton-Jacobi equation and since the function S enters only in the form of its derivatives, the solution* will be of the form

$$S = S(q_1, q_2, \ldots, q_m; \ \alpha_1, \alpha_2, \ldots, \alpha_m; \ t), \qquad (7\text{--}31)$$

where the α_k are constants. There will be an additive constant of integration that we shall ignore because we are interested only in the partial derivatives of S.

Suppose we have found S and know the initial values of the momenta p_k and coordinates q_k at $t = 0$. Then by Eqs. (7–15) we have m equations

$$p_k = \frac{\partial S(q_k, \alpha_k, t)}{\partial q_k} \qquad (k = 1, 2, \ldots, m) \qquad (7\text{--}32)$$

from which to solve for the α_k.

Now we arbitrarily *choose the new momenta of the system, P_k, to be the constants, α_k*, resulting from the integration. Then by Eqs. (7–15),

$$Q_k = \frac{\partial S(q_k, \alpha_k, t)}{\partial \alpha_k} = \beta_k \qquad (k = 1, 2, \ldots, m), \qquad (7\text{--}33)$$

where the β_k are constants. Recall that in our solution we have *forced* Q_k to be constant in time. Since the α_k and q_k are known from Eq. (7–32) and the initial conditions, we can solve Eq. (7–33) for the β_k. Having found the values of β_k, we may invert the solution of Eq. (7–33) to find the q_k as functions of α_k, β_k, and t, and the problem is solved.

The steps outlined above may be visualized by consideration of the electron moving in a central force field, a problem discussed in Section 6–2 by means of Hamilton's equations. There we found the Hamiltonian

$$H = \frac{1}{2m}\left\{p_r^2 + \frac{p_\phi^2}{r^2 \sin^2 \theta} + \frac{p_\theta^2}{r^2}\right\} - \frac{Ze^2}{r}. \qquad (7\text{--}34)$$

Substituting in Eq. (7–34) the momenta

$$p_r = \frac{\partial S}{\partial r}, \qquad p_\phi = \frac{\partial S}{\partial \phi}, \qquad p_\theta = \frac{\partial S}{\partial \theta},$$

we have by Eq. (7–29) the Hamilton-Jacobi equation,

$$\frac{1}{2m}\left\{\left(\frac{\partial S}{\partial r}\right)^2 + \frac{1}{r^2 \sin^2 \theta}\left(\frac{\partial S}{\partial \phi}\right)^2 + \frac{1}{r^2}\left(\frac{\partial S}{\partial \theta}\right)^2\right\} - \frac{Ze^2}{r} + \frac{\partial S}{\partial t} = 0. \qquad (7\text{--}35)$$

---

* An equation of this type is discussed, for example, in M. Morris and O. E. Brown, *Differential Equations*, 3rd edition. New York: Prentice-Hall, Inc., 1952, p. 225.

We assume a separable function,

$$S = S_1(r) + S_2(\phi) + S_3(\theta) - \alpha_1 t,$$

and substitute in Eq. (7–35) to obtain

$$\frac{1}{2m}\left\{\left(\frac{dS_1}{dr}\right)^2 + \frac{1}{r^2 \sin^2 \theta}\left(\frac{dS_2}{d\phi}\right)^2 + \frac{1}{r^2}\left(\frac{dS_3}{d\theta}\right)^2\right\} - \frac{Ze^2}{r} = \alpha_1. \qquad (7\text{–}36)$$

Multiplying Eq. (7–36) by r^2 and regrouping the terms, we have

$$r^2\left(\frac{dS_1}{dr}\right)^2 - 2m\alpha_1 r^2 - 2mZe^2 r = -\frac{1}{\sin^2 \theta}\left(\frac{dS_2}{d\phi}\right)^2 - \left(\frac{dS_3}{d\theta}\right)^2. \qquad (7\text{–}37)$$

But the left side of Eq. (7–37) is a function of r alone, and the right side is a function of ϕ and θ. This can be true only if both equal some constant, say α_2. Hence to determine S_1, we have the equation

$$\frac{dS_1}{dr} = \frac{1}{r}\sqrt{\alpha_2 + 2mZe^2 r + 2m\alpha_1 r^2}. \qquad (7\text{–}38)$$

In a similar way the right side of Eq. (7–37) can be separated by writing

$$\left(\frac{dS_2}{d\phi}\right)^2 = -\alpha_2 \sin^2 \theta - \sin^2 \theta \left(\frac{dS_3}{d\theta}\right)^2 = \alpha_3. \qquad (7\text{–}39)$$

Therefore,

$$\frac{dS_2}{d\phi} = \sqrt{\alpha_3}, \qquad (7\text{–}40)$$

$$\frac{dS_3}{d\theta} = \frac{1}{\sin \theta}\sqrt{-\alpha_3 - \alpha_2 \sin^2 \theta}. \qquad (7\text{–}41)$$

Equations (7–38), (7–40), and (7–41) yield the components of the substitution function, so that

$$S = \int \frac{1}{r}\sqrt{\alpha_2 + 2mZe^2 r + 2m\alpha_1 r^2}\, dr + \sqrt{\alpha_3}\int d\phi$$

$$+ \int \frac{1}{\sin \theta}\sqrt{-\alpha_3 - \alpha_2 \sin^2 \theta}\, d\theta - \alpha_1 t. \qquad (7\text{–}42)$$

We need not evaluate these integrals since we are interested only in the partial derivatives of S with respect to the α_k. Applying Eq. (7–33), we have

$$\frac{\partial S}{\partial \alpha_1} = \int \frac{mr\,dr}{\sqrt{\alpha_2 + 2mZe^2 r + 2m\alpha_1 r^2}} - t = \beta_1, \qquad (7\text{--}43)$$

$$\frac{\partial S}{\partial \alpha_2} = \int \frac{dr}{2r\sqrt{\alpha_2 + 2mZe^2 r + 2m\alpha_1 r^2}} - \int \frac{\sin\theta\,d\theta}{2\sqrt{-\alpha_3 - \alpha_2 \sin^2\theta}} = \beta_2, \qquad (7\text{--}44)$$

$$\frac{\partial S}{\partial \alpha_3} = \frac{1}{2\sqrt{\alpha_3}}\,\phi - \int \frac{d\theta}{2\sin\theta\sqrt{-\alpha_3 - \alpha_2 \sin^2\theta}} = \beta_3. \qquad (7\text{--}45)$$

Equation (7–43) provides the functional relationship between r and t; Eq. (7–44) gives r as a function of θ and hence is the equation of the orbit. From this equation, knowing r as a function of t, we could obtain θ as a function of t. Equation (7–45) gives ϕ as a function of θ or, if desired, ϕ as a function of the time. The constants α_1, α_2, α_3 and β_1, β_2, β_3 are determined by the initial circumstances of the motion. We leave this as a problem for the reader. The constant α_1 is, of course, the total energy of the system.

This example illustrates the general procedure for solving a multi-dimensional dynamical problem by the Hamilton-Jacobi method. Whenever the Hamiltonian H does not contain the time explicitly, as in the example just discussed, a separation of S into the sum of functions, $S = S_1(q_1) + S_2(q_2) + \cdots + S_m(q_m)$, is possible. Then a complete solution of the Hamilton-Jacobi equation is

$$S = S'(q_k, \alpha_k) - \alpha_1 t \qquad (k = 1, 2, \ldots, m), \qquad (7\text{--}46)$$

where the function $S'(q_k, \alpha_k)$ is the sum of functions, each of which contains only one of the q_k and at least one of the constants α_k.

Since $(\partial S/\partial t) = -\alpha_1$ in this case, the Hamilton-Jacobi equation may be written as

$$H\left(q_k, \frac{\partial S'}{\partial q_k}\right) = \alpha_1 \qquad (k = 1, 2, \ldots, m). \qquad (7\text{--}47)$$

The assumption of separability in S implies that the part of H containing q_1, $(\partial S'/\partial q_1)$ may be segregated, leaving all other q_k and $(\partial S'/\partial q_k)$ grouped. Thus,

$$H_1\left(q_1, \frac{\partial S'}{\partial q_1}, \alpha_1\right) = H_2\left(q_2 \cdots q_m, \frac{\partial S'}{\partial q_2} \cdots \frac{\partial S'}{\partial q_m}, \alpha_1\right). \qquad (7\text{--}48)$$

But this equation can be true only if both sides equal some constant, say α_2. We have then two equations,

$$H_1\left(q_1, \frac{\partial S'}{\partial q_1}, \alpha_1\right) = \alpha_2, \tag{7–49}$$

$$H_2\left(q_2 \cdots q_m, \frac{\partial S'}{\partial q_2} \cdots \frac{\partial S'}{\partial q_m}, \alpha_1\right) = \alpha_2. \tag{7–50}$$

Equation (7–49) can be solved as an ordinary differential equation for $S_1'(q_1, \alpha_1, \alpha_2)$. In similar fashion Eq. (7–50) can be separated to yield

$$H_2\left(q_2, \frac{\partial S'}{\partial q_2}, \alpha_1, \alpha_2\right) = H_3\left(q_3 \cdots q_m, \frac{\partial S'}{\partial q_3} \cdots \frac{\partial S'}{\partial q_m}, \alpha_1, \alpha_2\right) = \alpha_3, \tag{7–51}$$

and $H_2[q_2, (\partial S'/\partial q_2), \alpha_1, \alpha_2] = \alpha_3$ may be solved for $S_2'(q_2, \alpha_1, \alpha_2, \alpha_3)$. As a result of this separation repeated $m - 1$ times, we find ultimately

$$S' = S_1'(q_1, \alpha_1, \alpha_2) + S_2'(q_2, \alpha_1, \alpha_2, \alpha_3) + S_3'(q_3, \alpha_1, \alpha_2, \alpha_3, \alpha_4) + \cdots. \tag{7–52}$$

This is the substitution function for the problem. It is the time-independent part of S.

Having found S' by this separation technique, we may then choose the α_k to be either the new coordinates or the new momenta, as we did in the examples above. The concluding analysis follows.

Case I. $\alpha_k \equiv Q_k$. By Eqs. (7–10) we have, since S' is independent of t,

$$p_k = \frac{\partial S'}{\partial q_k}, \qquad -P_k = \frac{\partial S'}{\partial \alpha_k}, \qquad K' = H = \alpha_1 \qquad (k = 1, 2, \ldots, m), \tag{7–53}$$

where K' is the new Hamiltonian and is independent of the time. Then the Hamiltonian equations (7–11) yield

$$\dot{P}_1 = -\frac{\partial K'}{\partial \alpha_1} = -1,$$

$$\dot{P}_2 = -\frac{\partial K'}{\partial \alpha_2} = 0,$$

$$\vdots \tag{7–54}$$

$$\dot{P}_m = -\frac{\partial K'}{\partial \alpha_m} = 0,$$

so that

$$P_1 = -t - \beta_1,$$
$$P_2 = -\beta_2,$$

(7-55)

.

.

.

$$P_m = -\beta_m,$$

where the β_k are constants of integration.

Combining the second of Eqs. (7–53) with Eqs. (7–55), we have

$$\frac{\partial S'}{\partial \alpha_1} = t + \beta_1,$$

$$\frac{\partial S'}{\partial \alpha_2} = \beta_2,$$

(7-56)

.

.

.

$$\frac{\partial S'}{\partial \alpha_m} = \beta_m.$$

These equations may be solved for the coordinates q_k as functions of the time, and hence they constitute a solution to the dynamical problem.

Case II. $\alpha_k \equiv P_k$. By Eqs. (7–15) we have

$$p_k = \frac{\partial S'}{\partial q_k}, \qquad Q_k = \frac{\partial S'}{\partial \alpha_k}, \qquad K' = H = \alpha_1 \qquad (k = 1, 2, \ldots, m).$$

(7-57)

The Hamiltonian equations yield

$$\dot{Q}_1 = \frac{\partial K'}{\partial \alpha_1} = 1, \qquad \dot{Q}_k = \frac{\partial K'}{\partial \alpha_k} = 0 \qquad (k = 2, 3, \ldots, m),$$

(7-58)

so that

$$Q_1 = t + \beta_1, \qquad Q_k = \beta_k \qquad (k = 2, 3, \ldots, m).$$

(7-59)

Combining the second of Eqs. (7–57) with Eqs. (7–59), we have

$$\frac{\partial S'}{\partial \alpha_1} = t + \beta_1, \qquad \frac{\partial S'}{\partial \alpha_k} = \beta_k \qquad (k = 2, 3, \ldots, m).$$

(7-60)

These equations, solved for the q_k as functions of the time, constitute a solution of the problem. Both examples, discussed previously in this section, illustrate the procedure.

As a final example, consider again the spinning top discussed in Section 4–9. Using the values of T and V in terms of the Eulerian angles, we find

$$H = \frac{1}{2} \left\{ \frac{p_\theta^2}{I} + \frac{(p_\phi - p_\psi \cos \theta)^2}{I \sin^2 \theta} + \frac{p_\psi^2}{I_3} \right\} + mgl \cos \theta, \qquad (7\text{–}61)$$

where p_θ, p_ϕ, p_ψ are the momenta conjugate to the angles θ, ϕ, ψ (see Fig. 4–19). Since H is independent of the time, we shall assume $S = S'(\theta, \phi, \psi) - \alpha_1 t$ as the form of the substitution function. We have

$$p_\theta = \frac{\partial S'}{\partial \theta}, \qquad p_\phi = \frac{\partial S'}{\partial \phi}, \qquad p_\psi = \frac{\partial S'}{\partial \psi},$$

and the Hamilton-Jacobi equation is, by Eq. (7–47),

$$\frac{1}{2I} \left(\frac{\partial S'}{\partial \theta} \right)^2 + \frac{1}{2I \sin^2 \theta} \left(\frac{\partial S'}{\partial \phi} - \frac{\partial S'}{\partial \psi} \cos \theta \right)^2$$

$$+ \frac{1}{2I_3} \left(\frac{\partial S'}{\partial \psi} \right)^2 + mgl \cos \theta = \alpha_1. \qquad (7\text{–}62)$$

Since this equation does not contain the variables ϕ or ψ explicitly, we assume the function

$$S' = S_1(\theta) + \alpha_2 \phi + \alpha_3 \psi, \qquad (7\text{–}63)$$

where α_2 and α_3 are constants. Whenever cyclic or ignorable coordinates such as ψ or ϕ occur, the corresponding part of S' can be taken as a linear function of these coordinates. Then, substituting in Eq. (7–62), we have

$$\frac{1}{2I} \left(\frac{dS_1}{d\theta} \right)^2 + \frac{1}{2I \sin^2 \theta} (\alpha_2 - \alpha_3 \cos \theta)^2 + \frac{1}{2I_3} \alpha_3^2 + mgl \cos \theta = \alpha_1. \qquad (7\text{–}64)$$

Therefore,

$$\frac{dS_1}{d\theta} = \left\{ 2I\alpha_1 - \frac{I}{I_3} \alpha_3^2 - 2Imgl \cos \theta - \frac{1}{\sin^2 \theta} (\alpha_2 - \alpha_3 \cos \theta)^2 \right\}^{1/2}.$$

Hence,

$$S_1 = \int \left\{ 2I\alpha_1 - \frac{I}{I_3} \alpha_3^2 - 2Imgl \cos \theta - \frac{1}{\sin^2 \theta} (\alpha_2 - \alpha_3 \cos \theta)^2 \right\}^{1/2} d\theta.$$

Let the quantity in the brace be denoted by $F(\theta)$. Then we have for the substitution function,

$$S' = \int \sqrt{F(\theta)} \, d\theta + \alpha_2 \phi + \alpha_3 \psi. \qquad (7\text{–}65)$$

If for sake of variety we choose the constants α_k to be the new coordinates, Q_k, we have by Case I, Eqs. (7–56),

$$\frac{\partial S'}{\partial \alpha_1} = t + \beta_1 = \int \frac{I \, d\theta}{\sqrt{F(\theta)}}, \qquad (7\text{–}66)$$

$$\frac{\partial S'}{\partial \alpha_2} = \beta_2 = \phi - \int \frac{(\alpha_2 - \alpha_3 \cos \theta) \, d\theta}{\sin^2 \theta \sqrt{F(\theta)}}, \qquad (7\text{–}67)$$

$$\frac{\partial S'}{\partial \alpha_3} = \beta_3 = \psi - \frac{I}{I_3} \alpha_3 \int \frac{d\theta}{\sqrt{F(\theta)}} + \int \frac{(\alpha_2 - \alpha_3 \cos \theta) \cos \theta \, d\theta}{\sin^2 \theta \sqrt{F(\theta)}}. \qquad (7\text{–}68)$$

Equation (7–66) gives θ as a function of the time. The function $F(\theta)$ is equivalent to that appearing under the radical in Eq. (4–83) if we set

$$\alpha_1 = E, \qquad \alpha_3 = I_3 \omega_3, \qquad \alpha_2 = L_\phi.$$

These are all constants of the motion determined by the initial conditions.

Equations (7–67) and (7–68) give the functional relationships between θ, ϕ, ψ. Once θ has been determined as a function of t, the other variables may also be expressed in terms of t. These three equations constitute the solution of the problem.

The Hamilton-Jacobi theory, here discussed briefly, has been applied extensively in studies of planetary motion and in the development of quantum mechanics. The interested reader will find detailed studies of the method in the references listed at the end of the book.

7–3 Action and angle variables. Many physical problems are of a multiply periodic nature. For example, in the electron problem discussed in Section 7–2, the radius vector r goes through a cycle from minimum to maximum to minimum again as the angle ϕ varies from 0 to 2π. In the harmonic oscillator, the position coordinate is a periodic function of the time. In the latter case the momentum, too, oscillates between minimum and maximum values.

The Hamilton-Jacobi theory is particularly effective in handling such periodic systems. By a periodic motion of the system we mean that the projection of the representative point in phase space on any (p_k, q_k) plane is simply periodic in a one-dimensional sense. That is, the path in the (p, q) plane is a closed curve.

In order to study this cyclic motion, we introduce a special type of variable called the *action variable* or *phase integral*. This is defined by the equation

$$J_k = \oint p_k \, dq_k \qquad (k = 1, 2, \ldots, m), \qquad (7\text{–}69)$$

where the integration is to be performed over one complete cycle of the q_k involved. This amounts to defining J_k for each degree of freedom as the area in its partial phase space bounded by the path of the representative point.

Let us use as an example the simple harmonic oscillator discussed in Section 7–2. There we found the momentum to be

$$p = \sqrt{2m(E - \tfrac{1}{2}kq^2)} = \sqrt{2m(\alpha_1 - \tfrac{1}{2}kq^2)},$$

where the constant α_1 corresponds physically to the total energy of the system. Hence the action variable for this oscillator is

$$J = 4 \int_0^{q_0} \sqrt{2m(\alpha_1 - \tfrac{1}{2}kq^2)} \, dq. \qquad (7\text{–}70)$$

The upper limit q_0 in Eq. (7–70) is obtained by setting the integrand equal to zero. Thus $q_0 = \sqrt{2\alpha_1/k}$. The phase integral, Eq. (7–70), represents the area of the ellipse shown in Fig. 7–1. When the coordinate involved is an angle, such as the angle θ in the electron problem of the preceding section, the integration extends from 0 to 2π.

Since, by definition,

$$p_k = \frac{\partial S'(q_k, \alpha_k)}{\partial q_k},$$

we can write for the phase integral associated with the coordinate q_k

$$J_k = \oint \frac{\partial S'}{\partial q_k} \, dq_k. \qquad (7\text{–}71)$$

But q_k is only the variable of integration and does not appear in the final result. Hence each J_k is a function of the α_k, the constants in the solution of the Hamilton-Jacobi equation. Each set (p_k, q_k) of momenta and coordinates is independent. Therefore the various J_k are independent, and we have m equations from which to solve for the α_k. Thus

$$\alpha_1 = \alpha_1(J_1, J_2, \ldots, J_m),$$
$$\alpha_2 = \alpha_2(J_1, J_2, \ldots, J_m),$$

$$\cdot$$
$$\cdot \qquad\qquad\qquad\qquad\qquad\qquad (7\text{–}72)$$
$$\cdot$$

$$\alpha_m = \alpha_m(J_1, J_2, \ldots, J_m).$$

S' can then be written as a function of the coordinates and of these new quantities, the action variables. That is,

$$S' = S'(q_1 \ldots q_m, J_1 \ldots J_m). \qquad (7\text{–}73)$$

Now *we choose the J_k to be the new momenta in the canonical transformation.* Then, by Eqs. (7–15),

$$p_k = \frac{\partial S'}{\partial q_k}, \qquad Q_k = \frac{\partial S'}{\partial J_k} \equiv w_k, \qquad (7\text{–}74)$$

where we introduce the notation w_k to designate the new coordinate. Furthermore, by Eqs. (7–47) and (7–57),

$$K'(J_1, J_2, \ldots, J_m) = H(J_1, J_2, \ldots, J_m) = \alpha_1. \qquad (7\text{–}75)$$

Hamilton's equations then become

$$\dot{J}_k = -\frac{\partial K'}{\partial w_k}, \qquad \dot{w}_k = \frac{\partial K'}{\partial J_k}, \qquad (k = 1, 2, \ldots, m). \qquad (7\text{–}76)$$

Since K' is a function of the J_k alone, $(\partial K'/\partial w_k) = 0$, and J_k is constant in time. But then $(\partial K'/\partial J_k)$ is constant in time, and we may write

$$w_k = \nu_k t + \beta_k, \qquad (7\text{–}77)$$

where ν_k is a constant, thus far undefined physically, and β_k is a constant of integration. The quantities w_k are called *angle variables*. The constants ν_k will depend upon the J_k through the partial derivatives $(\partial K'/\partial J_k)$.

Let us now examine the physical significance of the ν_k. We compute first the change in a given angle variable, say w_1, due to a complete cycle of variation in any one coordinate, say q_k, while all the other coordinates are fixed. This will be

$$\Delta w_1 = \oint \frac{\partial w_1}{\partial q_k} dq_k. \qquad (7\text{–}78)$$

But, by Eqs. (7–74), $w_1 = (\partial S'/\partial J_1)$. Hence

$$\Delta w_1 = \oint \frac{\partial^2 S'}{\partial q_k \partial J_1}\, dq_k, \qquad (7\text{–}79)$$

or, reversing the order of the integration and partial differentiation,

$$\Delta w_1 = \frac{\partial}{\partial J_1} \oint \frac{\partial S'}{\partial q_k}\, dq_k = \frac{\partial}{\partial J_1} \oint p_k\, dq_k. \qquad (7\text{–}80)$$

We note, however, that the last integral in Eq. (7–80) is J_k. Therefore

$$\begin{aligned}
\Delta w_1 &= 1 \quad \text{if} \quad k = 1, \\
\Delta w_1 &= 0 \quad \text{if} \quad k = 2, 3, \ldots, m,
\end{aligned} \qquad (7\text{–}81)$$

so that w_1 increases by unity when q_1 goes through a complete cycle but is not changed by the variation in any other coordinate.

From Eq. (7–77) it follows that $\Delta w_1 = \nu_1(\Delta t)$, where Δt is the time required for q_1 to complete its cycle. Hence ν_1 must be interpreted as the *frequency* of the motion in the usual reciprocal time sense. In a similar way, each ν_k is found to be the frequency of the motion in the corresponding q_k.

The power of this method of analysis now becomes apparent. We can compute the frequencies of the periodic motions directly without finding the variations of the coordinates with time. We need only express $\alpha_1 = H = K'$ in terms of $J_1, J_2, \ldots, J_m$. Then the frequency $\nu_k = (\partial K'/\partial J_k)$ for each k.

Consider again the simple harmonic oscillator. We have from Eq. (7–70)

$$J = 4\int_0^{q_0} \sqrt{2m(\alpha_1 - \tfrac{1}{2}kq^2)}\, dq = 2\pi\alpha_1\sqrt{m/k}. \qquad (7\text{–}82)$$

Solving for α_1, we find

$$\alpha_1 = \frac{J}{2\pi}\sqrt{k/m} = K'. \qquad (7\text{–}83)$$

Hence, by Eqs. (7–76),

$$\dot{w} = \frac{1}{2\pi}\sqrt{k/m} = \nu, \qquad (7\text{–}84)$$

the frequency of the oscillation.

The Bohr theory of the hydrogen atom pictures the electron moving about the nucleus in prescribed closed orbits. Phase integrals, or action variables, play an important part in this mathematical model. If the electron moves in a plane curve represented by the coordinates r and θ,

$$ J_r = 2\int_{r_1}^{r_2} p_r \, dr, \qquad J_\theta = \int_0^{2\pi} p_\theta \, d\theta, \qquad (7\text{--}85) $$

where r_1 is the minimum and r_2 is the maximum value of r during a cycle. We have treated the motion of the electron in Section 6–4 and have found $p_r = \sqrt{2m\{E + (Ze^2/r) - (p_\theta^2/2mr^2)\}}$, $p_\theta = \text{constant} = \alpha_2$. In this treatment, E and what we have termed α_1 in Section 7–2 are the same. Hence

$$ J_r = 2\int_{r_1}^{r_2} \sqrt{2m\{E + (Ze^2/r) - (\alpha_2^2/2mr^2)\}} \, dr, \qquad J_\theta = 2\pi\alpha_2, \quad (7\text{--}86) $$

where r_1 and r_2 are the roots of $E + (Ze^2/r) - (\alpha_2^2/2mr^2) = 0$.

Integration yields

$$ J_r = \sqrt{(2\pi^2 mZ^2 e^4)/(-E)} - 2\pi\alpha_2 = \sqrt{(2\pi^2 mZ^2 e^4)/(-E)} - J_\theta. $$
$$ (7\text{--}87) $$

Solving for E, we have

$$ E = H = K' = -\frac{2\pi^2 mZ^2 e^4}{(J_r + J_\theta)^2}. \qquad (7\text{--}88) $$

Thus the frequencies are

$$ \nu_r = \nu_\theta = \frac{4\pi^2 mZ^2 e^4}{(J_r + J_\theta)^3}. \qquad (7\text{--}89) $$

In this case, where the frequencies are the same in the two coordinates, the system is said to be degenerate.

By the Bohr postulates, the phase integrals are quantized; that is, they can be only integral multiples of Planck's constant h. Hence we write

$$ J_r = kh \qquad \text{and} \qquad J_\theta = lh, \qquad (7\text{--}90) $$

where k and l are integers. From Eq. (7–89) we see that the frequencies are also quantized, depending on the total quantum number $n = k + l$, or

$$ \nu = \frac{4\pi^2 mZ^2 e^4}{h^3 n^3}. \qquad (7\text{--}91) $$

The energy likewise is quantized,

$$ E = -\frac{2\pi^2 mZ^2 e^4}{h^2 n^2}, \qquad (7\text{--}92) $$

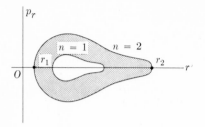

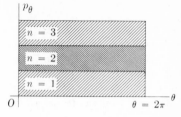

FIG. 7-2. Phase plane for radial motion of the electron.

FIG. 7-3. Phase plane for transverse motion of the electron.

where n takes on positive integral values. The energy changes in every atomic transition by discrete amounts, depending on the values of n.

The quantization of the phase integrals means that the areas in the partial phase spaces of the system are limited to certain values. In Figs. 7-2 and 7-3 these spaces are shown for the electron. Each successive curve corresponds to an integer n. The representative point must move on a curve defined by a specific value of n. For it to change from one curve to another requires an addition or subtraction of a discrete amount of energy in the atomic system. In such a transition from one excited state to another, the J_r and J_θ change by integral multiples of h.

An important property of the canonical transformation is the invariance of the phase integrals. The magnitudes of the variables J_k remain the same in any system of canonical coordinates we choose to use. In the case of the simple harmonic oscillator, for example, we found $J = 2\pi\alpha_1\sqrt{m/k}$, the area of the ellipse in Fig. 7-1. Taking the new momentum to be $E(\equiv\alpha_1)$, as in Fig. 7-1(b), we find the phase integral in the (P, Q) plane to be $2\pi E\sqrt{m/k}$, which agrees with J above. In the (P, Q) plane this is the area of the rectangle from $Q = 0$ to $Q = 2\pi\sqrt{m/k}$.

Problems

7-1. Show directly that the use of $L = \sum_{k=1}^{m} P_k \dot{Q}_k - K + (dS/dt)$ in Hamilton's principle leads to the canonical equations $\dot{Q}_k = (\partial K/\partial P_k)$ and $\dot{P}_k = -(\partial K/\partial Q_k)$. (Section 7-1)

7-2. Show that L from Eq. (7-16) in conjunction with Hamilton's principle yields the canonical equations of Hamilton. (Section 7-1)

7-3. Show that the transformation

$$Q_1 = a_{11}q_1 + a_{12}q_2,$$

$$Q_2 = a_{21}q_1 + a_{22}q_2,$$

$$P_1 = b_{11}p_1 + b_{12}p_2,$$

$$P_2 = b_{21}p_1 + b_{22}p_2,$$

is a contact transformation provided that $b_{ij} = (A_{ij}/\Delta)$ for all i, j where

$$\Delta = \begin{vmatrix} a_{11} & a_{12} \\ a_{21} & a_{22} \end{vmatrix}.$$

and A_{ij} is the cofactor of a_{ij} in Δ. All the a_{ij} and b_{ij} are constants. (Section 7-1)

7-4. Solve Eqs. (7-43), (7-44), and (7-45) for (a) r as a function of t, (b) r as a function of θ, and (c) ϕ as a function of θ under the initial conditions $\phi = 0$, $\theta = \pi/2$, $r = r_0$ when $t = 0$. Here r_0 is the minimum value of r. (d) What additional data would be required in order to fix the remaining values of the α_k? (Section 7-2)

7-5. A single particle of mass m moves in a field where the potential energy is $V(x, y, z)$. (a) Write the Hamiltonian function for the motion, (b) find the momenta and the Hamilton-Jacobi equation. (c) Apply the Hamilton-Jacobi theory to find the motion of the particle when $V \equiv 0$ and when $V = mgz$. The initial conditions are: for $V \equiv 0$, $x = y = 0$, $z = z_0$, $\dot{x} = \dot{y} = v$, $\dot{z} = 0$ at $t = 0$; for $V = mgz$, $x = y = 0$, $z = z_0$, $\dot{x} = v$, $\dot{y} = \dot{z} = 0$ at $t = 0$. (Section 7-2)

7-6. A projectile fired with a speed v_0 at an angle ϕ_0 with the horizontal moves thereafter under the action of gravity. By means of the Hamilton-Jacobi theory, find the equation of its path and verify by elementary analysis. (Section 7-2)

7-7. A small mass m slides smoothly on the interior of the surface $z = x^2 + y^2$. Assume that the mass is acted upon by the force of gravity and that the motion is restricted to a small region near the bottom of the surface. (a) Discuss the motion of m by means of the Hamilton-Jacobi theory. (b) Set up the phase integrals and find the frequencies of oscillation about the lowest point of the surface. Neglect the motion in the z-direction. (c) Compute the x- and y-displacements as functions of the action and angle variables. (Section 7-3)

7-8. Find the phase integrals for the electron problem discussed in Section 7–2. Express the new Hamiltonian in terms of J_r, J_θ, J_ϕ, and calculate the frequencies for the motion. (Section 7–3)

7–9. A pendulum with bob of mass m has an elastic supporting cord whose length is l when the bob hangs in equilibrium. At any time $t > 0$, let the elastic cord have a length $l + r$ and spring constant k, and let θ denote the angular displacement of the supporting cord from its equilibrium position. Assume that the oscillations are small so that $r/l \ll 1$ and take place in a plane. (a) Solve the problem by means of the Hamilton-Jacobi theory using $S'(r, \theta, J_r, J_\theta)$ as the substitution function. (b) Find the frequencies of oscillation and check the results by any other method. (Section 7–3)

7–10. (a) Solve by the Hamilton-Jacobi method the problem in Section 5–2 of two statically coupled masses. (b) Exhibit the canonical equations of motion. (c) Show that the Hamilton-Jacobi equation is not separable in the original coordinates. (d) Find a point transformation which will yield a separable equation. (e) Exhibit the transformed Hamiltonian in terms of the phase integrals and calculate the frequencies of oscillation. (Section 7–3)

7–11. A particle of mass m moves in the xy-plane in a field created by force centers at $(1,0)$ and $(-1,0)$. The potential energy $V = kr_1^{-1} + k'r_2^{-1}$, where r_1 and r_2 are the distances from the respective force centers to the particle; k and k' are constants. (a) Under what force law does the particle move? (b) In terms of elliptic coordinates (q_1, q_2) given by $x = \cosh q_1 \cos q_2$ and $y = \sinh q_1 \sin q_2$, write the expressions for the kinetic and potential energies. (c) Write the Hamilton-Jacobi equation and show that it is separable in the (q_1, q_2) system. (d) Exhibit the substitution function in terms of integrals and derive the equations of motion of the particle. (Section 7–2)

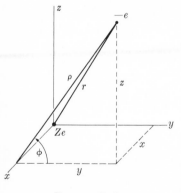

FIGURE 7–4

7–12. An electron is moving in a field produced by a nucleus of charge Z_e and is subjected to an external electric field of intensity $\mathbf{E} = E\mathbf{i}$, where $\mathbf{i}$ is a unit vector along the x-axis shown in Fig. 7–4. The potential energy is $V = -(Ze^2/r) + Eex$. The motion of the electron may be treated by the Hamilton-Jacobi theory if parabolic coordinates are used. Let $x = \frac{1}{2}(\xi^2 - \eta^2)$, $\rho = \xi\eta$, $\rho^2 = y^2 + z^2$.

(a) Show that

$$V = \frac{1}{2(\xi^2 + \eta^2)} \{eE(\xi^4 - \eta^4) - 4Ze^2\}.$$

(b) Show that an element of arc can be written $ds^2 = (\xi^2 + \eta^2)(d\xi^2 + d\eta^2) + \xi^2\eta^2\, d\phi^2$, and hence find the kinetic energy in terms of ξ, η, ϕ and the corresponding velocities.

(c) Set up the Hamiltonian, compute the momenta, and hence write the Hamilton-Jacobi equation and show that it is separable.

(d) Write the phase integrals but do not evaluate them.

References

ANDRONOW, A. A., and CHAIKIN, C. E., *Theory of Oscillations.* Princeton, N. J. Princeton University Press, 1949.

BERGMANN, P., *An Introduction to the Theory of Relativity.* New York: Prentice-Hall, Inc., 1942.

BIRKHOFF, G. D., *Dynamical Systems.* New York: American Mathematical Society Colloquium Publications, 1927.

BORN, M., *The Mechanics of the Atom.* London: G. Bell and Sons, 1927 (translation by J. W. Fisher).

CORBEN, H. C., and STEHLE, P., *Classical Mechanics.* New York: John Wiley and Sons, Inc., 1950.

GOLDSTEIN, H., *Classical Mechanics.* Reading, Mass.: Addison-Wesley, Publishing Company, Inc., 1950.

KRYLOFF, N., and BOGOLIUBOFF, N., *Introduction to Non-Linear Mechanics.* Princeton, N. J.: Princeton University Press, 1947.

LANCZOS, C., *The Variational Principles of Mechanics.* Toronto: University of Toronto Press, 1949.

MACMILLAN, W. D., *Theoretical Mechanics—Dynamics of Rigid Bodies.* New York: McGraw-Hill Book Company, Inc., 1936.

MACMILLAN, W. D., *Theoretical Mechanics—Statics and Dynamics of a Particle.* New York: McGraw-Hill Book Company, Inc., 1927.

McLACHLAN, N. W., *Theory of Vibrations.* New York: Dover Publications, Inc., 1951.

ROUTH, E. J., *Advanced Dynamics of a System of Rigid Bodies* (6th ed.). London: Macmillan and Company, 1905; Reprint by Dover Publications, New York, 1955.

ROUTH, E. J., *Elementary Dynamics of a System of Rigid Bodies.* London: Macmillan and Company, 1882.

RUTHERFORD, D. E., *Classical Mechanics.* Edinburgh and London: Oliver and Boyd; New York: Interscience Publishers, Inc., 1951.

SLATER, J. C., and FRANK, N. H., *Mechanics.* New York: McGraw-Hill Book Company, Inc., 1947.

STOKER, J. J., *Non-Linear Vibrations.* New York: Interscience Publishers Inc., 1950.

SYNGE, J. L., and GRIFFITH, B. A., *Principles of Mechanics* (2nd ed.). New York: McGraw-Hill Book Company, Inc., 1949.

WEBSTER, A. G., *The Dynamics of Particles and of Rigid Elastic and Fluid Bodies.* Leipzig: Teubner, 1904; New York: Hafner Publishing Company, 1949.

WHITTAKER, E. T., *A Treatise on the Analytical Dynamics of Particles and Rigid Bodies* (4th ed.). Cambridge, England: Cambridge University Press, 1937. Republished by Dover Publications, New York, 1944.

255

INDEX